Guide to Managing PC Networks

Tools and Techniques for Running LANs

BY STEVE STEINKE

With Marianne Goldsmith, Michael Hurwicz, Charles Koontz

Prentice Hall PTR
Englewood Cliffs, New Jersey 07632

Library of Congress Cataloging-in-Publication Data

Steinke, Steve
  Guide to managing PC networks : tools and techniques for running LANs / by Steve Steinke with Marianne Goldsmith,
  Michael Hurwicz, Charles Koontz.
      p.   cm.
    Includes bibliographical references and index.
    ISBN 0-13-185497-6
    1. Local area networks (Computer networks)—Management.
  I. Title.
  TK5105.7.S785   1995   94-34836
  004.6'8—dc20   CIP

Prentice-Hall, Inc.
A Simon and Schuster Company
Englewood Cliffs, NJ 07632

Trademarks

A number of entered words in which we have reason to believe trademark, service mark, or other proprietary rights may exist have been designated as such by initial capitalization. However, no attempt has been made to designate as trademarks or service marks all personal computer words or terms in which proprietary rights might exist. The inclusion, exclusion or definition of a word or term is not intended to affect, or to express any judgment on, the validity or legal status of any proprietary right that may be claimed in that word or term.

Names

Company and personal names used in examples and illustrations are used with permission or are fictional. Any resemblance to real persons or companies from which permission has not been obtained is coincidental.

Prices

All prices included in this book are manufacturers' list price, accurate at press time.

Credits

Interior Design: Marianne Ackerman, Amaryllis Design
Illustrator: Laurie Wigham
Cover Design: Lundgren Graphics
Editor: Charles Drucker
Typesetter: Nancy Adams

The publisher offers discounts on this book when ordered in bulk quantities.
For more information, contact: Corporate Sales Department, Prentice Hall PTR, 113 Sylvan Avenue, Englewood Cliffs, NJ 07632,
Phone: 800-389-3419, FAX: 201-592-2249, E-mail: dan_rush@prenhall.com.

Printed in the United States of America

10 9 8 7 6 5 4 3 2 1

ISBN 0-13-185497-6

Prentice-Hall International (UK) Limited, London
Prentice-Hall of Australia Pty. Limited, Sydney
Prentice-Hall of Canada, Inc., Toronto
Prentice-Hall Hispanoamericana S.A., Mexico
Prentice-Hall of India Private Limited, New Delhi
Prentice-Hall of Japan, Inc., Tokyo
Simon & Schuster Asia Pte. Ltd., Singapore
Editora Prentice-Hall do Brasil, Ltda., Rio de Janeiro

6 / Performance Management

7 / Planning for a Secure Network

8 / A Note on Accounting Management

Preface

Guide to Managing PC Networks is a reference book on LAN management designed specifically for the business person who needs to understand networking technology. A new kind of computer book, it combines elements of technology books and business books to address the distinct needs of the computerized work place, where there may be 5 or 50 thousand employees.

Guide to Managing PC Networks focuses on the basic issues of network management. It includes strategies for effectively managing PC networks and offers lessons learned from network pioneers in all types of businesses. At the same time, it provides the information—from tools to solutions—that companies need to make their networks work best for them. In clear, non-technical language, it examines what is practical and cost-effective. And it looks ahead to what businesses can expect in the network management field.

Although downsizing from mainframe and minicomputers to PC networks is the most important trend in business today, the job of managing LANs is often given to employees with no formal training in this field. So if it's your job to keep the network running, or if you're a department manager or executive who needs to understand networking technology, this book is essential reading.

Guide to Managing PC Networks was produced by Vanstar Corporation, which, in early 1994, changed its name from ComputerLand Corporation. The book reflects 17 years of frontline experiences of thousands of Vanstar experts—from systems engineers to corporate trainers, from sales reps to help desk staffers. These people work with all kinds of computer users—employees in small firms as well as is large corporations. Their collective experiences are offered to you here in this book.

—Karen Sharpe,
Publisher

Introduction

I began writing *Guide to Managing PC Networks* because it became clear to me that Vanstar (which was called ComputerLand Corporation during the ten years that I worked there) and its customers are now facing a major problem with their PC networks.

The problem is the paradoxical quality of PC networks—from an everyday, operational standpoint, they are much more attractive than they are reliable. On the one hand, the economic and structural advantages of installing networks of personal computers are strongly compelling. On the other hand, these networks combine technologies from several very different sources, making them inherently unpredictable—too unpredictable for the core functions performed by industry, commerce, government, education and other serious institutions. The consequence is that many organizations are becoming increasingly dependent on PC networks, but, in effect, are exempting them from the traditional reliability standards of mainframe computer systems—near 100 percent up time, orderly problem resolution, predictable performance and controllable security.

There has been no single source of information regarding potential solutions to this problem. The networking trade press—*Network Computing, Communications Week, LAN Times, LAN Technology* and *LAN Magazine*, as well as more general-interest PC publications such as *Byte, PC Magazine, PC Computing, PC Week, InfoWorld, PC World* and the rest—regularly addresses aspects of the problem of network management and reviews the products that purport to address the problem. Inevitably, these varied sources contradict one another, not so much on matters of fact as on how they map the terrain of the problem.

Several other sources of information offer particular maps of the terrain, but lag behind the marketplace in their commitment to PC technology. The International Standards Organization, with its Open Systems Interconnect standards, has the support of governmental bodies around the world; the Internet community's network management standards dominate the installed base today; IBM set the whole world's expectations for computing reliability; and other hardware and software suppliers all have more or less parochial views of the network management issue. Similarly, the engineering textbooks that discuss network management principles stay close to the practice of the telephone companies (and government agencies), whose networks predate the personal computer. These books don't even begin to consider the implications of PCs for network management problems, either as causes or as potential solutions.

In 1992, Rich Melnikoff and Glenn Massaro of ComputerLand Corporation's (now called Vanstar's) Networking Services group developed a list of PC network management functions and a list of tools available to perform these functions. Their work helped me clarify the problems of network management and in some sense inspired this book.

Guide to Managing PC Networks is a reference book designed for the people responsible for implementing and operating networks of PCs. In most organizations, that responsibility extends in two directions: to managers and executives, whose missions depend on networks of PCs, and to the beleaguered people who have day-to-day accountability for these fragile, ever-changing organisms.

Managers and executives can use the book to develop strategies for ensuring that the management of networked PC systems will be practical, cost-effective and able to grow with the network. Network specialists and systems engineers will find this book to be an organized source for product specifications, basic network management theory and lessons from pioneers who have crossed this treacherous terrain before. It is my hope that this book will, at the very least, provide a framework for future discussion of PC network management—that it will help organize our thinking and therefore our development and procurement of new network management tools.

Three overlapping subject areas form the principal contents of this book:

- The facts of computing life in organizations with management hierarchies, budgets and missions to accomplish;
- The networking technology that is rapidly permeating those organizations;
- The products that have begun to grow out of this technology and offer some hope of helping to provide better control.

To ground these discussions of organizations, technologies and products, and to provide some real-life content, I included interviews with some of the people responsible for network management in actual organizations.

The book is divided into four major parts. Part One deals with the organizational context out of which today's PC networks evolved, and within which these systems currently operate. Chapter 1 is an overview of the historical and technical background for today's network management issues. Chapter 2 offers some examples and ideas on the costs and benefits of network management, an appreciation of which can help organizations establish the appropriate scale for pursuing management solutions. Chapter 3 discusses the decisions organizations must make about their networks and network management in the context of the basic network technological notions. My intention in this chapter is to hold the attention of readers who thoroughly understand talk of protocols, APIs and architectures without intimidating those readers who understand what is at stake in the organization but lack training in some of these esoteric subjects.

Part Two discusses each of the five generally recognized categories of network management, describing the specific products that help perform these functions now, and, wherever possible, considering what to expect regarding future products. Chapter 4, on fault management, discusses the ways an organization can deal with trouble on the network, and ways to prevent it. The specific tools developed to help manage faults on networks of PCs are grouped together and their principal features are discussed. Chapter 5, on configuration management, and Chapter 6, on performance management, follow a similar structure. They begin by introducing the tasks each type of management must perform and then investigate specific products that may help accomplish those tasks. Chapter 7, written by Charles Koontz, is a discussion of security issues. It describes how an organization can plan for the right level of security for its data and other computing resources. Chapter 8 is a succinct discussion of the accounting function with respect to PC networks.

Part Three looks at PC network management as an evolving discipline. Chapter 9, written by Michael Hurwicz, discusses the emergence of the unified management platform, a much-needed development as our organizations grow ever more dependent on PC networks. Chapter 10 summarizes the conclusions of the previous chapters and assesses the state of the art of networking. Part Four concludes the book with a series of technical appendices and resource lists that may prove useful to the reader. Note that all prices in this book were current at the time of printing, but are subject to change at the manufacturers' discretion.

Interspersed throughout the text are interviews with people responsible for network management in real organizations—LAN administrators, design consultants, MIS personnel, systems engineers and others. Each has a unique perspective to bring to the subject, and the diversity of their opinions demonstrates how rapidly the field is evolving. Background information on these individuals and their organizations, some of whose names have been changed to preserve anonymity, is included as Appendix A beginning on page 305.

Acknowledgments

Throughout the long and complicated gestation of this book, the people at Vanstar (formerly called ComputerLand) Books have been overflowing with constructive ideas, patient with my shortcomings, and gracious to collaborate with. David Gancher conceived this series of books and, along with Karen Sharpe, brought it to actuality. Charles Drucker solved the strategic problems that arose during the writing of this book with great ingenuity. I owe most of such writing skills as I may possess to Charles and David for their aggressive editing and high standards when I wrote and edited for *ComputerLand Magazine*. Karen and Charles both read the manuscript and contributed many valuable suggestions. Fortunately for all of us, Carol MacDermond organized the many traffic flows and deadlines as the actual production heated up.

Mike Hurwicz provided me with many useful stylistic and substantive revisions, as well as writing Chapter 9. Charles Koontz contributed portions of Chapters 7 and 8, as well as some of the product descriptions appearing throughout the text. Dave Fogle and Jonathan Angel also read the manuscript and made valuable suggestions that were incorporated into the book.

The interviews interspersed throughout the text were conducted by Alison Prince and Marianne Goldsmith, who also edited the transcripts. Anyone with an interest in network management will realize just how busy and preoccupied network management people are, and appreciate the remarkable combination of persistence and tact that was needed to collect these stories. I am also grateful to the interviewees for contributing their time and energy; I hope that in return they will find the book useful. I especially thank Dianne Danielle—who has wide experience with network management in large organizations and who never fails to enlighten in her *Network Computing* columns—for her valuable insights, which the rest of us would not have uncovered on our own.

Mary and Nicky sacrificed their regular family life for many months as I worked on this book. I am particularly thankful for their forbearance and love.

PART ONE

The Organizational Context of Network Management

1 / Why Is Managing PC Networks Such a Challenge?

To understand the importance and the depth of the PC network management challenge, consider the roots of PC networks. In broad terms, four factors have contributed to the difficulties that organizations face in working with these valuable but unpredictable systems. First, PCs have increased dramatically in importance. Understanding the forces propelling PCs into organizations will help to determine the nature and severity of the management problem and whether a long-term solution makes more sense than a short-term patch.

Second, PC networks have proved difficult to control. The installed base of PCs has both technical and organizational limitations, and ways in which networked personal computers can remain *personal* are complex and subtle.

"Network management is either ad hoc *or theoretical."*

—JAMES BRENTANO

Third, the technology of PC networks is divided among noncommunicating, even hostile, camps. Investigating the history of computer networking helps define the various constituencies of the networking world and their interests.

Fourth, the problems of PC networks have several dimensions of complexity. The more components a system has, the less predictable it becomes. All too often, people responsible for planning projects involving mission-critical PC networks underestimate just how difficult the problems of network management are.

In this chapter, we begin by discussing how, in light of the forces favoring PC networks, these four factors have contributed to the network-management problem. Then we describe the organizational response to the problem—some of the ways that responsibility for managing networks can be divided within an organization, and the traits of the people who tend to occupy these positions. Finally, we distinguish between network management and two closely related activities: network administration and troubleshooting.

The Advantages of PC Networks

The Invisible Hand is unplugging mainframe and minicomputers at an accelerating rate, replacing them with networks of personal computers and workstations. The economic advantages of these smaller systems are profound:

- The cost of computing power on a PC is as little as 10 percent of the cost on a mainframe.
- The size of the market for PC products has resulted in economies of scale based on true mass production.
- Unlike proprietary mainframes and minicomputers, much PC equipment is standardized, leading to powerful downward pressures on cost.
- PC maintenance and service expenses are lower as a side effect of mass production.
- Software costs are proportionately low.
- An inventory of PCs and PC peripherals can be redeployed much more readily than a mainframe—PC assets are much more liquid.

If the economic arguments are not sufficiently convincing, there are also compelling organizational and operational reasons for running critical business functions on networks of PCs. Custom software development is normally much more flexible and responsive on PC platforms. Client-server computing, with its inherent scalability and flexibility, is only of practical significance for networks of PCs and workstations. Off-the-shelf or "shrink-wrapped" software, which has permitted huge productivity increases in today's organizations, is a phenomenon of the PC world. It is inevitable that more and more of the tools we use in our daily lives, both the business and personal aspects, will present themselves to us via personal computers and their networks.

The Problem of Management

Although personal computer networks can offer significant benefits, many corporate executives and MIS department managers are appalled by the difficulties inherent in managing these systems. Even with today's relatively robust network operating systems and sophisticated management utilities, moving critical business functions from mainframes or minicomputers onto PC networks still requires a leap of faith and some professional risk-taking.

What makes PC networks so hard to manage? Complexity is part of the problem. As many disparate devices are hooked together, the potential for unanticipated side effects and novel problems quickly grows. Other challenges derive from the unique history of the personal computer industry, and the fact that no one organization or institution is responsible for all the technology that underlies PC networks. Let us consider the history behind that complexity.

Personal Computers and Their Operating Systems

The first personal computers to be installed in organizations—these include Apple's products and the first generation of IBM PCs (and their clones)—had very limited processing capability by today's standards. Their operating systems—MS-DOS and the Macintosh System—were crude compared with those of larger, more costly systems. Capabilities such as multitasking and memory protection, well-understood technologies for creating robust operating systems, were luxuries the early PC processors could not afford. The consequences of losing data on a standalone computer were minor, and there was no demand for linking these computers together.

These operating systems constituted a foundation for thousands of peripherals and pieces of software. This installed base, in turn, exerted a powerful conservative force on operating systems and PCs. Given these operating systems, PC connections to networks were unreliable, difficult to install and troubleshoot, and subject to disruption whenever new software or hardware was introduced.

"It's a rare corporation where LANs were brought in from the top down through the traditional MIS department."

—DIANE DANIELLE

The place of PCs in organizations and the informal ways they have been acquired contributed to the problem. PCs have often been purchased by individual departments or even employees. Stand-alone PCs don't have to maintain compatibility. Even if the organization's management had thought to plan for eventual networking, no central authority was in place to enforce a plan. Nor was reliable information available on how to plan for networking PCs. For example, connecting Macintoshes with IBM-compatible machines makes networking an order of magnitude more difficult than it would be with either type alone, but few organizations knew this before they had installed bases made up of both. Even today, when network connections are inevitable for practically every new PC acquisition, there is little central control in many companies and offices.

PC networks sprang up in individual departments much as PCs themselves did. Administration and maintenance don't usually impose unacceptable overhead costs for purely local networks with fewer than 20 or 30 connections. Upper management could afford to ignore LANs buried in the budgets of a few departments. But as they got connected together, and organization-wide applications came to depend on the internetwork, the costs of keeping crucial network services available rapidly came into focus.

IBM Turf

The International Business Machines (IBM) Corporation presided over the installation of computers at the foundation of enterprises throughout the world—corporations, governmental bodies, universities, research entities and other nonprofit organizations. Between 1955 and 1985, IBM's domination of mainstream computing was all but unchallenged.

As one would expect, the network and its components were—in the eyes of IBM—secondary to the mainframe. When 70 percent and more of the world's computing resources were made by IBM, the company had few incentives to interconnect its devices with those of other manufacturers. In fact, it had powerful competitive reasons to make interconnection as difficult as possible. While IBM conducted advanced research and even introduced products in many areas that led to today's client-server/networked PC environment, it would be fair to say that until as late as 1991 or 1992, large constituencies within IBM, and many of the large corporate customers whose careers were intertwined with IBM, continued to believe that all mission-critical computing tasks ought to be performed on mainframes or minicomputers.

> *"LANs have grown in size much faster than the industry has grown in its ability to provide tools to manage them."*
>
> —Diane Danielle

Before 1974, when IBM introduced its Systems Network Architecture (SNA), the company offered numerous incompatible interconnection technologies for hundreds of different products. Even the early versions of SNA, the all-encompassing (but IBM-only) unification scheme, provided customers with little more than hierarchical terminal access to mainframes—hardly networking as we know it today. IBM's teleprocessing and networking efforts were geared to dedicated private communication links. The original goal of SNA networks was to link subsidiary terminals and preprocessors to mainframe computers at the top of the hierarchy. This hierarchical architecture is difficult to reconcile with the client-server architecture of PC networks—it was late in the 1980s before SNA networks began to be moderately friendly to other networks.

With their IBM mainframes, organizations learned to expect reliable and secure computing resources with predictable performance. While this reliability, security and predictability were tremendous accomplishments, they were possible only in environments with all IBM components. In today's organizations, the yardstick for measuring the accomplishments of network management is the reliability, security and performance of that mainframe environment.

As networks grew in importance through the middle and late 1980s, IBM's policies generally fragmented the LAN marketplace rather than unifying it. The company introduced its broadband IBM PC Network that ran over CATV-type coaxial cable in 1984. This essentially proprietary, low-performance system was installed in schools and training centers, but was never intended to support business applications. IBM's support for token ring technology—a superior solution for some applications—succeeded in developing market share more or less equal to that of Ethernet. The IBM LAN Server Program, a version of Microsoft LAN Manager based on the OS/2 operating system, has never been higher than fourth place in the PC network operating system standings, with no more than 5 percent of the market. Perhaps the most constructive action IBM has taken to unify the LAN market was its endorsement in 1991 of Novell NetWare, which culminated in IBM selling NetWare under the IBM logo.

Overall, IBM has been understandably reluctant to fan the flames of PC network computing. While it remains a fundamental part of the computing landscape and a major producer of PCs and networking hardware, the IBM Corporation makes up only one of the constituencies of the LAN world. People trained to apply the traditional IBM guidelines for systems management may be shocked by the absence of tools for managing heterogeneous PC networks. Their objections to this absence may give them reputations for trying to hold back the tide.

AT&T and Telephone Company Turf

The telephone network is the public transportation system of networked computers. Like public transport, special services, such as high-capacity lines or optical fiber cabling, may be available only at certain places. Pricing for many services is set by regulators, not the marketplace. Change is slow, as the installed base casts a long shadow over new development. Sometimes there is a temptation to look for an alternate ride. Nevertheless, without the public telephone system, PC networks would be strictly *local* area networks, well out of the mainstream of organizational computing tasks.

Packets of digitized voice and packets of digitized data are indistinguishable, and the problems of routing, acknowledgment, security, accounting and so forth are much the same for both industries.

AT&T, unlike IBM, has long been in the middle of the networking arena, albeit for voice circuits with analog, not digital, signals—at least until recently. If IBM traditionally looked at networks as a way to connect IBM peripherals to IBM mainframes, the telephone company looked at networks as a quasi-public infrastructure: a collection of assets such as real estate, rights of way, millions of miles of wire and trucks with cherry pickers on them. AT&T got into the computer business because it needed to build switching equipment for its telephone network. (Incidentally, AT&T also invented the Unix operating system and the C programming language, both of which are important components of the PC network world.) As the telephone companies began to lose their grip on equipment installed on customers' premises, they began to insist on boundaries between their network and whatever the customer might have connected—telephone, PBX or computer. Before and after the points where the phone company provided connections, you were on your own—it wasn't their job. The management tools developed by the telephone companies and familiar to the people with that background are not applicable to the environment on the other side of the connection, which includes the local components of PC networks.

Telephone network services are very reliable and flexible, thanks in part to the suite of network management tools the phone service providers have at their disposal. The management problems that arise with respect to the telephone network are often not technical but economic and organizational. For example, any company can connect its warehouse to its office across the country at the full speed of an Ethernet network, but it will probably have to pay $30,000 a month for the dedicated line. Alternatively, one can use a much cheaper line by sacrificing speed, and therefore the volume of transmissions, but that would require rewriting the applications software and installing a completely different collection of hardware.

"When I had to move a large group of people from one building to another, the users kind of expected that maybe the phone system wouldn't work quite right, or possibly they wouldn't be able to get to the mainframe. But they expected the LAN to be up and running the Monday morning they came in."

—DIANE DANIELLE

In the 1980s, the prospective merger of data processing and telecommunications became a cliché of management seminars and conventions in both industries. AT&T, the telecom behemoth, would go after IBM's turf at the end of the cable, while IBM (which acquired Rolm) would begin providing services that competed with AT&T's. The truth at the core of the cliché is that packets of digitized voice and packets of digitized data are indistinguishable, and the problems of routing, acknowledgment, security, accounting and so forth are much the same for both industries. So far, neither King Kong nor Godzilla appears to have captured much of the other's territory. IBM sold its stake in Rolm in 1990. Its domination of the computing world is less secure today than it has been for at least 30 years, but not because of anything AT&T did. The computer hardware offerings of AT&T, its subsidiaries and allies have remained marginal in the broad marketplace. AT&T now faces competition from other interexchange carriers (IECs) such as Sprint and MCI. The local exchange carriers (LECs) AT&T used to own are now regional Bell operating companies (also known as RBOCs or Baby Bells), possibly competing with the former parent for new services.

Naturally, organizations want the best of both the traditional computer and the telecom worlds: full control over the network, but the low costs of a shared public network; the utmost reliability, but the low costs of nonproprietary computer hardware and software. The mainframe environment and the telephone system both have effective management tools at their disposal, but these tools do not go very far toward solving the management problems of networked PCs.

The Internet

"The frustrating thing about network management is there are so many changes going on. We're in the business of change, so we're constantly imposing change on end users. But change is being imposed on us by vendors with products, with new versions of everything that's being put out there. The business itself is exciting. If your goal is to be in an environment that is pretty stable, this is not the place to be."

— RANDY HOWLAND

In the late 1960s and early 1970s, the U.S. Department of Defense funded a great deal of research on the problems of interconnecting computers. Universities with advanced computer science research departments were the first to connect to the Advanced Research Projects Agency Network, or ARPANET, which was made possible by their findings. (The agency was for some years known as the Defense Advanced Research Projects Agency, or DARPA.) The networking technology that grew out of these activities is embodied in the Internet Protocol (IP) and Transmission Control Protocol (TCP), among other standards. Almost any computer running the Unix operating system, which is practically ubiquitous in universities, can connect to the Internet using a modem over public phone lines.

The Internet is the oldest and largest multivendor computer network. In many respects it has served as a laboratory for the kinds of problems facing networked PC systems today. Unlike the technologists at IBM and the telephone companies, the developers of the Internet were committed to open systems—to interoperation among many different kinds of computers and peripherals.

One of its most significant contributions to network management is the collection of standards known as SNMP, the Simple Network Management Protocol. This protocol was formally introduced by the Internet Engineering Task Force (a subcommittee of the Internet Activities Board) in May 1990. Devices that implement this protocol can provide information about their activity and respond to commands across the network.

The Internet world, with its strong academic flavor and deep roots in the U.S. government—the Department of Defense in particular—provides yet another important strand of influence on the challenge of managing PC networks.

Heterogeneity and Complexity

"In the LAN world even the brightest people can make the wrong decision, because it's a very fast-moving arena. You need to be aware of the new technology, but you need to get your feet wet slowly. The key is to keep your eye focused on the business."

— DIANE DANIELLE

With these various institutions contributing to the evolution of PC networks, four primary reasons emerge for why PC network management problems are so hard. First, while single-manufacturer PC networks are (barely) conceivable, almost every real-world PC network has components from multiple producers. As a result, no one producer can exercise responsibility over (or take control of) these systems.

Second, while industry-wide standards can enable products from multiple producers to work together, in the world of PCs (and computer technology in general) manufacturers are often reluctant to sacrifice perceived competitive advantages to their customers' desire for uniformity. As a result, PC networking standards are often weak, late and ignored.

Third, the technology of networking is necessarily complex and specialized.

Fourth, and finally, this already complicated landscape is continuously destabilized by the rapidity of technological change.

Heterogeneous Components and Their Combination

The very reasons that explain why personal computers became the preeminent components of information processing and transfer they are today also explain why networks run out of control. Thousands of different companies have built PCs, add-on components, peripheral devices and software. These manufacturers competed aggressively to provide high performance at low prices, ready access to computer functions by civilians and deliverance from the MIS Department's backlog. One of the hidden costs of this competition was limited compatibility among these components when the time came to connect them together.

"Vendors who make software, even the ones that have LAN in huge letters on the box, still think in terms of individual computers with local hard disks."

—DIANE DANIELLE

It is not too difficult to spell out all the explicit incompatibilities between two devices or programs. It is practically impossible to predict all the potential negative side effects of a network with dozens or hundreds of components. To get a sense of the way individual PC configurations proliferate exponentially, consider just two networked PC workstations. To make it easier, imagine that the two PCs are of the same model, with the same version of ROM BIOS and the same version of DOS. In addition, they have the same model and version of network interface card. The symptom: With a network connection in place, Windows works fine in enhanced 386 mode with one PC but not the other. Possible explanations include these:

- One user installed more RAM than the other.
- One user configured memory to take better advantage of the RAM that was installed.
- One user installed a second internal hard drive with a driver that conflicts with the network card.
- One user installed a terminate-and-stay-resident utility program that is incompatible with Windows on a network.
- One user neglected to install, or inadvertently deleted, a special Windows patch that is placed in service by copying a file to the Windows subdirectory and editing the SYSTEM.INI file.
- One user installed a scanner that interferes with the network interface card.
- One user has a bus mouse, while the other has a serial mouse.
- And many more.

The problem of heterogeneity has several dimensions. The most obvious source is the multitude of manufacturers supplying components. Even when the same manufacturer supplies all the components of one type—PCs, for instance—there are still compatibility issues across the different models. In addition, almost any sizable PC network has some kind of IBM, DEC or HP host to contend with, Macintoshes connected somewhere and, increasingly, SQL databases or other critical Unix installations. Multiple vendors are inevitable here; not even IBM can claim to offer complete solutions in these complex networks.

"The fun part of being a network manager and solving problems is the detective aspect of the work. The drag is when you have no suspects."

—JAMES BRENTANO

The time/version dimension of heterogeneity affects practically any piece of PC hardware or software. For all practical purposes, the makers of the least expensive IBM-compatible PC clones source their ROM BIOSs, their disk drives, their supporting chip sets, their RAM, perhaps even the microprocessor itself, from the lowest bidder. In the very worst cases, the producer goes out of business with no forwarding address. In cases almost as bad, the producer can't trace the etiology of the computer through serial numbers or production codes and can only replace an entire subsystem with another, hopefully more compatible, one. But even major producers, with whole departments dedicated to documenting and solving networking problems, have to distribute service bulletins and CD-ROM databases describing intricate side effects that result from combining particular versions of hardware, firmware and software—side effects capable of causing data loss or system failure.

A new version of a network operating system (NOS) software usually requires new add-on utilities, such as print spoolers and backup managers. It will probably require configuration changes on every user's system. While NOS version changes provide significant advantages to the fortunate subnets with large enough budgets to upgrade, they can provoke major techno-political conflicts in organizations. The e-mail system, or the directory services or the network management arrangement may not work for the whole network unless everyone upgrades. Even simple management utilities and troubleshooting techniques can founder on older versions of the network operating system.

In the final analysis, networks are as heterogeneous as their user populations. Organizations that, for good reasons or bad, accommodated PC adoptions from the ground up have opinionated, self-sufficient users and, therefore, a broad selection of hardware and software. Organizations with close control over PC procurement have well-standardized components if they have listened well to their users and stayed in front of the tools users need to get the job done.

The Success and Failure of Standards

"It's not a problem here to establish standards, because most of the IS people have mainframe backgrounds. They understand that a network is no different than a mainframe, outside of the distribution divisions. You need fail-safe backup and recovery procedures, and sometimes these get overlooked."

— ARTHUR GRANT

Standards are detailed descriptions of how products interact with each other. If the appropriate standards are set and adhered to, products can be interchanged freely without fear of incompatibility. Standardized products offer customers the further advantage of setting the stage for a bidding process with assurance that those products will perform as expected when combined with other conforming products. Standards are widely implemented throughout the world economy, for screw threads, photographic film, drugs, tires and innumerable other categories of goods. Industries that don't change as rapidly as the computer and networking industries don't need to discuss standards as often as they do. But as a reminder of what is at stake in standards decisions, remember the VHS vs. Betamax videotape format controversy.

Standards can be set either through a coup d'état undertaken by an accepted industry leader or through a quasi-legislative committee process. The first method has the advantage of speed; the second has the advantage of consensus. An example of the first is the IBM PC specification. An example of the second is the Ethernet 10BASE-T twisted pair wiring standard.

Standards always have limits. That is, the entire performance of a hardware or software product will never be defined by standards. It is not in the interests of the developers who create and subscribe to standards to completely specify a device or a program because there must be room to differentiate one developer's product from another's. Furthermore, technological change itself requires flexibility in standards. If a standard is too brittle, it will be passed by in the blink of an eye. For instance, the BIOS in the IBM PC provided orderly video functions to programs that were written for DOS. Because these functions were relatively slow, software developers such as Lotus Development Corporation wrote programs that took over the video hardware directly. Almost no commercial software used the standard video BIOS routines after *1-2-3* and other software set the performance benchmark.

Standards Organizations

The International Standards Organization (ISO) is a gathering of national standards bodies that includes ANSI (American National Standards Institute), DIN (Deutsche Industrie Normal) and similar groups from some 90 nations. There are ISO sub-committees for many industrial and commercial products and practices. The Open Systems Interconnect (OSI) Reference Model is the ISO's framework for international networks with components produced by many different suppliers. The seven-layer OSI Reference Model spells out in great detail the responsibilities of devices and programs that interoperate via networks.

The lower layers of the OSI Reference Model were first established by an official international agency, the Comité Consultatif International Télégraphique et Téléphonique, or CCITT. The CCITT is part of the International Telecommunication Union, an agency of the United Nations. The voting members of the CCITT are government postal, telegraph and telephone bureaus from around the world. (The interests of the United States are represented by the State Department.) The X.- and V.-series of standards (X.25, V.32bis and so on) are CCITT products. The ISO is a nonvoting member of the CCITT, and the two bodies often cooperate closely.

The Institute of Electrical and Electronic Engineers (IEEE) is a professional organization that has its own standardization committees. Standards in the 802.-series (802.2, 802.5, etc.) were created by the IEEE. The ISO has incorporated these into its LAN standards. Committees on network management from the IEEE, the ISO and the Internet Activities Board are the primary sources of consensus-based network management standards.

"When you get up to the hundred-node network, the several-hundred-node network, the multithousand-node network, network management becomes a multi-person rather than a single-person responsibility. You're likely to have a true 'manager,' someone who may or may not know anything about computers, but who is the manager for the entire environment."

— DIANE DANIELLE

Standards arrive from many directions, with many different and conflicting missions. The OSI (Open Systems Interconnect) standards have been developed by European and North American phone bureaucracies and companies with telephone networks in mind. Computer networks were something of an afterthought to this group. The IP standards began as a mechanism for government and university researchers to transfer data among themselves. Xerox, DEC and Intel spearheaded the Ethernet standard, while the token ring standard is forever tied to IBM.

Part of the extreme heterogeneity of the PC world results from the imperial drive of PC technology, which regularly engulfs whole families of competing equipment. The dedicated word processor and a major portion of the typewriter market have been displaced by PCs. Despite the rapid growth of the facsimile industry, PCs will inevitably take over a large part of fax traffic. Dumb terminals are increasingly superfluous as PC performance increases and prices drop. The low end of the typesetting business has been taken over, and some of the more specialized parts of the high end, such as photo retouching and color separation, may soon be performed routinely on PC-based systems. PCs can perfectly well support point-of-sale and distribution applications, with bar-code readers and other specialized peripherals.

"There is always going to be complexity. I think the more reliable you can make your servers, the more you eliminate emergency management."

—Dave Fogle

As PCs have overthrown these technologies, they have inherited the need for standardization from all of them. From word processing came the need to maintain the format of a document across a network. From typesetting came page description languages and the need to handle fonts gracefully on networks. From terminal emulation came the telecommunications standards for modems, cluster controllers and a host of other equipment.

Without a doubt, the hard work of standards committees will continue to aid the user community. Also, the results of standards committees will undoubtedly continue to be too little, too late for desperate users. The fundamental reasons that standards will always lag behind are the complexities of network technology and the pace of technological change.

Complex Technology

Individual PCs and peripherals seem robust and predictable until they are networked together. One reason is the inherent unpredictability of events at the other end of a wire. (This principle is equally applicable to modem communication processes, which are also much more likely to be troublesome than the operations of devices no further away than one's own desktop.) Another reason is the exacting demands that are made on network devices—data-transfer rates must be almost as fast as a local hard disk drive. Furthermore, the single-user, single-tasking PC operating systems of the 1980s— MS-DOS and early versions of the Macintosh System—were installed on millions of computers before the need for PC networks became apparent. As a result, PC behavior on networks can be brittle and inflexible, rarely capable of recovering from anomalies introduced by the network.

A multiprotocol networked system spanning multiple sites compares in complexity with a nuclear power plant. (Such a system might include mainframe and minicomputer connections, scores of file servers, an assortment of database servers, communications servers, fax servers, backup servers, high-speed communications links and program-to-program links between systems.) No two of these networks have more than glancing similarities. No individual has deep knowledge of all the components; few have more than the most superficial knowledge of more than one component. Even if someone thoroughly understood all the components, understanding all the interactions and side effects would still present a tremendous challenge.

Accelerating Rates of Technological Change

Network managers with a year or two of experience are grizzled veterans. Much ten-year-old experience is utterly off the map of relevance to today's problems. Freshly minted engineering graduates need to be retrained before they can start working. While other technologies are also changing rapidly, the technology for interconnecting personal computers is indisputably one of the fastest changing and most significant.

Certain changes, such as the cost of a million instructions per second (MIPS) of computing capacity, the cost of a megabyte of RAM or the cost per megabyte of hard disk capacity, follow reasonably predictable linear or exponential trend lines. Other changes—the rise of the PC, the rise of PC networks, the rise of the graphical user interface—seem fundamentally unpredictable. These discontinuous changes are perhaps the greatest contributors to the difficulties faced by network managers. Decisions that are difficult on technical grounds often have tremendous organizational implications: Will that department's computers work with this application? Will all the users need to add $500 worth of new options to their PCs to run the application? No customer or manufacturer has the resources to bet on every horse, but in the world of networked PCs, the favorites run out of the money more often than the odds would suggest.

Network Management Career Paths

I think most of the people who got into the LAN world got into it specifically because they liked the technology or were interested in it. In a lot of cases they had to, because most of us were bringing LANs into companies that didn't know anything about them, and we usually had to fight pretty hard to get them installed in the first place because a LAN was this strange animal. But network management today is definitely something that people think of as a career.

It's a career in transition simply because of the increasing size and complexity of the networks and the way companies keep trying to figure out who does what. In these environments, at some point most people must decide whether they want to stay at a technical level solving problems, working on implementation, looking at new things, or whether they want to move up into management, where they're dealing more with vendors and with other parts of the company, with managing other people. In most technical areas in corporations, this can be a real point of strain.

Corporations generally have limits on how far you can move in a technical career ladder. So at some point, if you want to earn a better living, you must either go some place else or move yourself up into management. Then maybe you give up things that were interesting to you before because now you're managing people and budgets and you're not spending any time doing the technical jobs you liked.

It's become much like other technical computer areas within a company. The trick is to figure out what it is about the environment that you like, what you want to do, and see if you can stay in the area that particularly interests you.

—*Diane Danielle, industry columnist and President of Danielle Associates, a network consulting firm*

Organizing for the Management of Networked PCs

"Some things look great in memos, but on a practical level are not that useful. Business will have to decide what's important."

— RANDY HOWLAND

As corporate networks grow in size and complexity, some organizations respond by hiring additional network gurus to keep the system working. More commonly, the incumbent network gurus are expected to extend their working schedules, master new technologies and somehow prioritize the never-ending stream of problems.

Expecting a single person to hold the system together, however, is a strategy that rapidly disintegrates. A PC network of any size requires the talents, background and time of a number of part- or full-time professionals. Companies vary considerably in the organization of their networking groups, but, by and large, the network management tasks that must be done include planning, implementing, problem-solving, maintenance and repairing. In the real world, one person or one team may have responsibility for more than one of these functions. My condolences to those who have to do them all.

High-Level Designers

Planning and implementation functions are critical for expansion and equally critical for platform migration and other kinds of system improvements. Working down the scale from the most general level, planning positions might include titles such as systems architect, network architect, network designer and network project planner. In the order listed here, these titles are associated with progressively more tactical concerns. A systems architect might be the CIO or an outside consultant. Because decisions about systems can have unexpectedly profound consequences throughout an organization, it is crucial that the highest levels of management understand the organization's systems profoundly and participate to a greater degree than simply delegating their crucial decisions and rubber-stamping someone's recommendations. Too often an ostensibly technical decision, such as whether options will be provided to users or whether batch or interactive processing will be used, defines the culture of an organization—and the customers' experience of that organization—for years to come. In comparison to the systems architect, a network architect might be responsible for only the networked part of the organization's systems. Network designers may implement a network architect's plan or develop their own. The project planner may be a sort of general contractor, mobilizing cable installers, movers, network administrators and purchasing agents on a large scale. In another organization this person may perform all these functions solo.

Planners and Implementers

It would be natural to include project planners in the implementation category since detailed planning and execution are closely related. On the whole, few planners have the luxury of devising plans and handing them off to others, and it's probably a good thing that they don't. Other implementers can be broken out by specialty: cable installer, telecom installer, mainframe link specialists, people who understand phone company tariffs and how to negotiate with long-distance services and so on.

Problem-Solvers

The activity of problem-solving is not closely related to that of planning and implementation, though poorly planned and implemented networks inevitably have more problems than those that are well-planned and well-implemented. On a large networked system, asking a planning/implementing employee to respond to random problem events could be asking for trouble. The organization will be lucky if any of the jobs get done well. Help desk workers are typically first-line problem-solvers. They filter out routine user errors, talk through simple configuration hassles, document problems and quickly escalate serious difficulties to those who can handle them. The people the help desk escalates to are the gunslingers of the network. Their job titles may be systems engineer or network specialist. They wear beepers. They know the meaning of pressure. It is to be hoped that they thrive on it, even when they complain about it. A down server or a nonfunctioning network segment is *ipso facto* a crisis. An unsuspecting user who innocently asks one of these troubleshooters for configuration help when the system is down will likely get an earful. If they have to do help desk duty for a while they will undoubtedly experience adrenaline withdrawal. As a rule, troubleshooting types are not strong on administrative duties; they are probably not inclined to populate a trouble ticket database. They justifiably hunger for training. It is not unreasonable for these employees to spend 15 to 20 percent of their time in class.

The Network Management Team

There are four levels of network management services that we use at the company. They have departmental LAN administrators; four network administrators in the microcomputer department; our MIS management; and corporate management. They also work with telecom. The whole telecom operations group is responsible for adds, moves and changes, setting up the SynOptics concentrators, checking the router and resetting it if something goes haywire. They maintain the T1 line between the three sites, and this is a happy marriage. They have weekly operations meetings between each site with the telecom staff, MIS staff, microcomputer staff as well as our facilities staff. They've found that we needed to include facilities people on-site since they often find out what's going on with people moving around before MIS does.

There used to be a fire drill every time somebody wanted to move. They'd have it all worked out with the facilities department. The facilities staff would arrive on the site and find a mainframe connection and a LAN connection. They'd call us and we'd have to drop everything and go do the move, so we've done a lot of proactive things to stop that from happening, such as weekly operations meetings.

Our other building at this site was an older building and we had to do a lot of work to get the cabling up to spec there. We had some serious problems with wires that were just not terminated properly or were otherwise causing errors. Our cable is specified for 500 feet, but sometimes things are just out of spec and it doesn't work. These are the hardest problems to solve. We've bought a cable scanner, but we have problems getting into the switch room to set it up at the other end. We've had to work very closely with our telecom group to get them some test equipment that we understand and teach them how to use it, since they're not PC people, they're data people. They tell us 'The line works, we tested it.' We've sent them to Novell training and they've sent us to data communications training. So cross training has really helped a lot in solving cabling problems.

—*Jane Shea, Sr. Technical Analyst, AmSys Telemanagement*

Consistent Terminology in Network Management

Because of the multiple sources of technology that intersect in the realm of PC networks, there are many times that a word can mean several different, or even contradictory, things. The following sections discuss some of the worst potential sources of confusion so that at least the terms used in this book will be clear and consistent.

The term *organization*, throughout this book, refers to the networked system's customer-institution; the problems of networked systems in businesses are also found in government offices, educational institutions and other nonprofit organizations.

Networks, Hosts and Other Terminology

Network management is sometimes defined narrowly as the process of collecting and presenting information about, and controlling, network-specific devices, especially concentrators, hubs, gateways, routers, bridges, telecommunications lines and equipment and the cable plant. In this pre-PC terminology, widely used in discussion about standards such as SNMP and CMIP, workstations, servers and mainframe or minicomputer hosts are attached to the network, but are not themselves the subjects of network management. (The notion of a host on the customer premises and, on the other hand, a public network is, of course, a telephone company distinction. The best definition of a host is any computer that runs applications programs. Internet terminology tends to adopt this host/network manner of speaking, with additional components that have been variously named Interface Message Processors [IMPs], intermediate systems [ISs] or routers. PCs and workstations, especially if they run client-server applications, overlap in function with traditional multiuser hosts and terminals. Their existence can make it confusing to speak any longer of hosts where networks of PCs are involved.)

Managers and users of networks, and the producers of network support tools, do not often limit themselves to these terminological boundaries. If users can't access e-mail and other applications they normally load from the network, they are liable to say that the network is down in spite of the fact that the network itself (narrowly defined) is working fine and only their server or workstation is not working properly. The people who work in PC network management or network support departments are typically responsible for correct server operation and the compatibility of workstations as well as the components of the network defined narrowly.

This book will try to avoid muddling useful distinctions by referring to the problem of *managing networked PC systems* as its primary subject. Systems can include networks, hosts of any size, workstations,

> *"Everybody expects all of these to work together, they want to be able to share files, they want to be able to share data, they want this to be transparent. You get all of the hype in the news about being able to get to any data anywhere on the network or the mainframe with just the click of a button. Nobody is saying this is what your goal is, or this is what you want. No one has any concept of what's involved down here in the practical layer to make that work."*
>
> — DIANE DANIELLE

servers and software. However, the temptation to use the term *network management* the same way that the book's readers would is irresistible. If the occasion arises to use *network management* in the narrow sense, I will call out the special sense.

Network Administration

Much of what may appear to a user to be fault correction, performance enhancement or security provision is network administration, not management. Network administrators perform the routine, but critical, jobs a PC network requires. Adding, deleting or moving a workstation or a server, setting access rights for users and backing up files systematically are all examples of network administration tasks. Network administration is a crucial function that overlaps the role of systems management. For example, the improper assignment of file rights—an error in an essentially clerical function—may cause an automated process responsible for storing and forwarding a large volume of files to fail so spectacularly that data is lost. On the other hand, a well-managed networked PC system will inevitably be easy and efficient to administer.

"Probably the best thing any network administrator can do is get involved in user groups, to get onto the Internet or some of the CompuServe forums, and to talk to other people who have similar environments."

— DIANE DANIELLE

Network administration presents an organization with many of the same problems that other security-oriented occupations do. It is critically important to the organization that data be kept secure from anyone unauthorized to use it and from disasters of many kinds. An ill-trained administrator could leave data unprotected in a multitude of ways, so the temptation is to give supervisor access only to the most advanced troubleshooting personnel. But since the nature of this task is basically administrative—dealing with passwords and authorizations, performing regular backups and communicating with users about issues like disk space and e-mail setup—it lacks the kind of intellectual challenge that an advanced troubleshooter would like to see. One solution is to create a group of local administrators with sufficient authorization to perform day-to-day maintenance activities, but not enough to harm other parts of the organization. Despite the intimate connection between management and administration, network administration in itself is not the central concern of this book.

Troubleshooting

"The fact that I'm known means that I've slipped up somewhere. When a network runs smoothly, nobody cares who's in charge of it."
—ARTHUR GRANT

Troubleshooting is another organizational role that overlaps with networked systems management. In the sense the term appears in this book, troubleshooting is a tactical and local activity; the main thrust of this book is comparatively strategic and global. However, many of the tools this book discusses are useful for troubleshooting problems on networked PC systems. Troubleshooting guides typically consist of flow charts that begin with specific problems, prescribe actions to get closer to a solution and provide multiple potential paths to pursue based on the results of those actions. A well-managed system of networked PCs has ready access to the troubleshooting tools its users and managers need, including manuals and other documentation, help desks, public online services and specialized hardware. A properly planned and maintained—that is to say, a well-managed—networked system is much easier to troubleshoot than one that is poorly planned or maintained. But troubleshooting itself is not the focus of this book.

The Problem Provides the Solution

The burgeoning and still-evolving field of network management embodies a certain irony in that personal computers present both a problem and a solution. While these systems contribute complexity, incompatibility and instability to a network, they are also ideal for the jobs of monitoring the elements of a networked system, generating problem alerts and sending them to the right destination, and even automatically reconfiguring or otherwise repairing a troubled network. In the end, the promise of PC network technology can only be realized if management tools evolve sufficiently to keep these networks running reliably, inexpensively and without the need to train 5 or 10 percent of the world's workforce on how to troubleshoot these problems.

2 / Thinking About Costs and Benefits

In tight money times everyone is fighting the budget battle, but network managers have to struggle for dollars that in the mainframe world are just taken for granted. They have to struggle because there is no understanding of what those dollars can buy, because there isn't a budget history.

—*Diane Danielle, industry columnist and President of Danielle Associates, a network consulting firm*

This chapter is an effort to think through some of the ways networks of PCs are productive assets of organizations, and some of the ways they generate expenses. There may be an accounting methodology that can perfectly allocate costs to various business units, maximize the productivity of the invested capital and maximize the productivity of employees responsible for the network, but don't expect to read about it here. This book makes no pretense of being an original contribution to the subjects of cost accounting, depreciation or the time value of money, though these important factors shouldn't be overlooked. There can, however, be little doubt that a well-managed network will save expenses over the long term and improve the productivity of assets and people.

To make long-term plans and day-to-day purchasing decisions with regard to network management, it is essential to understand: (1) the value of the network as a collection of capital equipment; (2) the recurring costs associated with operating the network; and (3) the network's role as a factor in the organization's productivity.

Capital Investment

Networks of PCs sometimes infiltrate organizations from the ground up. There may not be a separate asset account on the books for networks of PCs. The problem can be compounded when the organization moves to take centralized control of the network. Suddenly all kinds of expenditures for capital equipment that were buried in department budgets surface in one place, and it appears that the network department wants huge capital budget increases every year.

Patterns of Growth

The mainframe world is used to buying machines that cost millions of dollars and software products that cost fifty thousand or a hundred thousand per machine. They have gargantuan budgets. Even if the company is limiting growth to 5 percent a year, out of a $10 million budget there is still a fair amount of money that's going to be coming down the pike in the following year.

When you look at local area networks, you see that somebody started out with two computers or three computers and a server. They had a small budget. And then they need to add 20 more machines. Well, this is not a 5 percent increase. Or they want to triple or quadruple the number of machines; they're working on budget paths that are orders of magnitudes of growth per year. But all the corporation can see is that you're asking for a 30 percent increase, or a 50 percent increase. The corporation's not looking at it from the point of view that the total dollar amount is still going to be well within the limits of what it's paying on the mainframe side.

I worked in an area of a corporation that owned and operated a mainframe. Sometimes, if I needed something for the LAN, I convinced my manager to postpone buying one string of drives or one software package for a month. That would be enough money to get me something that I needed for the network. It wasn't so much the dollars as just the percentage of budgets and changes that we're talking about.

—Diane Danielle, industry columnist and President of Danielle Associates, a network consulting firm

A physical inventory of PC assets may be onerous for the staffers who have to perform it, but it is one way to start tracking these assets. An automatic inventory application may help simplify the inventory. (See Chapter 5, Configuration Management.) As the detailed cost figures in Table 2-1 make clear, the capital amounts (or lease payments) tied up in networks are sizable enough to track insistently.

Table 2-1 Typical Network Capital Investments

Node Components	Low	Mid	High
Personal computer or workstation (including display, RAM, mouse, system software)	$1,500	$4,000	$15,000
Network interface card	150	300	4,000
Cabling (PC to wiring closet or hub)	50	200	750
Structured wiring elements (hubs/concentrators, wiring closet to backbone or server)	0	200	1,000
Per node total	$1,700	$4,700	$20,750
Server Components			
Server CPU (including RAM, disk drives)	$3,000	$20,000	$50,000
Backup system	600	2,500	8,000
Uninterruptible power supply	400	1,500	3,000
Network operating system	2,000	7,000	12,000
Additional software services (Macintosh support, messaging, etc.)	0	4,000	15,000
Per server total	$6,000	$35,000	$88,000
Internetworking/WAN Components			
Local bridge	$3,000	$7,000	$15,000
Remote bridge	5,000	10,000	25,000
Multiprotocol router	6,000	15,000	25,000

A medium-sized network of 100 nodes and 2 servers could easily have cost more than $500,000. Multimillion-dollar networked systems are common in large and medium-sized companies. These figures have the advantage of being tangible and easy to compile. Network management products can be cost-justified as leverage for these sizable assets.

Operating Expenses of a Network

The costs of operating a network can be elusive. The grassroots origins of many networks has left a legacy of part-time network administrators, informal peer-to-peer technical support and hidden help desk services. Nevertheless, most network-using organizations recognize that the ongoing costs of supporting a PC network add substantially to the cost of hardware, software, and design and installation services.

Network Administration

Even the smallest network needs to be administered: new users must be added and departing users deleted; people forget their passwords and need help getting connected; users need access to services or files they haven't received network permission to use; people buy new devices and want them connected. As more and more people load software from the network, organizations have obligations to software licensers to live up to their agreements—this many concurrent users, that many nodes with local copies, so many server copies. While upgrading server-based software is much easier than upgrading individual workstations, problems are still inevitable: some workstations will need hardware or other software upgrades or conversions. Spending for training can offset administration (and help desk) costs disproportionately. On many networks, a set of standardized menus shields users from low-level interactions with networks and reduces training and administration requirements.

Help Desk or Technical Support

"I can't log on to the network." "I get an error message inside e-mail that says 'Error reading device Network.'" "I lose my network connection whenever I use the modem." "It took 10 minutes instead of 30 seconds to load my database file today." These requests for help inevitably arise, and someone in the organization just as inevitably must respond to them, whether it is another, slightly more experienced user, an informally designated power user, a formal MIS help desk or an outside service. In the first two instances, no budget will be charged for servicing these requests, but the cost in lowered efficiency and lost productivity is certainly higher than in situations where formal, well-tracked help services are available.

More Difficult Than Managing Mainframes

The lack of sufficient head count in network management is nightmarish. It goes back to the fact that senior management often thinks PCs are toys. In a lot of corporations there is one support person for every 80 to 100 PCs, which is totally inadequate.

Managing local area networks is infinitely more complex, infinitely more difficult than managing mainframes. It's more difficult because every one of those machines sitting on someone's desk is a computer in and of itself. When you're managing a local area network you're not managing a bunch of dumb terminals.

—*Diane Danielle, industry columnist and President of Danielle Associates, a network consulting firm*

Diagnosis and Repair

When the network or a segment of it goes down, someone has to identify the fault, reestablish an environment that allows users to do their jobs and get the network back to normal. Most organizations identify these situations as emergencies to the degree that the network is part of the organization's mission rather than a convenience. Budgets often lose their usual privileges in emergencies. (Chapter 4, Fault Management, discusses possible strategies for repairs.)

Training

The award for the most lip service paid (in lieu of actual spending) perennially goes to training, but especially training in the productive use of computers. Employees are too busy, budgets are too constrained. But the fact is that new users are being trained every day, probably by someone who is harried and grudging of time, which is not the best way to teach or learn. Isn't there a likelihood that it will be cheaper to conduct a real class, with clear objectives and measurable results?

Outside Services and Miscellaneous Expenses

Design and installation expenses are unavoidable with new networks and major enhancements. New installations of unfamiliar products—SQL database servers, high-speed wide area links, fiber-optic or microwave connections, Electronic Data Interchange—can often get off the ground faster and cheaper with outside help. Consultants may be required to solve other kinds of specialized problems. Organizations unable to justify the expense of a protocol analyzer can rent one, or hire an outside provider to troubleshoot especially difficult problems. Third-party providers can also supply help desk services (outside normal business hours or full time), hardware maintenance, administration services, performance monitoring, training and more.

Telecommunications charges for wide area links may also be included in operating expenses. Internal support personnel need PCs, software and probably a collection of basic test equipment. Support staff may spend significant sums downloading operating system patches and bug fixes, or seeking answers from online conferences.

Network Budgets vs. Mainframe Budgets

We need to start managing the desktop the way we manage the mainframe. We have to stop thinking about desktop machines as if they were typewriters that you bring in, set down on the desk and leave for the next 20 years. What we need to do is something that's very common in the mainframe world—create an automatic turnover cycle. The mainframe department will turn over the machine every 2 to 3 years. Your depreciation will stay constant because you're looking at different dollars. But you're getting more power.

Desktop computers are likely to be useful for 5 years, a not untypical depreciation period, only if you're in an environment where you can keep pushing machines lower and lower in the corporate hierarchy. But at some point the base-level machine that is required by the computing environment will be higher than the oldest machines on the premises. If you haven't planned for this obsolescence, you'll be in trouble.

A manager once told me that desktop systems didn't really earn their keep until they were fully off the books. Once the machine's gone off the books, if there's no new machine to pick up the depreciation level, then the depreciation line goes down. If you want to increase it, you're faced with an incredible hurdle.

—*Diane Danielle, industry columnist and President of Danielle Associates, a network consulting firm*

Table 2-2 Typical Monthly Operating Expenses (Per 100 Users)

	Low	Mid	High

Network administration (adds, moves, changes, passwords and permissions):
Mid = half of $2,500 salary
    + 23% burden
    + 10% training
    + 10% occupancy cost;
High and Low are ±20%
	$1,430	$1,790	$2,150

Help desk (mixture of application support and specific network support): Low = third-party rate; Mid is 25% greater than Low; High is 20% greater than Mid	1,200	1,600	1,920

Troubleshooting and repair:
Mid = half of $4,000 salary
    + 23% burden
    + 10% training
    + 10% occupancy cost, 4-hour
        hardware maintenance
        contract on two servers,
        $500 each per month
	3,290	3,860	4,430

Per 100 user monthly total	$5,920	$7,250	$8,500

Assumptions:

1. Network administration, narrowly defined (passwords, access rights, backups, etc.), is assumed to take one staffer's time for 200 users.
2. Help desk services cover application support and end-user network issues.
3. Troubleshooting and repair covers salary and burden for one systems engineer for every 200 users and adds cost of outside repair services. (The actual costs of internally provided service capabilities include costs of stocking spare

parts; spares' obsolescence, tracking and shrinkage; training for repair personnel; manuals, special tools and test equipment; and additional occupancy cost.)

Support Costs—The Bottom Line

Based on the numbers in Table 2-2, it is clear that the annual operating costs of a network, consisting mostly of salaries (or outside services), can easily be half of the capital costs of the hardware and software. These are personnel-based figures, not including the costs of dedicated phone lines or other services. If outside contractors supply cabling services, those expenditures must also be added. Though some of these costs may be disguised by informal support provision and others by long work weeks on the part of systems engineers exempt from overtime requirements, network management tools will clearly multiply the productivity of these staffers.

Networks, Lost Productivity and Lost Revenue—General Principles

The principal determinant of how much productivity is lost as the result of a down network or a down server is the extent to which the network is "mission-critical" rather than a "productivity enhancer" or a "peripheral cost reducer." If the manufacturer's assembly line, the travel agency's link to the airlines or the law office's document storage and retrieval system can't work without the network, a down network is no different than a power failure. If it lasts more than a few minutes, people take an early lunch and check back later. If it lasts an hour or more, people are likely to go home.

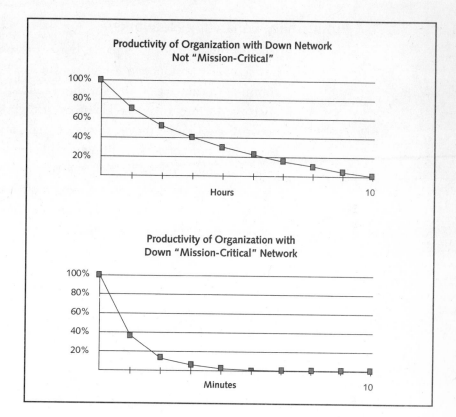

Figure 2-1 The Costs of a Down Network

Mission-Critical Networks

With fully mission-critical networks, you can conservatively multiply the organization's monthly payroll, benefits and occupancy cost by the fraction of a business-month the network is unavailable and produce the numbers. The results are frightening. (Four hours is about 2.5 percent of a working month.) The costs could easily be $30 to $70 per active user per hour—that is, $3,000 to $7,000 per hour for an average-sized network of 100 nodes. Under these conditions, fault tolerance is a good deal at almost any price.

Productivity-Enhancing Networks

What if the network is valuable, but not essential to the conduct of business? For instance, a router goes down but the local office can continue to transact business without uploading to corporate headquarters. Or users have local copies of their software, so when the network goes down they lose only e-mail, access to files stored on the server and network printing. On this end of the "mission criticality" scale, it is possible that the cost to the organization in lost productivity is minimal, even nonexistent. Users perform tasks in a different order, or they use different tools, but their jobs continue to get done until the network comes back up.

Unfortunately, networks fitting this description grow insidiously into mission-critical networks: Someone says that the "productivity enhancer" network can supply 3270 emulation services to desktop PCs through a communications server or an SNA gateway for a fraction of the cost of the terminals on those same desktops. The terminals are taken away, and the mission-critical order-entry function is on the network. One of the most attractive features of a standards-based PC network is its amazing flexibility. Once the basic network infrastructure is in place, expanding the services the network provides is cheap, simple, and in most cases irresistible.

Intangible and Human Costs

The opportunity cost of a down network is difficult to quantify, but no less a significant cost for that reason. The orders booked by the competition, the disgruntled customers who won't be back, and the overtime costs to get back on schedule are all real costs of down networks.

The preceding kinds of accounting miss certain hard-to-quantify, but still apparent costs. Users dread jobs that require them to repeat work over and over. A network manager's marriage suffers from a series of all-night assignments. Skilled people's wasted effort carries a kind of charge that cost calculations can't capture.

Underestimating PCs

Senior management has grossly underestimated the penetration of PCs in companies, the value of those PCs and of local area networks or wide area networks, and the degree to which their businesses have become dependent upon this technology. It's an underestimation because a single PC is a small dollar item. It's not a $2.5 million mainframe. Many large corporations probably have as much, if not more, sheer dollars invested in desktop machines than in their mainframe networks. They just don't know it.

—*Diane Danielle, industry columnist and President of Danielle Associates, a network consulting firm*

Costs of a Down Network Beyond Lost Productivity

Productivity costs may be more or less disguised, but certain other costs are not:

- Compensation for the employee or contractor who tracks down the fault and corrects it: probably $75 to $150 per hour. Charges are likely to accrue for longer than just the time the network is down. The first priority is to reestablish the essential network functions by any means necessary, whether by temporarily replacing a server or router or by reinstalling a prior version of a program or operating system. Then fault diagnosis can proceed in parallel with normal functions. Ultimately, these services may take days even though the network was back in operation in an hour or two. Typical costs could easily amount to $1,000 for each event.

- The cost to restore any lost or damaged information: perhaps $50 to $100 per hour, though specialty disk recovery services can cost thousands of dollars for a single hard-to-recover drive. A typical cost might be $500 per event.

- The time users spend rebooting their systems, reattaching to the network and recovering or reentering data lost when the network went down: anywhere from $5 or $10 per active user for simple restoration of normalcy to hundreds of dollars for people who have to spend days rekeying lost data. A typical cost might be $500 per event on a 100-user network.

Costs and Clones

It doesn't make sense for me to look at using a clone or a cheaper box. Money is not the issue when it comes to providing 99.9 percent up time for our applications 24 hours a day. It's critical. So we look to buy the best piece of hardware we can.

If you don't, you pay for it in the long run, with technical costs and troubleshooting costs that you wouldn't have if you spent the money up front either to bring in the right resources to help you get it done right or to provide good hardware and the right products.

—*Jane Shea, Sr. Technical Analyst, AmSys Telemanagement*

The Costs of Security Disasters

Security disasters may be difficult to quantify, but the magnitude of the potential loss is undeniable. Any organization that carries insurance should be sufficiently prudent to protect against the following kinds of events.

Fire and Rain

Although the facility has been damaged, phones, desks, partitions and PCs can be set up elsewhere, quickly. Yet if the organization's data—customer lists, credit files, inventories, accounts receivable, personnel files, all kinds of correspondence—are lost, and not backed up offsite, there may be no point in trying to start again. Even in the best circumstances, starting again may be unnecessarily painful, expensive and prolonged without timely backups.

Confidentiality

Try to quantify the cost of "Yes" answers to any of the following questions: Could a competitor log on to the network remotely and appropriate trade secrets? Could embarrassing or damaging e-mail messages get forwarded to everyone in the organization? Are there confidentiality obligations for information kept on a network that will be difficult to live up to because the network is not secure?

The Disgruntled Employee

If the right networking precautions are not taken, stealing data, erasing files, and other kinds of sabotage may take only a few seconds. Backups provide insurance against sabotage, but not against theft.

Viruses

Unsecured networks are frighteningly vulnerable to computer viruses. Infections can get into backups and wreck data again after it has been restored.

Chapter 7, Planning for a Secure Network, discusses possible remedies for these kinds of threats.

The SPA Audit

The penny-wise MIS director loaded up the company's eight file servers with single-user copies of all the PC software the organization used and encouraged users to copy them locally—in violation, needless to say, of the license agreements of the programs. He "saved" $40,000.

One wintry day, a sales rep who had installed six of these programs on her laptop lost an argument with her boss over a fine point of the company's compensation plan. She dropped a dime to the Software Publishers' Association.

A week later a team of SPA auditors and the FBI turned up at headquarters, demanding to see proof of purchase for each extant copy of every flavor of software in the building and in the field.

The company managed to avoid criminal prosecution by (1) purchasing licenses for every copy of every program on the spot ($100,000 cash, since lots of people had copies they didn't really need), (2) settling with the SPA after the kind of negotiations that corporate lawyers hate to be involved in ($200,000 cash) and (3) ejecting the MIS director (who had just been promoted to MIS VP) onto the street so fast the wind whistled in his ears.

The point of this parable is that misappropriating software is easy for network users and risky for organizations. Network management can control software proliferation and meter concurrent execution, thus guarding against this nightmare scenario.

The Impact of Network Management on Costs

Managed networks experience fewer instances of down networks and less total downtime than unmanaged networks. Fault management tools can help identify and isolate faults rapidly. Configuration management tools can streamline administrative procedures and minimize many of the overhead costs of networks. Performance-monitoring tools can anticipate problems and alert the people who can correct them. In some cases, problems can be corrected before they bring the network down. Planning for security minimizes the risks associated with PC networks. Ultimately, investing in network management is a business decision like many others. The danger lies in failing to recognize just how high the stakes may be.

Costs and Benefits for a Sample Management Project

Table 2-3   Costs of Converting a 100-node, Thin Ethernet Network to a Managed 10BASE-T Network

Transceivers for workstations	(Workstations already have coaxial cable interface boards)	100 x $75	$7,500
Managed hubs	Managed modular concentrators	2 x $3,000	$6,000
	10BASE-T modules	10 x $1,600	$16,000
Capital outlay subtotal		$295/node	$29,500
Workstation installation	100 x 15 minutes x $50/hour		$1,250
Wiring closet installation	2 x 8 hours x $50/hour		$800
Labor subtotal		$20/node	$2,050
Total cost		$315/node	$31,550

The principal benefit of this sample project is the reduction in network downtime. Coaxial cable Ethernet segments regularly go out completely when any single connector or terminator has a problem. With centrally managed hubs and 10BASE-T wiring, cable-related outages can be almost completely prevented. One rough way to calculate a breakeven period for this project is to calculate the average monthly downtime cost and divide it into the total project cost. If downtime costs $5,000 per hour, the old coaxial network is down 4 hours per month, and the new 10BASE-T network is down half an hour per month, the breakeven period is: $31,550/(4 hr/mo - 0.5 hr/mo) x $5,000/hr = 1.8 months. If downtime costs $1,000 per hour, the breakeven period is 9 months. If the unshielded twisted-pair cable must be installed from scratch, at a cost of $100 per node, and the downtime cost figure of $1,000 per hour is used, the breakeven period is still less than 12 months.

Other cost savings follow from this sample project. Troubleshooting problems other than those relating to the cable, such as bad network interface boards or improper user configurations, will be speeded up. Users' network performance may be improved if the old cable was marginal. Performance with the managed hub can be baselined and monitored to proactively identify future problems.

LANs and Mainstream Computing

Even when LANs are large, and even when they extend to wide area networks, they still aren't mainstream computing for a lot of companies. Most major corporations can easily tell you how much money they've got invested in their mainframes. They can tell you what's invested in their telecommunications network or satellites or their T-1 network. But if you ask them what they've got in terms of PCs or LANs or Macintoshes, they probably haven't the foggiest notion, because it's still very decentralized. There are pockets of PCs all over—they may actually be quite large, but they're still pockets.

—Diane Danielle, industry columnist and President of Danielle Associates, a network consulting firm

3 / Planning Networked Systems for Management

Anarchy and Totalitarianism
The Configuration Platform
The OSI Model and Planning
Layers 1–7 of the OSI Model

PC networks grow opportunistically. Departments, task forces and subgroups assemble them and suddenly need to attach to the rest of the organization. This chapter is intended to assist in developing successful plans for managing networked systems. Implementing those plans is an entirely different challenge, a political one that is closely related to budgeting and purchasing practices.

The context for planning is defined by the way an organization chooses to structure itself. Before discussing some of the technical choices that affect network manageability, this chapter will look at the primary techno-political decisions that must be made prior to other kinds of meaningful planning. Then some of the more purely technical issues affecting planning will be considered. These decisions are grouped according to the layers of the Open Systems

Interconnect (OSI) Reference Model. For the benefit of readers unfamiliar with the seven-layer model, the discussion includes some explanation of the basic concepts.

Network Anarchy and Network Totalitarianism

The two limiting possibilities for organizations' political stances regarding the network are anarchy and totalitarianism. These tendencies can be completely independent of an organization's overall management; thus highly decentralized organizations may be network-totalitarian and strongly hierarchical organizations may be network-anarchic.

"Pretty soon we might not even allow people to have the gateway of their choice. We might force them to use our gateway. We want to reduce the number of choices a user has."

—JERRY WHITE

The hypothetical network-anarchic organization permits decentralized purchasing of all kinds of computing equipment. Any planning is done at the department level, making overall coordination unlikely. There are no guidelines for the types of PCs used as workstations or servers, so many brands and models are freely intermingled. New protocols can be introduced whenever users decide that their applications need them. Users modify their configurations at will. Decisions about cabling, wide area connections and internetworking are made at the department level. Backup is the responsibility of each user or department. So is training. The network management staff is the servant of the users, committed to setting up and maintaining the ever-expanding mixture of components.

Network-totalitarian organizations, which are not hypothetical, centrally procure PCs, peripherals and software, as well as networking-specific components. There are standard-issue workstations for users, with no floppy disks or local hard disks. Users see only the organization-wide menuing system when they turn on their workstations. They never attempt to improve the system's performance by adding memory, changing the configuration files or installing a replacement printer driver. If they do, Network Control Central knows immediately and reverses the modification (with a letter to the user's personnel file generated automatically). All the data on the network is carefully backed up with off-site storage. Users are fully trained in the techniques and applications they need to know. The network managers are the enforcers of uniformity, if not the masters, of the network. This group identifies deviations, reverses them, and takes action to prevent them in the future.

Table 3-1 Anarchy vs. Totalitarianism

Anarchy	Totalitarianism
Users control workstation configurations	Organization controls workstation configurations
Users have floppy drives and local hard disk drives	Users have diskless workstations
Users boot locally and may run applications from local drives	Users boot from the server and run only network applications
Network support department (if there is one) is the servant of the users	Network support department makes the rules for the users
Difficult and costly to support with respect to help desk, troubleshooting	Easy and cheap to support
Flexible—work can continue when the network is down	Brittle—no network, no work
Resourceful users maximize the productivity of the network	Resourceful users have to fill out forms and wait indefinitely to try out a good idea
Resourceful users waste time tinkering	No one tinkers

Most organizations are far removed from both of these poles. However, in organizations with network-anarchic tendencies, planning is greatly complicated because procurement is often decentralized. Coordination likely has to be mandated from the top. Even if department managers agree to establish an approved list of products or organization-wide backup standards, a lone dissenter can bring down the whole house of cards by not budgeting for the agreed-upon items or by authorizing the purchase of nonstandard items.

On Control

We have a different attitude toward it than the mainframe guys. Those of us who come from the distributed side have the attitude 'Unless we tell you not to, go ahead,' and their view is 'Unless we tell you you can, you can't.' They have a kind of mainframe-centric, we-control-everything attitude.

Our department does a lot of training and tutorials. This is how we maintain control. Control stays in the local area via the system administrators we train.

—*James Brentano, Network Specialist at a West Coast utility company*

Very little meaningful planning can take place without centralized procurement control over the following:

- the physical infrastructure, including cabling and connections
- the components of network architecture, including the network interface elements and the concentrators or hubs that establish backbones and the overall topology
- internetworking components such as bridges, routers, gateways and wide area services
- items that require the support of new network protocols—previously unused operating systems (Unix, Macintosh, OS/2) or certain classes of new applications
- e-mail and other store-and-forward services, e.g., Lotus *Notes*
- network directory services
- network diagnostic and management tools

Organizations with network-totalitarian leanings find the task of planning relatively easy. Migrations to different workstation technologies, version upgrades and rolling out new applications are all greatly simplified by central control over the network. Support and training costs are also minimized.

Automating Standards

I think it's more important to make a choice and establish standards than to have a variety of choices. Standards are key. Before our client-server information delivery system was installed in user environments, we insisted upon the establishment of ongoing standards. We spent time building the user environments so that each individual user didn't have a different log-in script. Directory tree structure and search paths are set automatically, so they are the same everywhere.

Our standards are in automated form, available within Lotus *Notes*. Our generic network specifications are listed. The system explains how a file server should be constructed. The organization prefers U.S.-built equipment. Various other guidelines must be followed internationally. Our software will allow us to install *Notes*, Lotus *CC:mail* and other Windows applications automatically.

We want to avoid excessive administration effort in the branches in the U.S. and around the world. It took a year and a half to develop this way of setting and communicating standards. It's not a problem here to establish standards, because most of the IS people have mainframe backgrounds. They understand that a network is in many ways no different than a mainframe. You need fail-safe backup and recovery procedures, and sometimes these get overlooked. When someone has only desktop experience, they don't do anything about these issues until they run into trouble.

We spent a lot of time discussing the benefits of this approach with those who were relatively autonomous in the organization. Eventually people realized that working together is a good direction. The resistance we encountered at times was due less to technical snobbery than to a concern for job security. Another reason I was able to persuade divisions to cooperate with setting standards was there weren't a lot in place at the time.

—*Arthur Grant, IS officer for a commercial development corporation*

The Configuration Platform

One method of controlling combinatorial proliferation is to establish a small group of well-defined platforms from which the organization's server and workstation needs are filled by orderly extensions. If a case can be made for Macintoshes on an AppleTalk network for one department, or for a Sun database server in another, these devices can be connected in an orderly, well-documented way, with "firewalls" that can isolate them if trouble arises.

"We're trying to limit the number of protocols on a wide area network. For example, we do not have IPX packets going across the wide area network. So a user can't log in from a DOS workstation running IPX to look at a server. This is something that was set up in terms of designing the wide area network."

— RANDY HOWLAND

On a large network, there may be dozens or hundreds of changes made on user configurations every day. Most of these changes have no effect on the operation of the network, but if they go untracked for very long, the network environment can soon become an overwhelming mystery factor whenever problems arise. A platform configuration serves as a starting point for troubleshooting difficult problems. With a documented platform, a server or even a group of workstations in a misbehaving network can be reconfigured in a condition that is known to have operated properly at one time. If the basic platform configuration won't run correctly, the problem should be one of a very few possibilities. If the platform configuration runs normally, extensions can be added back systematically until the problem resurfaces.

The foundation of a DOS workstation platform might consist of a minimum amount of RAM, specific versions of DOS and Windows and particular configuration parameters (extended memory setup, environment size, disk cache guidelines, for example). On Apple Macintosh networks, the basic requirements include a minimum amount of RAM and a specific version of System software. Requiring the same model computer and the same model network interface card at each workstation makes the management job much easier but may be difficult to achieve politically.

Similarly, network server configurations can be extended from a basic platform. The essential components of a server platform include the version of the network operating system, minimum RAM requirements, specific extensions to the operating system (NLMs or VAPs for NetWare servers), disk drive configurations (duplexing, mirroring or other fault-tolerant methods), print queue specification and diagnostic software. As with workstations, a standard model computer and network interface card is highly desirable.

Extensions to the basic platforms must be documented religiously with their implementation date. If problems arise that cannot be diagnosed with the available tools, the extensions can be rolled back in an orderly fashion. Network inventory software can make the job of documentation easy or even eliminate much of the need for manual configuration collection. In organizations with a sizable installed base of PCs and servers, the best that can be done is to begin to migrate to platforms.

Standards and Efficiency

Set your standards for workstation configuration and follow them. The worst thing you can do is to do the same thing five different ways. We had a group of technicians who were not consistent in the way they set up a station. Every time we had a problem, we had to check on how the workstation was configured and they were all different. Every server had the printers configured differently, or they had the printers configured three different ways. There was no documentation available. It was very difficult to work this way.

You have to set standards and follow them. You have to
decide, 'This is how I'm going to handle printers. I'm going to
use Novell PSERVER and set up my HPs as clients to PSERVER.'
You can't set up Novell PSERVER and then set up an HP printer
as a print server. Then you never know when something's
wrong, where to check.

I'm now involved in setting up a new LAN/WAN. We're not
going to allow nonstandard machines on the network. If
someone wants to put an Acme garage machine on the network, we'll say, 'Do it yourself.' We're going to have a set
number of protocols we support. If somebody wants to run
OS/2 or NetBIOS, forget it. We're not going to support that.
If they don't comply, we won't let them on the network. We
don't think they will want to do it themselves.

I'm now working on building a series of large, standardized file
servers—a 250-user Novell license, with 10GB storage. We
are in the documentation phase now. We've set up one large
server. We will not be adding any users until the documentation is complete. I've never had the luxury of doing that
before. Once we complete work on this server, we will add
users and refine our procedures. Then we will have a template
in place, and we can roll out 20 of these.

—*Jerry White, Network Manager for a West Coast financial
institution*

The OSI Model as a Template for Planning

Much thought and discussion about networks can best be organized
in terms of the International Standards Organization's Open Systems Interconnect (OSI) model. This structure divides network
operations into discrete layers, each of which provides specific functions. Each of the layers isolates a specific set of problems that must
be solved to provide reliable, accurate and efficient data transmission. A layer of the model communicates only with the layers

"The users are going to want the network managers to do the technical research for them. Most department managers don't really want to get involved in technical details; they just want to perform their business function in the organization. They don't want a LAN administrator in their department. So the decentralized era of the bank is over, and this bank is on the way to becoming centralized as far as LANs are concerned."

—JERRY WHITE

directly above and below it, so it can be focused on very specific operations and not have to anticipate how to cope with the complexity of the rest of the network environment. In many cases, a particular implementation of a layer can be interchanged with another implementation to improve performance, reliability, security or manageability. (See Figure 3-1.)

In many ways, the operation of a data network resembles that of a mail delivery system with strict hierarchical rules. For a letter to be delivered, it must first go into an interoffice mail envelope, which indicates a mail stop within the company. This envelope must be put into a Federal Express envelope, which has an end address where the package can be signed for (Post Office Box numbers not being permitted). Federal Express puts the package into an airplane container, which indicates the destination airport. At the destination, the process is reversed. This model is closely analogous to the OSI Reference Model. (See Figure 3-2.)

Competing layered models, such as IBM's, can generally be overlaid on the OSI map without much loss of basic concepts. The OSI's mission is much more ambitious than providing the technological community with reference materials, though. It defines its own protocols for each layer of the reference model. Thus there are the standardized functions of, say, the OSI Reference Model session layer (layer 5), which may need to be performed on any network, and the OSI session layer protocols, a document named ISO 8327, which defines an implementation for an OSI network. (See Appendix B.)

The formats and rules for interaction that have been identified and agreed upon for particular layers are known as protocols. The OSI standards committee has the most complete set of these protocols, but its protocols are not necessarily the most widely adopted ones in the real world. At many layers, proprietary protocols from IBM,

Figure 3-1 The Open Systems Interconnect Reference Model

LEVEL 7

Application Layer

Provides the interface between network services and the local node's application software or operating system. Application layer services include directory services, messaging and terminal emulation.

LEVEL 6

Presentation Layer

Translates data—texual, numeric or other types—for the application layer or for applications or system software. For example, the presentation layer converts EBCDIC text to ASCII text.

LEVEL 5

Session Layer

Controls and synchronizes dialog between two processes or users at the ends of a network link.

LEVEL 4

Transport Layer

Provides end-to-end connection services to the session layer, breaking up the elements of the session if necessary, sending them via multiple routes if necessary, and reassembling them as they arrive.

LEVEL 3

Network Layer

Routes packets of data from one internetwork node to another on the way to the ultimate destination.

LEVEL 2

Data Link Layer

Provides a reliable, acknowledged frame delivery service to the network layer. It includes two sublayers, the Logical Link Control sublayer and the Media Access Control sublayer.

LEVEL 1

Physical Layer

Presents an intelligible stream of bits over a communications medium. This layer determines how the digital data in the data link layer will be converted to electromagnetic impulses for transmission.

Figure 3-2 The Interoffice Mail System Reference Model

LEVEL 5

User Mailbox Layer

Provides a repository for users to pick up and send mail (in interoffice mail envelopes or other labels that identify the mail stop within the building).

LEVEL 4

Interoffice Mail Layer

Picks up bins of mail and sorts mail bound for local offices from that bound for remote locations. Routes local mail to user mailboxes and passes remote mail to remote mail function.

LEVEL 3

Remote Mail Layer

Sorts remote mail among U.S. Mail, UPS, Federal Express and local courier service. For Federal Express, encloses interoffice envelope in a Fed Ex envelope or package.

LEVEL 2

Federal Express Truck Layer

Encloses Federal Express envelope in tray with other envelopes with similar destinations and delivers it to the airport.

LEVEL 1

Federal Express Container Layer

Loads all trays with the same hub destination into a container bound for that airport and unloads them at the destination.

Novell, Sun and Apple, for instance, are the ones most commonly encountered on PC networks. The Internet protocols are much more widely implemented than the OSI protocols for many layers, and its network management standards are far more popular than the OSI's.

The discussion that follows climbs through the layers of the OSI Reference Model. It identifies the principal problems a network has to solve at each layer and discusses the most common solutions in the PC network world. At each juncture, it indicates the key choices that must be made when a PC network is designed, implemented, expanded or modified. As far as possible, it spells out the implications of those choices for managing the system.

There is a tendency to think that all the levels of the OSI Reference Model are equally significant. Perhaps they are to the OSI standards committee. For this discussion of PC networks, the choice of protocols at layers 1 and 2 is very important for day-to-day network management. The protocols of layer 3 are also very important, although networks, usually small ones, can be implemented without them. Layer 4 protocols are moderately significant in some networks, and necessary for SNMP management. Layers 5 and 6 rarely have practical effects on PC networks. Layer 7 is important for network management and can also be significant for ordinary problem-solving.

In decisions related to layers 1 and 2, a network planner has a broad range of choices. Many different physical media and access-sharing methods have been documented, standardized, offered commercially and used practically. To a great degree, these media and access-sharing methods can be substituted interchangeably for reasons of cost, existing infrastructure or performance requirements.

In most cases, the protocols at layers 3 and 4 (and 5, if any are used) are inherent in the network operating system that is selected. Only recently have users gotten the ability simultaneously to employ multiple protocols at these middle layers. It is still rare to find a network that employs only a single protocol that is not the default set, although this state of affairs may not last. In any event, middle-layer protocols are not so much chosen as they are accepted as part of the network operating system. The real decisions are whether or not to support one or more additional protocol suites beyond the one included by default.

"When we started instituting local area network technology, one of our key goals was interoperability across OS/2, DOS, Macintosh and Sun workstations. To that end we selected technologies that would allow us to provide file services and print services across all of those platforms."

— RANDY HOWLAND

The protocols at layers 6 and 7 are usually transparent to the user and built into the software; only in exceptional cases do the protocols supported at these layers determine purchasing decisions. Software applications may make use of standardized services at these upper layers of the OSI Model. However, these layer-7 services, including directory facilities, messaging mechanisms and network management itself, are not normally bundled together as a take-it-or-leave-it proposition. It may even be necessary to look at the fine print in the software's documentation to determine whether one of these standards is supported. Many of the best-known network software applications use their own proprietary methods rather than supporting any standards at the seventh layer.

Setting Standards

Establishing standards is important for any downsizing industry. We need to be able to support a large number of people with as few people as possible. Part of the way that any group is going to accomplish that goal is through the use of common products, common tools, common standards. The more products out there, the more support it's going to take to administer and to handle them. Same with the network. Standards become a way to maximize the people that we have for support and for performing architecture work across a wide base.

So we use common protocols, common methods and techniques, and applications for accessing all these different things. This means we can deliver to any workstation a series of services—connectivity to Vaxes, Suns, hosts, modems, dial out faxing—via one network connection. Our goal is to set those standards and to try to provide a clear direction within the company for people who need to connect with any kind of host.

—Randy Howland, Network Manager for a Fortune 500 technology company

Layer 1 of the OSI Model—The Physical Layer

The physical layer of the OSI Model is concerned with electromagnetic or optical impulses. The standards at this layer define what kinds of signals are allowed on the cable (or other medium) and how to distinguish a 1-bit from a 0-bit. They also address the physical and electrical properties of cables and connectors. As far as the physical layer is concerned, network traffic is simply a stream of bits with no further differentiation.

When the lion's share of installed LANs consisted of Ethernet buses running on coaxial cable, problems with poor connector attachments, improper termination, excessive run lengths and other poor installation practices were rampant. On these early LANs, which were less likely than those of today to support multiple protocols or to be interconnected with other networks, as many as 80 percent of the faults could be traced to the cable plant. As token ring networks began to grow, and especially after the establishment of the Ethernet 10BASE-T standard in late 1990, the problem of the unstable cable was essentially solved. The physical star topologies of these newer cabling methods, combined with hub technology that automatically disconnects nodes that threaten the operation of the network, eliminate what was the largest source of faults on the most popular network installations.

Present-Day Cable Technology

The cable plant or wiring infrastructure of a building (or an enterprise) sets the outer bounds of manageability. Because cables run through special channels, or above the ceiling, or even inside walls, it is essential for the network, not to mention the management scheme that runs on the network, that the cable plant be absolutely solid—comparable in reliability to the cables that provide telephone service and electric power.

Shielded Twisted Pair

This cabling medium is associated with IBM, which specified the characteristics of shielded twisted pair when it spelled out its Premises Distribution System for systematically connecting workstations and other computing devices throughout buildings. Its resistance to electrical interference and its ability to propagate undistorted waveforms are superior to that of unshielded twisted pair. Therefore shielded twisted pair supports greater overall distances between the components of a token ring network than unshielded. Its cost is also higher.

Unshielded Twisted Pair

Many modern buildings are fully equipped with this type of cable at each workstation because the telephone cable infrastructure uses it. (It is not the same as "silver-satin" wiring used for analog phone lines, however.) Some fortunate organizations can install networks without incurring costs for running new cable. Both 10BASE-T Ethernet networks and 4-megabits-per-second (Mbits/sec) token ring networks are officially supported on data grade unshielded twisted pair. Until 1992, IBM was unwilling to support 16-Mbits/sec token ring networks on unshielded twisted pair cable, though other token ring suppliers installed the higher-speed networks successfully on it. Internode distances must be shorter at 16 Mbits/sec than at 4 Mbits/sec. ARCnet can also run on twisted pair cables with some sacrifice in the overall distances allowed.

Unshielded twisted pair cable is classified as type 3, type 4 or type 5, depending on its bandwidth specifications. In general, type 3 is acceptable for 4-Mbits/sec token ring networks and 10-Mbits/sec Ethernet installations. Type 4 is roughly 20 percent more costly, but readily supports 16-Mbits/sec token rings and probably contributes to a more flexible and stable Ethernet. Type 5 is not widely installed today, but may be required for 100-Mbits/sec copper systems in the future.

Coaxial Cable

This type of cable was the most common medium for Ethernet networks before the 10BASE-T standard was adopted. These networks were defined with a bus topology. Nowadays coax is used mostly for backbones, if at all, in new installations. It supports greater distances than 10BASE-T wiring. The early Standard Ethernet cabling (10BASE-5) required a cable 0.4 inch in diameter, which was costly, hard to install and difficult to attach to. Thin Ethernet, sometimes called Cheapernet, was standardized by the 10BASE-2 specification. This cable has a diameter of 0.2 inch and offers lower cost and better attachment flexibility. ARCnet networks can operate on RG/62 coaxial cables, which have been installed in many buildings to support IBM 3270-type terminals.

Fiber-Optic Cable

These cables conduct light, not electrical signals. They are therefore impervious to the usual sources of electrical interference, such as fluorescent lighting fixtures and elevator motors, which can degrade the performance of copper-medium networks. Running fiber between buildings can prevent electrical mismatches that might interfere with networks connected by copper. Fiber has inherent security advantages since it is impossible to tap without physically penetrating the cable, unlike copper wires. Optical transceivers can convert Ethernet signals to light using the Fiber Optic Inter-Repeater Link (FOIRL) specification. With this technology, Ethernet backbones can run as long as 1,000 meters, twice as long as standard thick Ethernet coax. Some, but not all, of the standards necessary for actually implementing Fiber Distributed Data Interface (FDDI) have been adopted. These networks run at 100 Mbits/sec and use token ring data link technology. Standards for running FDDI to workstations over copper wire have been proposed and discussed, but agreement and adoption may be years away.

Wireless LANs

Infrared and microwave radio transmission equipment that can create networks without cable connections is available commercially. In theory, the high cost of this special equipment can be offset by cutting expenses for adding, moving and changing cable connections. In practice, today's wireless LAN technology requires performance sacrifices compared to cable, and some of the systems are subject to electrical interference or vulnerability from line-of-sight impairment. When all the factors are considered, wireless networks only make sense in organizations where the volume of cabling changes is large, the cost and hassle of rewiring is particularly high, and conditions don't prevent their proper operation.

LANs can be connected together at full Ethernet transmission rates with microwave transceivers. If the distance that must be covered is a few miles and high speed is necessary, this technology may provide the best price-performance ratio. The technology is mature, but specialized. As with fiber-optic cable, the usual tools for troubleshooting copper cables are not much help in managing these links.

Cable Specs

We had some cable we knew was not Level 3 Cable but we wanted to use it to install a network. It had originally been used for SNA. We had some distance concerns, as there were long distances involved in this network. We knew it was shielded, and 10BASE-T cable specifies unshielded. It was 22 gauge, but we thought it would probably work. The integrator came out, we picked some sample cables and scanned them with a cable tester and, for the most part, they came out great. The cable scanner told us that the longest distances were over spec, actually over 400 feet, but all the other measurements were within spec. Based on that evaluation, we decided to go ahead. We bought equipment and installed a LAN and it worked.

—Jerry White, Network Manager for a West Coast financial institution

Management and the Physical Layer

Management traffic on network cable is the same as any other traffic. It will travel over any medium that is set up correctly. Nonetheless, network fault identification, performance analysis and security can be strongly affected by the choice of medium. The following list addresses some of the implications of physical layer choices.

Once a well-structured network runs correctly, faults arising from the cable infrastructure will be local and minor.

1. Unshielded twisted pair provides adequate performance at the lowest possible cost for many of today's networks. For applications that use traditional types of data—text, numbers, database inquiry and most publishing—this cable infrastructure should suffice for the foreseeable future.

2. In many installations, shielded twisted pair would constitute an unnecessary expense if today's technology stopped developing. The superior electrical qualities of this medium will allow it to perform better than UTP on high-speed networks in the future. The incremental cost will be a worthwhile investment provided, firstly, that workstations on the network will need to run applications that require a greater bandwidth than today's Ethernet and token ring, and, secondly, that FDDI running on copper wire or a similar standard gets established.

3. Traditional coax-based Ethernet networks and others with a bus topology often display "all or nothing" faults: The whole segment will not function until the fault is identified and corrected. Management resources permanently on the network, such as monitoring stations, will stop functioning at the same time as the network segment itself. The specialized equipment that can identify cable faults can only be used on a down network. Network managers lacking a time domain reflectometer (and the skill to use one) will find themselves disconnecting workstations sequentially, to

isolate faults by trial and error. Most everyone would agree that it is inefficient to assign highly trained and well-paid people to crawl along the floors in an office, using trial and error to find a bad connection.

4. Optical fiber and wireless network segments don't suffer from the "all or nothing" faults of Ethernet buses—one faulty workstation or cable won't prevent the overall network from operating. But when faults arise or performance degrades, there is a greater difficulty certifying that these media are working correctly than there is with copper wire. The special tools required are costly, and the skill to apply them is rare. In practice, specialists must be brought in when problems appear.

5. Cabling can contribute to network faults in unexpected ways. Different suppliers, or even different production runs of the same medium, may cause problems if they are intermingled on a network segment. With modern structured wiring techniques, physical-layer faults can usually be isolated. Once a well-structured network runs correctly, faults arising from the cable infrastructure will be local and minor.

Structured Wiring Schemes

While coaxial cable is commonly associated with bus topologies, shielded and unshielded twisted pair installations are almost always installed as part of a structured wiring system. From the point of view of the architect or facilities manager, structured wiring includes standardized construction practices for distributing cables throughout buildings. From the network manager's point of view, it includes physical star topologies implemented with wiring hubs or concentrators. IBM and AT&T have published detailed specifications for two competing structured wiring methods. Physical star configurations bring all node connections to a common point before they are distributed to user workstations. In many installations, the hub or concentrator resides in the wiring closet that serves as the telephone distribution center.

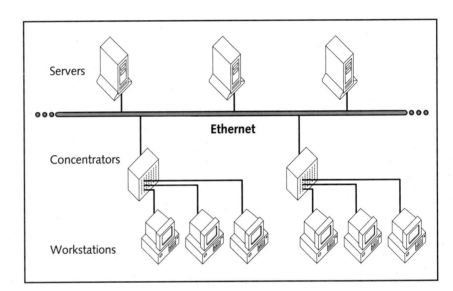

Figure 3-3 Backbone and Hub Topology (Ethernet)

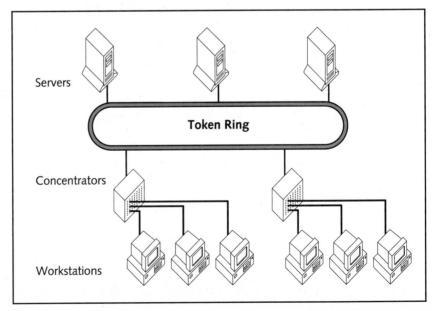

Figure 3-4 Backbone and Hub Topology (Token Ring)

The network backbone segment is the starting point for structured wiring installations. All the servers are connected to the backbone, but as a rule no workstations are. To attach workstations to the network, the backbone is connected to a hierarchical system of concentrators and hubs. If fault tolerance is required, there are many opportunities in such a configuration to provide redundant capabilities that can keep the network performing despite failures of single components.

The hub is the focal point of the physical star, where a number of workstation connections come together to be attached to the backbone. Hubs or concentrators link the backbone or the server with multiple workstations. They usually have the ability to disconnect any node that malfunctions. Most models provide diagnostic indicators that show which connections are active and perhaps indicate traffic. Some have serial ports that allow them to be controlled remotely even when the network is down.

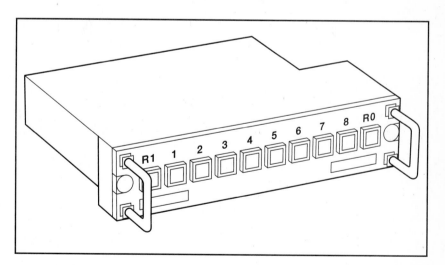

Figure 3-5 Fixed-Port Hub

Fixed-port hubs have a set number of connections and support a specific medium—unshielded twisted pair, shielded twisted pair, coaxial cable or fiber—and a specific data link method—token ring,

Ethernet, ARCnet or FDDI. Some models include configurable connections to the backbone or server, but the workstation connections are fixed. If you need to change to unshielded twisted pair from shielded twisted pair, you must buy a different hub.

Figure 3-6 Modular Concentrator

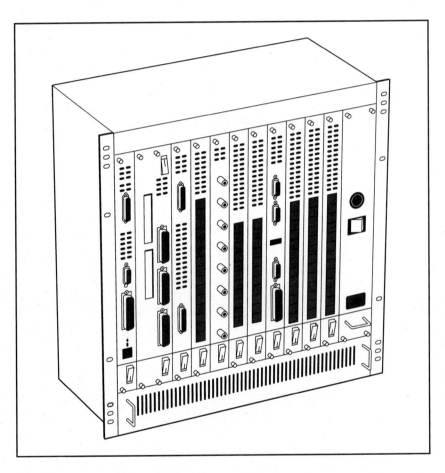

Modular concentrators have slots for media attachment modules to plug into (see Figure 3-6). Some concentrators support only Ethernet, but permit modules for different media to be used at the same time. Others support multiple data link methods, permitting simultaneous token ring, FDDI and Ethernet connections from the same box. Concentrator slots can also be dedicated to bridges or routers that provide internetworking services. Management capability can be added by installing a management module. Other slots may be used for redundant power supplies so that a failure in the first power supply won't bring down the entire subnetwork.

Stackable hubs provide some of the scalability of modular concentrators. As many as four or more of these hubs can be interconnected with short cables so that the number of nodes connected to them can be almost as high as a modular concentrator would permit. With some vendors' stackable hubs, one higher-cost manageable hub can provide management services for additional low-cost unmanaged hubs.

Figure 3-7 Stackable Hubs

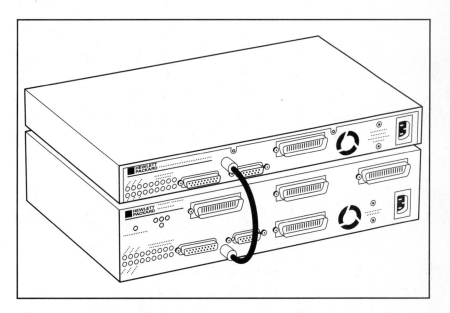

Intel and other vendors have begun manufacturing hub boards for personal computers. With these products and supporting software, such as Novell's Hub Services Manager, managed hub services can be provided by the file server PC itself, or by a PC specially configured for the job, at a very low cost per port.

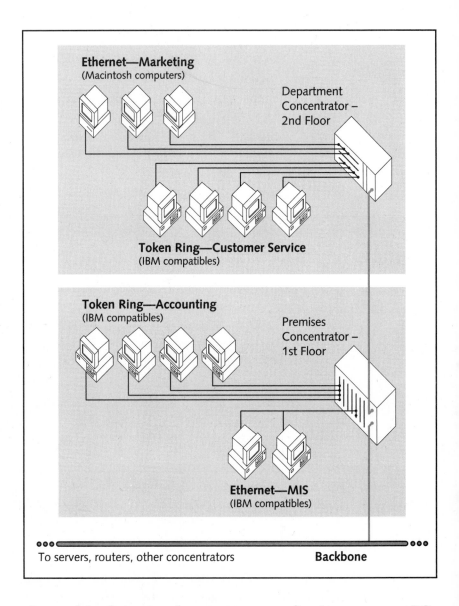

Figure 3-8 Structured Wiring Installation

Some of the first network management applications to run on PCs were hub managers. A hub without management capability is no less structured than one that has it, but the managed hub can be diagnosed and controlled from a central console. This is possible because the managing components capture performance information systematically and send it to the console. Managed hubs can be controlled as well as polled from the console. For instance, a malfunctioning workstation that did not trigger automatic disconnection could be shut off.

Anticipating Future Needs

The rapid pace of change may always keep network cabling from being as reliable as that of our older utilities. As network traffic increases, with digital images (in paper replacement and workflow projects, for instance), audio annotation and perhaps full-motion video someday, the 10-Mbits/sec bandwidth of Ethernet and the 16-Mbits/sec bandwidth of token ring will prove to be inadequate. Various nonstandard technologies that provide 100-Mbits/sec service over existing wiring have been built and demonstrated. Installations with shielded twisted pair wiring (often specified for token ring networks) may be more likely to have the ability to run high-speed traffic than those with unshielded twisted pair wiring, although AT&T and Hewlett-Packard have proposed a standard for 100-Mbits/sec Ethernet running over unshielded twisted pair.

Some forward-looking enterprises have invested in fiber-optic cabling, in some cases even running fiber to individual workstations rather than confining it to a backbone. In a new or newly remodeled building, the costs of laying in fiber in addition to traditional copper cables are not excessive. At this writing, however, network interface boards for high-speed fiber cost five to ten times as much as Ethernet and token ring boards. All the diagnostic equipment for fiber-optic cable is specialized and expensive—obviously the cable testing and measurement equipment used for copper cables is useless on nonconductive fiber-optic cables.

Many of the same considerations apply to wireless network connections. Microwave and infrared interconnection technology is available, but identifying faults and performance problems calls for substantial additional investment in equipment and training.

Layer 2—The Data Link Layer

The data link layer is responsible for providing error-free transmission to the higher layers. This job is accomplished by creating delimited frames (discrete bundles of data) on the physical medium, with acknowledgments confirming that they reach their destination. The data link layer controls access to the physical medium, enforcing a set of rules that manage or prevent contention between customers of the bandwidth the physical medium provides.

Some workstation-originating problems would be easier to solve if management agents were widely installed in desktops.

Ethernet and token ring, the two most widespread data link implementations, account for more than 90 percent of PC network installations today. With structured wiring practices, neither data link method offers important advantages over the other with respect to management. Of course, the people who support the network will be more successful with technology they understand fully.

Apple Macintosh workstations have built-in network access capabilities that make use of a proprietary standard, LocalTalk. LocalTalk cables run between workstations and printers in a bus configuration, though third-party hubs can be installed to run LocalTalk over twisted pair cable in a star configuration. LocalTalk networks have a much lower bandwidth—230 kilobits per second—than Ethernet and token ring. For some applications, this narrow bandwidth results in unacceptably slow performance. In those cases, Ethernet or token ring adapters can be installed on Macs.

ARCnet suffers the disadvantage of never having been officially standardized. Therefore, fewer manufacturers support it, and users have reason to doubt whether the ARCnet technology will offer the latest advances in management capability. For example, few producers of modular concentrators supply ARCnet modules for their systems. Proprietary data link schemes attract even less support than ARCnet from the network management industry. Users of these products are at the mercy of the original manufacturer for diagnostic and management tools, as well as for upgrades and bug fixes.

The optical fiber standard FDDI will doubtless be fully standardized and manageable in the near future. Especially when it is limited to establishing high-performance backbones, most organizations would not have to sacrifice manageability to take advantage of FDDI.

Some manufacturers have begun to put management capabilities into network interface cards. Without this capability, the central management console's visibility of network traffic ends at the hub. The hub can isolate the problem, identifying a particular workstation and the detailed symptoms, but it can't distinguish between problems induced by cabling, the network interface card or the workstation software. Some workstation-originating problems would be easier to solve if management agents were widely installed in desktops. Whether this set of problems is important enough to justify the expense of desktop management is subject to debate.

Layers 3, 4 and 5—The Network, Transport and Session Layers

The network layer (layer 3) of the OSI Reference Model is responsible for getting packets from one network segment to another, along the way to their destinations. (The data link layer is aware only of its own segment.) This service is known as *routing*. Any form of internetworking, whether of two LANs in the same office or thousands of segments around the world, needs the services governed by the network-layer protocols.

The transport layer (layer 4) is the lowest layer with an awareness of both ends of a network connection. Thus it may be capable of using multiple network-layer routes to maintain a connection between two nodes or of managing the use of one connection by multiple programs simultaneously.

The session layer (layer 5) provides additional services to transport-layer connections, including such things as dialog control, token management and synchronization. These services can be important to particular applications, but unlike the OSI practice, the world of PC networks rarely sees session-level protocols called out by name.

Choosing Protocols

Planning for management with respect to the three middle layers of the OSI model can be divided into two stages: deciding whether the organization needs multiple protocols and deciding which protocols those will be. The protocols in these layers are determined primarily by the choice of network operating system and secondarily by the operating systems of computers, large and small, that are connected to the network. Choosing a set of protocols to support is not particularly difficult if it is established in advance that there will be only one. However, in an environment as competitive as that of today's PC technology, limiting the network to one protocol stack is not easy. Once there are multiple protocols on the network, management issues that require resolution mount up rapidly.

The protocols from these layers commonly encountered on networked PC systems include NetWare's IPX/SPX (Internet Packet Exchange/Sequenced Packet Exchange), Apple's DDP/ATP/ASP (Datagram Delivery Protocol/Apple Transaction Protocol/ Apple

Session Protocol), LAN Manager and LAN Server's Net-BIOS/NetBEUI (Network Basic Input Output System/NetBIOS Extended User Interface) and the protocols used by many Unix systems, the Internet's TCP/IP (Transmission Control Protocol/Internet Protocol).

Internetworking

Once a network's cabling infrastructure is sound, the biggest challenges for network managers arise from connecting networks together. A bridge can be employed to connect networks simply and inexpensively. Using the data link-layer information (level 2 of the OSI Reference Model) in each packet, a bridge determines whether the packet's destination is local to its segment or not. If the packet is not local, the bridge passes it on to the other segments it is connected to. If the packet is local, it ignores (filters) it. The bridge is indifferent to information from layers higher than layer 2. It doesn't care whether the packet came from a Sun workstation using TCP/IP, a Macintosh using Apple's protocols or a DOS-based PC using IPX/SPX.

Bridges are useful not only for connecting networks, but also for segmenting them. If particular users make up a disproportionate share of a segment's traffic, installing a bridge between them and the other users can prevent their traffic from degrading everyone's performance. Special diagnostic tools may be valuable in identifying situations like this one, but the actual installation of a bridge is usually simple. Most of the major producers of modular concentrators supply bridges that can be installed in a concentrator slot. Some bridges can be managed remotely from a console with network management application software.

Routers, which concern themselves with information from layer 3 of the reference model, are more complex than bridges and constitute a greater management challenge. First, they must decode each packet more thoroughly than a bridge. Then they must decide what action to take. All in all, they are presented with a much larger processing job than bridges. Networks with traffic that uses more than one layer-3 protocol probably need a multiprotocol router. Such routers may need to make different routing decisions for each packet based on the protocols they find at the network layer. Router implementation choices can have tremendous effects on network performance.

Routers are critical components of wide area networks. They control the specific paths data must take to move from one system to another. On a WAN, communications charges are likely to be a significant consideration. Properly installed routers can maximize reliability and performance while minimizing cost.

The best way to install routers and bridges is not intuitively obvious most of the time. One of the primary justifications for using protocol analyzers (such as Novell's LANalyzer or Network General's Sniffer) is their ability to help optimize internetworking decisions. Managed routers and bridges can deliver ongoing information about their traffic and thus provide the raw material for problem-solving and performance tuning as the network changes and grows. Managed routers and bridges can also be reconfigured remotely.

The Importance of Visualization

People have to be able to visualize a network. One of the things we've observed as we've brought people from an SNA environment with terminals connected to a host, to a local area network-based environment, is the importance of visualizing the network and where certain services are located.

With a mainframe, the connection is terminal-host, period— you have a terminal connected to a controller connected to an

IBM host. We've had to radically change that view and show people, through some charts and graphs, what the local area network looks like and what the wide area network looks like. We want them to understand that we're in a building with a local area network, and that we're connected to file and print servers that give us certain types of services, and that we connect to a mainframe in another state. When they put something on the network, it leaves this building through a router that goes to another building, and on to a router to another building—and at some point there's a gateway that will actually do some translations for them.

It's important for a network manager to get a visual sense of the network across to some of the end users, to remove that 'black hole syndrome' that they're connected to something, but where is it? There's no mystery, other than that they're running a network operating system versus a local workstation operating system. So there's no major mystique, and creating charts and diagrams to allow the end user to visualize networking services can help.

—Randy Howland, Network Manager for a Fortune 500 technology company

The Hazards of Multiple Protocol Internetworks

The protocols in these three layers have roots in different technologies. People with Unix networking experience have a good understanding of TCP/IP; Novell-experienced people understand IPX/SPX; IBM mainframe people know the SNA protocols; Macintosh specialists understand Apple's protocols. Furthermore, some of them are inclined to think the others are mentally deficient for being unfamiliar with principles, practices and tools that they use every day.

The foremost difficulty is that very few people have in-depth knowledge of more than one of these technologies. The networking industry has not yet figured out a good way to develop and reproduce the skills necessary to manage multiprotocol internetworks.

You Can't Get There From Here

Network traffic can be compared to vehicular traffic in some respects. Certain roads are designated as truck routes, while others are off-limits for trucks. A truck may need to take a roundabout route to make a delivery at a nearby location. There may be a low overpass or narrow spot that prevents it from getting to a particular place at all.

Unless a router recognizes a particular packet as one it is prepared to handle, the packet may be limited to the segment it is on. For instance, an AppleTalk packet may not be able to get to any segment other than its own if there is no AppleTalk router on the segment. (See Figure 3-9.) This can present serious practical difficulties for networks that include NetWare 2.X segments, because the router functions in those versions support only the IPX protocol. The users of these networks are faced with the competing expensive prospects of installing multiprotocol routers or upgrading all the NetWare 2.X segments to higher-numbered versions that have AppleTalk routing capabilities.

If subnetworks are not able to route packets, there can be no question of managing them. A morass of cabling problems, improper print queues and other defects may plague one of these segments that is invisible to the tools used to troubleshoot the dominant network, whether that is NetWare, AppleTalk, Unix or SNA.

Compatibility Issues

The elements of a network are subject to unexpected compatibility problems. Network interface cards may not support a particular protocol (e.g., AppleTalk Filing Protocol) and therefore not be able to support routing services for the network. Others may not support

"To accomplish what we wanted with our network using Novell would have been crazy, because Novell networks are not designed for WANs. Therefore, we would have had more administration and a lot more hoops to jump through."

— ALEX DEL RIO

*Figure 3-9 Packet's
Eye View of the
Network for Different
Types of Packets*

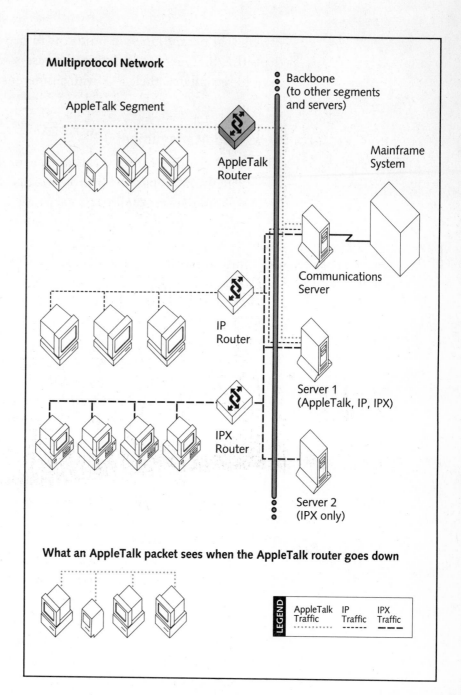

Multiprotocol Network

AppleTalk Segment

Backbone
(to other segments
and servers)

Mainframe
System

AppleTalk
Router

Communications
Server

IP
Router

Server 1
(AppleTalk, IP, IPX)

IPX
Router

Server 2
(IPX only)

What an AppleTalk packet sees when the AppleTalk router goes down

LEGEND

AppleTalk Traffic	IP Traffic	IPX Traffic

drivers that permit multiple protocols to be loaded simultaneously (e.g., IPX/SPX and TCP/IP) so that users with this requirement need to reconfigure their PCs with a different card.

Protocol Stacks and Management

The most common basis for network management is SNMP, the Simple Network Management Protocol. SNMP was created by the Internet community, so all of its early implementations employed TCP/IP as the underlying vehicle. There is no standard-based or technical argument to prevent SNMP implementations from using other protocols at the transport and network layers to carry management information and commands. Novell, for example, has implemented SNMP over IPX/SPX in some of its management offerings.

The OSI standard for network management is the Common Management Information Protocol or CMIP. Like some of the other OSI proposed standards, full seven-layer implementation of CMIP requires a substantial amount of processing overhead. This overhead, and the absence of an installed base, deters builders of products for the PC and workstation market from designing fully compliant OSI-based products. Commercial implementations are hard to find, if they exist at all. One alternative from the Internet community is Common Management Information Services and Protocol Over TCP/IP, or CMOT. This standard employs TCP/IP at the network and transport layers while using the OSI standards at the higher levels. TCP/IP requires fewer processing resources and is much more widely implemented than OSI protocols at the network and transport layers. CMIP is implemented at the application layer, layer 7, so it could theoretically be implemented over any protocol stack. Very little CMOT development is underway today. In practice, SNMP-based products constitute the lion's share of the marketplace.

Network Operating Systems

Network, transport and session protocols are not selected in and of themselves. The choice of a network operating system (NOS) generally determines the protocols for these layers and the upper layers as well. The most common PC network operating systems are Novell NetWare, Microsoft LAN Manager, Banyan VINES, IBM LAN Server, Apple Computer AppleShare and various versions of Unix.

Network operating systems include both client (or workstation) operations and server operations. The server provides access to files on its drives, network printing devices and perhaps other kinds of shared hardware, such as asynchronous communications devices and modems. To be useful, the NOS must provide these services reliably and securely. Other services may be agglomerated onto the server, though they are not intrinsically part of a network operating system narrowly defined. These services include internetwork routing, message storing and forwarding, database operations, network directory functions and accounting.

At the workstation, the client software enables local programs to get to the server transparently when they need its services. The network client software is implemented as an extension to the local operating system. Thus network volumes appear to the workstation operating system as local drives and network printing queues appear as local printer ports.

In broad outline, a network file operation from a workstation works like this: a local program, such as a word processor, asks the local operating system to open a file; the network client extension (NETX) recognizes that the request is for a network file and intercepts the request; this extension software, also known as the network shell, formats the request in terms the server can understand and passes the request to the local protocol stack; and the request is encapsulated repeatedly by the lower layers of the reference model—the network

"It's difficult to test this stuff in the sense that you have to know so much just to do the testing as well as to know what to test. You also have to take a person who is highly skilled off the support group, put them into testing, and see that it's valuable up front."

—JAMES BRENTANO

layer takes responsibility for finding the server, the data link layer manages the access to the physical medium, and the physical layer produces actual impulses on the cable. (See Figure 3-10.)

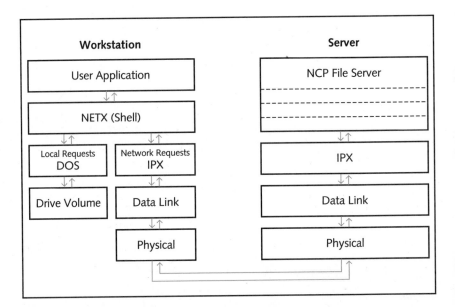

Figure 3-10 Network Workstation Shells

At the server, the process is reversed as the request for file access moves up the layers of the reference model. The physical stream of electrical (or optical) impulses is captured as a packet of data. The data link "envelope" is discarded. The network header is ignored if the server is the destination of the request. The file request can now be executed by the server program and the file itself can be returned to the client through the same process in reverse.

In theory, the client and server processes of a network operating system could use any or every protocol stack to communicate between them. In practice, the leading NOSes all have a native protocol stack that provides optimal performance and supports their unique features. Nevertheless, the day may come when network operating systems readily permit seamless protocol stack substitution and supplementation.

NetWare

Novell NetWare is by far the leading network operating system today, whether you consider market share, the extent of services offered to users, the breadth of third-party products that support it or the breadth of support it offers for client platforms. It is difficult to imagine that personal computer networks would have the important role they do today if Novell had not developed the market with NetWare.

The day may come when network operating systems readily permit seamless protocol stack substitution and supplementation.

NetWare's native protocol at the network layer (level 3) is the Internetwork Packet Exchange protocol, better known as IPX. All versions of NetWare, including 4.X, 3.X, 2.X, Novell DOS 7 and Personal NetWare, employ this protocol. Most DOS workstations that are clients of NetWare servers have IPX installed. OS/2 workstations can also install IPX. At the transport layer (level 4), Sequenced Packet Exchange (SPX) is available to programs that need its services.

NetWare versions 3.0 and higher support loadable extensions to the basic operating system called NetWare Loadable Modules (NLMs), which provide additional services to clients. NLMs that support the AppleTalk protocols, the Internet Protocols (TCP/IP) and the OSI protocols are available. If a server has these NLMs installed, workstations can access the server using their native protocols and need not have IPX capabilities.

In addition to the network protocols, a network operating system must support the file-organizing conventions of the clients. NetWare NLMs are available to support the Network File System (NFS) commonly employed by Unix clients, the Macintosh file system and the File Transfer Access and Management (FTAM) standard specified for clients using OSI protocols. File organization is considered to be a layer 7 (application level) function in the OSI reference model.

Novell has an entire division devoted to network management. The company produces a great variety of tools, from monitoring hardware to single-console management platform development software. These items are discussed in various parts of this book. Much of the NetWare installed base consists of version 2.X and earlier implementations. Support for multiple protocols and file systems is limited on these networks and on NetWare Lite peer-to-peer networks. Novell's own management software can cope with these IPX-only networks, but they are not readily accessible to management programs based on SNMP using TCP/IP. Similarly, the ability to feed management data to IBM's mainframe-based network management application, NetView, was implemented as an NLM, so only NetWare 3.X and higher can perform this task.

"To manage a network well, cooperation between the groups that are involved is critical."

—JANE SHEA

LAN Manager

Microsoft LAN Manager provides clients a collection of file and print services comparable to NetWare's. It fully supports DOS, OS/2, Macintosh and Unix clients. The server component of LAN Manager version 2.2 and below runs on OS/2 version 1.3. As IBM and Microsoft have emphasized competition over partnership, LAN Manager has faced uncertainty. Microsoft does not plan to migrate LAN Manager to OS/2 version 2; instead, future versions will run on Windows NT, the recently released, general-purpose operating system Microsoft is offering as an alternative to OS/2.

LAN Manager offers a choice of protocol stacks at the middle layers of the OSI model. Its NetBIOS protocol corresponds roughly to the session level, layer 5. NetBIOS can run on top of NetBEUI (NetBIOS Extended User Interface), TCP/IP or other protocols. NetBEUI and TCP/IP are included in the standard package. NetBEUI does not implement a network layer. Networks that use source routing—primarily those consisting of token ring nodes—put routing and other network layer functionality in the data link layer, so they don't necessarily need an explicit network layer. Many installations of LAN Manager that include multiple network segments will choose to install TCP/IP for the transport and network layers.

Macintosh, OS/2 and DOS file structures are supported by LAN Manager. Current versions do not include support for NFS (Unix) or FTAM (OSI) file services.

VINES

Banyan's VINES (VIrtual NEtwork operating System) is a proprietary version of Unix optimized for network services, particularly wide area network services. The default network layer protocol is VINES IP, which is not quite the same as IP. Regular IP can be installed on VINES servers, however.

In the current version, 5.5, VINES provides native support for Macintosh clients as well as DOS/Windows clients.

The best thing VINES has going for it is its distributed directory service. The online network directory, StreetTalk, makes it easy for widely separated users to identify network services and one another. Big worldwide organizations are the ones most likely to grasp immediately the advantages of an integrated network, but VINES can hold its own with respect to performance and price as a purely local area network, and appeals to smaller organizations as well. Banyan has even produced its Enterprise Network Services (ENS), which can provide integrated directory services for Novell servers.

AppleShare

AppleShare is Apple Computer's network operating system, which runs on top of either System 7, the default Macintosh workstation operating system, or Apple's Unix implementation, A/UX. AppleShare uses proprietary Apple protocols for all the layers above the data link layer. (These are AppleTalk Filing Protocol—AFP—and

Printer Access Protocol—PAP—at the application layer, AppleTalk Session Protocol—ASP—at the session layer, AppleTalk Transaction Protocol—ATP—at the transport layer and Datagram Delivery Protocol—DDP—at the network layer.) There is even a proprietary data link/physical protocol, LocalTalk, which is built into all Macintosh models.

What Apple has achieved with its lone-wolf strategy is local area networking no more difficult to set up than a stereo sound system for the primary target customer—an organization with no more than a few dozen users at one site. It has not been a high priority for Apple to support additional protocol stacks on AppleShare servers. DOS workstations with the Apple protocol stack and workstation shell can connect to AppleShare for file and print services, though there is currently no native support for OS/2 or Unix workstations.

With rare exceptions, AppleShare installations will be almost purely homogeneous Macintosh shops.

Unix

Computers running Unix have constituted the lion's share of the Internet's nodes from its beginning, and TCP/IP is supported on most versions of Unix. Thus Unix is no stranger to wide area networking. Sun Microsystems' development of a de facto file-sharing standard, NFS (Network File System), made Unix a credible offering for LANs as well. Non-Unix network nodes that can run NFS and the lower layers that support it can use a Unix file server.

Layers 6 and 7—The Presentation and Application Layers

Presentation-layer protocols (layer 6) permit a properly received stream of bytes to be meaningful. Data structures—text, numeric data and even arbitrary collections of bits such as a digital representation of an image or a sound, as well as the combinations of these structures that might be found in arrays or database records—are susceptible to different representations or encodings in different computers. For instance, IBM mainframe text data using EBCDIC encoding rules must generally be converted to and from the ASCII encoding used by most of the rest of the world. "Big-endian" to "little-endian" translation (whether the most significant digits of a number are the rightmost digits—IBM mainframes and Motorola—or the leftmost digits—Intel and DEC VAX) is another issue for the presentation layer. Data compression and encryption are also problems for the presentation layer to solve. PC networks handle these issues transparently. Network management personnel rarely meet with problems arising from the presentation layer. When data from "foreign" computers must be converted, the programs that otherwise establish the connection also solve this problem.

"As a network manager, you need to focus on what the application is, how do people work and what you can do to affect them working smarter, working better, working faster."

—JANE SHEA

Many of the applications that users run on their PCs—word processing, spreadsheets, desktop publishing, accounting and so forth—are network-indifferent. The network operating system client software makes the network services appear to be local resources—drives, files, printers and modems, for example. The application layer (layer 7) of the OSI Reference Model deals with services that a user program, or perhaps a user addressing the operating system directly, requires. Some of these services include file access, file transfer, file locking, login processing, directory capabilities, e-mail and terminal emulation. Network management itself is an application-layer service. When the network operating system producer or other supplier can implement these functions according to specific standards, application programs that need the functions don't have to implement them themselves.

For instance, the development of Lotus *Notes*, an application that provides synchronized text databases in multiple locations, was a mammoth job in part because the message-handling and synchronization functions were proprietary implementations. If the developers had had access to acceptable standard methods for these application-layer functions, they could have saved a great deal of effort in implementing those functions in the first place and also in ensuring compatibility with the rest of the world later on.

Communications Servers

Communications services are an important class of application-layer tasks that can be performed efficiently and cheaply on a network. Some of these tasks include mainframe or minicomputer terminal emulation, online transaction systems and providing remote access to the networked system over dial-up lines. Individual workstations can often perform these jobs with their own dedicated communications lines and modems, but the traffic they produce is often so light that many sessions can run simultaneously over one physical network connection.

A communications server that maintains contact with an IBM mainframe adds a new set of protocols, Systems Network Architecture (SNA), to the networked system. The communications server is a gateway, responsible for converting all layers of the reference model from the LAN to the host and vice versa. The appropriate software must be installed and configured on the mainframe before the communications server can establish contact. The mainframe side of this communications link is another specialized area in which few PC-world people have in-depth experience.

On NetWare and LAN Manager networks with communications servers installed, information about the network can be passed to NetView, IBM's mainframe application for managing networks. Mainframe-centered organizations, and those that hope to consolidate management for all their computing platforms under the IBM umbrella, can make use of this capacity.

Asynchronous Communications

Remote users may simply want to pick up and send e-mail messages while they are on the road, or they may want to use the full resources of the network, including mainframe access, database services and file transfer. While modems have become quite inexpensive, outside communications lines for them to connect to have not, particularly in office buildings. Many users need only a few minutes of connection time per day, so routing asynchronous communications over the network to a shared modem pool can save a lot of money.

Asynchronous connections are much slower than LAN connections, so it is not feasible to maintain a full LAN-like session over a serial line. One solution to this problem is to use LAN workstations as proxies for remote users who dial in to them. The serial line is responsible only for transporting keyboard and screen activity, which is duplicated at the proxy; the proxy does the real computing. If multiple users take advantage of this capability, each needs an open computer to dial in to. Novell and other manufacturers have addressed this problem by providing special software or building special devices for multiple simultaneous dial-in sessions that can be attached to the network and to multiple modems.

One management area where issues are sure to arise when dial-up lines are involved is security. The telephone network is a public utility, and a competitor or a vandal may attempt to get into any network that can be accessed over the phone. Passwords may not offer sufficient protection. One option is to set up specific telephone numbers in advance. A remote user initiates a session by dialing in, but the system hangs up and dials back to establish the working connection.

Compatibility can be a serious problem for networked systems with asynchronous communications services. The absence of true standardization in the async communications area is surprising in light of the accomplishments of the much newer LAN technology. Not all PCs have the correct hardware to make full use of async communications on the network. Modem compatibility can also be a severe problem, with proprietary interfaces to communications software and conflicting protocols for error correction and data compression. So many factors can generate difficulties that troubleshooting is hard—noisy phone lines, modem cabling problems, numerous weird communications settings that must be chosen correctly and digital PBX systems in hotels and offices are just a few examples.

The limitations of DOS as an operating system may result in hung-up sessions over the network. Remote users usually cannot reboot the machine they are dialing in to, so they typically hang up and redial, potentially using up all the dial-in resources as they get stuck repeatedly.

If the compatibility issues aren't worrisome enough, consider the problem of supporting users who face those issues. Support organizations for networks with async dial-ups face a substantially greater workload than those without them. Nevertheless, between traveling workforces, increased telecommuting and the spread of cellular communications capabilities, the pressure to provide remote access to networked systems will only increase in coming years.

Client-Server Database Access

Network operating systems are true client-server applications, with client programs on the workstations communicating with server applications on other computers. The most common services today are basic file retrieval and storage, but database services are a natural extension of operating systems in the PC realm, just as they are on mainframes and minis. There are several issues of network plumbing that must be resolved before a database server can be used successfully.

The most significant of these issues is the problem of general inter-process communications. Interprocess communications are instances of one computer task requesting results or actions from another. The other task might run on a different computer from the requester. Operating system actions, the interprocess communications that make networks and computers work at all, are generally simple and straightforward from the point of view of the computers. On the other hand, a database transaction, such as an interbank funds transfer, likely involves many linked actions, with provisions at every step for rolling back the whole thing if any step is compromised. These actions may take place on computers far from one another, with relatively slow wide area links connecting them. The systems may not have been designed with these kinds of transactions in mind.

The protocols for interprocess communications don't fit smoothly into the OSI reference model. They are often discussed along with session and transport layer issues. Applications developers for some versions of Unix and NetWare can use a mechanism called Remote Procedure Calls to implement remote interprocess communications. Microsoft and IBM, with support from Novell and Banyan, provide applications with remote sessions called Named Pipes, which act like files to the programs at both ends of the link. Because support for these approaches has not come together completely, installing a distributed database application on the network will likely raise numerous issues of proper workstation setup, protocol support, routing and compatibility.

Beyond the application layer, there is an ANSI standard for database queries, Structured Query Language or SQL. This standard concerns itself with text commands that can be passed from program to program, and does not address the details of physical implementation. Most SQL products include proprietary extensions to the standard features, so interoperability among the different SQL products is not complete. Nevertheless, SQL database servers (or back ends) have been implemented on every class of computer, and front ends exist for DOS, Windows, Macintosh and Unix workstations, the most common user platforms.

SQL-based client-server databases will be the foundation for migrating indisputably mission-critical applications from traditional mainframes and minicomputers to microcomputers and RISC-based systems. It is not clear that the management tools available to cope with the problems of the network that connects clients and servers are sufficient to deal with all the potential problems of the system.

E-mail and Groupware

Once electronic mail is installed more or less universally in an organization, it rapidly becomes a mission-critical application on its own as it insinuates itself into all kinds of processes. The applications roughly classed together as groupware, which include distributed document sharing (e.g., Lotus *Notes*), workflow management (e.g., Action Technologies *Coordinator*), shared calendaring (e.g., *Network Scheduler*) and other office automation tools, are becoming more important all the time. These distributed systems can be thought of as extensions to e-mail, or to the message-handling infrastructure required for e-mail.

If an organization begins to use e-mail, there is great pressure to make it work on all the desktops. Like other applications where interoperability becomes a job and not just a catchword, installing e-mail on multiple platforms highlights the differences between the different systems and surfaces many problems.

One important decision point is the choice of message-handling services. Many e-mail and groupware producers have proprietary message-handling mechanisms. These message handlers are not often available for multiple operating systems. There is a worldwide CCITT standard, X.400, for messaging systems, which provides the developer community with a target for e-mail interoperability. The most widely installed e-mail systems used today are not X.400-compliant. Other messaging systems include the Internet's Simple Message Transfer Protocol (SMTP); at least three from IBM (Systems Network Architecture Distribution Services or SNADS, DISOSS and PROFS); at least two from Digital (All-In-One, VMS Mail); and Novell's PC-oriented Message Handling System (MHS). Various corporations and consortiums have proposed standard programming interfaces for message handling. These include Microsoft's MAPI, Lotus' VIM, Apple's OCE and, from a group supporting X.400 standards, XAPI.

"It took years to put e-mail in because they didn't have every-body doing things the same way. We didn't want to connect a couple of thousand people on an e-mail system and be unable to connect up to the 7,000-10,000 people at the parent company."

—JANE SHEA

Message-handling services are responsible for storing and forwarding messages and files attached to them. Dial-up lines usually provide the links between message servers, so the server must manage asynchronous communications sessions between messaging hubs. Messaging networks do not necessarily look the same as the overall data communications network, with independent message routing and message gateways translating between systems. The job of administering messaging and e-mail users could be simplified by close links between the message-handling service and the network operating system, but in practice this job is often completely manual.

One factor that raises the stakes for successful electronic mail implementation is the rapid rise of Electronic Data Interchange (EDI). More and more large corporations and government entities each day set requirements for their suppliers to provide standard message dialogs for purchase orders, order confirmations, invoices, delivery schedule updates and other day-to-day operational information. While EDI is independent of any particular platform, the greater development speed and flexibility of microprocessor-based network platforms makes them prime candidates for the application when the company's largest customer says that in six months it will stop ordering from anyone who has not implemented full EDI capability. The likelihood of messaging's turning into a mission-critical application increases the pressure more than ever on those responsible for managing the network.

Directory Services

Network directories are an essential infrastructure of any network, controlling access (and other forms of security) and enabling any kind of accounting or logging to take place. Network administrators especially appreciate features of a directory that make them more productive, such as the ability to replicate user profiles for multiple servers. Global or network-wide directory services, such as Banyan's StreetTalk, make the network much more accessible to users as well as administrators. The global directory is the network equivalent of a phone book, listing other users and services available throughout the network—special printers, mainframe links, mailboxes, fax gateways and so forth.

"I just hope I live to see and experience global naming of directory services."
— RANDY HOWLAND

The CCITT standard for directory services is designated X.500. The network operating system suppliers may someday migrate to this standard, but it is not implemented today by the market leaders. One of VINES's most attractive features is its StreetTalk global directory, which wide area network users find especially useful. Novell, Microsoft and IBM, all of whom have roots in strictly *local* area networks, are hurrying to provide similar capabilities for their products. Banyan has introduced an add-on product for NetWare networks called Enterprise Network Services (ENS), which provides global network services for them.

With an internetwork directory, the systems management mission can be greatly simplified. Without the information the directory provides, a manager may have to use alternate means—a local list or database, a phone call—to find out what devices and services are active on a remote network.

Keeping Up With Technology

The role of the network manager is to stay up with all of the new products and new techniques. Fax machines came out, and the next thing you know, they're part of every business in the world. Now we've got portables that have fax capability, and everyone is asking for fax at the desktop, even to print a document. At some point, you'll be able to get almost full motion video right at the desktop level and incorporate some of those things into a node or into a message. And there are even some areas we haven't yet begun to tap into.

The technology is expanding and there will be demands on the network for support. Business will have to decide what's important. Is the fax from a desktop important or is video important? Is the ability to put voice annotation into mail messages more important than something else?

—Randy Howland, Network Manager for a Fortune 500 technology corporation

PART TWO

The Five Categories of Network Management

4 / Fault Management

This chapter is the first of five that roughly follow the five functional areas defined by the Network Management Forum of the OSI organization: fault management, configuration management, performance management, security management and accounting management. The discussion of specific management practices and tools follows this breakdown broadly—but many of the tools and topics are applicable to more than one of these categories as they are defined narrowly by standards committees. The reason for this overlap and category redundancy is that the OSI standards committees, and to a large extent the Internet standards committees, have historically focused more on the issues of wide area networks than upon PCs and their local networks. Thus a prospective designer of PC network management tools could expect little or no guidance from the standards committees regarding product features and interfaces to other devices and systems.

Fault management, as defined by the OSI's Network Management Forum, has to do with preventing and eliminating service interruptions. *Configuration management* involves mapping and controlling the setup of the network. *Performance management* is the process of improving speed, responsiveness, bandwidth, flexibility and other desirable aspects of the network. *Security management* includes contingency planning and the assurance of data integrity and confidentiality. *Accounting management* includes apportioning the costs of network services.

No matter how narrowly these categories are defined, they remain intricately interdependent. Many ostensible performance problems turn out to be subtle faults in devices or programs. The boundary between system faults and inappropriate configuration is not crisp. The issues of security and accounting overlap substantially. Gathering the information required for detailed accounting may impose performance penalties on the networked system.

Most of the products designed to help manage networked systems do not fit well into one particular OSI functional category. (Nor is there any reason that they should, except for the convenience of organizing books about them.) To some extent, the choice to discuss particular products under one or another heading is arbitrary. Different aspects of some products are considered in more than one functional chapter.

Networked System Faults and Their Management

This chapter discusses some of the principal ways faults can be prevented on PC networks. Then it addresses the subjects of fault detection, isolation and repair. Finally it discusses the tools that are available to help with fault management.

Faults occur when the networked system is unable to provide services that a reasonable user expects. The aim of fault management is to detect faults, isolate them and repair them with the minimum loss of services. Fault management often assumes a high priority in an organization's plans because many faults have immediate, serious consequences.

Faults are, in some respects, the environment that networked systems inhabit. Without electromagnetic noise, bottlenecks in the data path, irregular cable installations, out-of-date hardware, buggy software, configuration errors and all the other contributors of faults, there would be no need for the elaborately layered architecture of computer networks.

Many of the functions implemented in a stack of protocols are designed to hide or get around some kind of potential problem. The data link layer, for example, contains a Cyclic Redundancy Check (CRC) field carrying a checksum that verifies the accuracy of the data component of the frame. A bad bit of data caused by a burst of noise on the cable is caught by this check. At the network layer, there is a mechanism to make packets go away if they have not reached their destinations after a certain number of internetwork hops. If a destination disconnects from the network, packets sent to it are prevented from circulating forever, and eventually using up all the capacity of the network. The transport layer is responsible for reassembling fragmented packets in the correct order; if one is missing, it requests retransmission. Even on the simplest network, there is always a great deal of acknowledgment and confirmation traffic. Wide area networks are often constructed with redundant paths among their components, so the complete failure of a router may not be immediately obvious to users.

Consider, for example, an Ethernet segment. If two nodes transmit at the same time, a collision occurs: Both data frames are garbled.

"Most of the energy of vendors of network management software is going to what I would like to call wire management. That's looking at packets coming across the network, managing the traffic, trying to figure out where the bottleneck is. And this is definitely important. The larger your network, the more you're internetworked, the more critical that is. But it's only one piece of the puzzle."

— DIANE DANIELLE

But Ethernet is designed to detect collisions and inform the senders that they need to retransmit the lost frames. So a collision is not a fault. An Ethernet network that is approaching saturation experiences many collisions, to the point where retransmission activity can outweigh normal traffic. Nevertheless, under these conditions the Ethernet interface cards are doing just what they were designed to do, even though users are experiencing poor responsiveness, and little or no productive data is moving on the network.

Avoiding Downtime

When the network goes down, everybody suffers. Everyone complains, the paging starts and the phones are ringing and it's total insanity. I don't know any way short of migrating into the superserver environment that will change that situation.

—*Jane Shea, Sr. Technical Analyst, AmSys Telemanagement*

Proactive Fault Management

An impeccable design is the most effective way to prevent and minimize service disruptions. Faults that result from poor design are the most difficult to eliminate. In addition, servers, workstations, network interface cards, hubs and other components must be completely compatible and of high quality. Once a key component, such as a particular model of token ring or Ethernet board, is known to work compatibly, substituting something else for price reasons alone is probably a false economy. Likewise, any shortcuts taken by the cable installers can haunt the network forever. If pilot projects and other tests can be performed on new devices and software before actual productive service, potential faults can be resolved with minimal disruptive consequences.

Dealing with faults is impossible without good information about the devices on the network. Documenting the network is much easier before and during installation than it is later. There are network mapping and inventorying tools that can help to automate this function and keep the documentation up to date as the network changes. Chapter 5, Configuration Management, discusses these tools in more detail.

Any organization that keeps records of network faults would be well served to compile a representative sample of the data. (Organizations that don't keep such records should begin to keep them, and perhaps attempt to reconstruct the last few months' worth of faults as accurately as possible.) It should be a straightforward project for the network management group to use the data to produce a "Pareto Chart" (a series of columns ranked in descending order) like the following one.

Figure 4-1 Causes of Fault Events on a Mythical Network

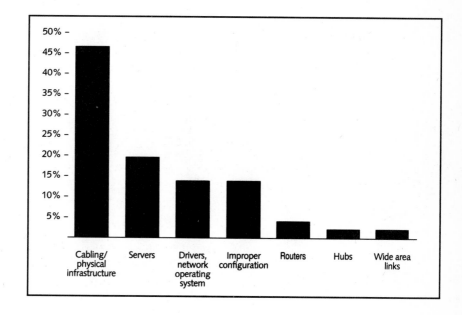

The bars in this high-level chart can be further decomposed until they point to a specific unambiguous cause.

Figure 4-2 Causes of Cabling Fault Events on a Mythical Network

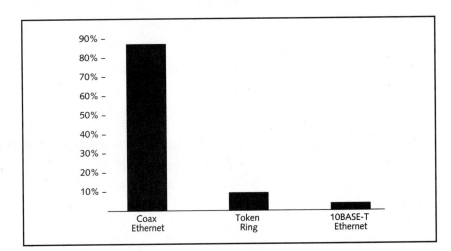

This data clearly spells out the most productive candidates for fault-management projects.

Figure 4-3 Causes of Server Fault Events on a Mythical Network

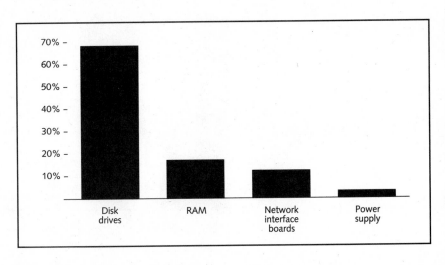

The Disappearing Server

We had a wide-scale problem which we called the Disappearing Server Problem. The symptom was that sometimes, from some servers, you couldn't see a list of other servers in the company. If a server wasn't on the list, we couldn't get information about it.

The problem turned out to be a combination of two things. First, there was a bug in the VINES operating system software, so the services were not sending out a packet that they were supposed to be sending out every 12 hours. In a stable state (that is, with no changes in the directory), what is supposed to happen is that the servers send out a 'keep alive' or summary message. If you don't get one of these messages in 96 hours, you assume the server is gone. This problem was exacerbated on our networks because the Cisco routers were dropping packets randomly. The combination of the two problems meant that sometimes there would not be enough packets sent out to confirm the existence of the server, and it would drop off of the list.

We used two key tools to find the solution. The Sniffer was one, and the other was the logs that come with the operating system. VINES provides logs that are basically an audit trail for the service. (Servers have multiple services.) We had three choices. We had to figure out whether these packets weren't being sent, whether they were not making it through the network, or whether they were making it through and then were being ignored. It turned out to be a combination of these factors: Sometimes they weren't being sent and sometimes they weren't making it through.

The bug was that the servers weren't sending those messages. But there are other ways to generate those packets. For example, if you make a change in the server's directory, you will send out a packet, and that has the effect of telling the other servers 'I'm here.' What was happening in this situation was that the summaries weren't going out and the details weren't always making it across to all parts of the network.

> The Sniffer could prove to us that the packet was leaving the server and it could tell us when the packet arrived at another server. Then we could confirm that the logs were correct. Once we knew that the logs were telling us the truth, we could review the logs and try to figure out what was missing. It boiled down to a matter of looking at the size of the network, the way the routers were configured, the amount of traffic and the version of the software we were running—a number of things.
>
> In the end, we got Banyan to fix a bug in the software. We changed the way the routers were routing. This improved their efficiency, and they stopped dropping packets.
>
> —*James Brentano, Network Specialist at a West Coast utility company*

Fault-Tolerant Devices

Fault-tolerance is a term applied to equipment that can experience particular kinds of failure and keep on providing service. It is implemented by making redundant components somehow available without a service disruption. The most failure-prone components are the logical place to begin providing fault-tolerance.

Drives and Drive Arrays

On PC-based network servers, the disk drives are the subsystem most likely to fail. The network operating system and the server hardware can cooperate to provide fault-tolerance through disk mirroring, drive duplexing or various kinds of disk arrays.

Disk mirroring involves duplicating a hard disk drive. Data is written to both drives all the time. If one drive fails, the other one can carry on. Drive duplexing duplicates the drive controller as well as the drive, providing insurance against failures of that component.

Drive arrays treat multiple drives as a single logical unit. While they can be configured for performance improvements only, there are several options for using some fraction of the array's resources for redundant storage. One common method is to use one drive as a parity device, much as a ninth bank of RAM chips is used as a check on the other eight. If any drive fails, the array can use the parity drive and the information on the surviving drives to reconstitute the data on the failed drive. While mirroring and duplexing cost twice as much as nonredundant storage, the parity method may cost only 25 to 35 percent more. Mirroring and duplexing can provide better performance than nonredundant storage because the secondary drives can work in parallel to read data. Parity techniques do not improve performance compared to nonredundant arrays, and performance after a drive failure is degraded severely as the controller and drives labor to recreate the data.

Some CPU and drive manufacturers support the hot swapping of drives. On these products, a failed drive can be disconnected and a new one connected and reconfigured without shutting down power to the system. Systems that must run around the clock need this capability.

Novell refers to mirrored disks and duplexed drives as System Fault Tolerance (SFT) Levels I and II, respectively. The next degree of redundancy is a mirrored server, SFT Level III. The mirrored server runs each CPU instruction at the same time the primary server does, with complete communication between the two constantly underway. If the primary server undergoes any kind of hardware failure, the mirrored server takes over. SFT Level III clients are protected against all kinds of server hardware failure— RAM, power supply, CPU and the rest. However, a software problem that brings down the primary server will do the same to the mirrored one.

"Our view is that if a hard disk crashes, we want to be running in realtime, so we are doing full mirroring on the file servers at this point. We viewed that as our risk when we implemented the file servers. If the file servers go down and a hard disk crashes at 9 in the morning, how long would it take us to fix that? We don't even want to know."

—RANDY HOWLAND

Most of these server fault-tolerance functions are supported by proprietary hooks between the server, the drive controllers, the network operating system and perhaps even the network interface boards. The chances of substituting components not specifically named by the manufacturers are slim.

Concentrators, Hubs, Bridges and Routers

Like a server, a wiring concentrator constitutes a single point of failure for many users. In critical installations, concentrators can be configured with redundant power supplies in case one fails. Each stackable hub has its own power supply, so those configurations automatically provide a degree of fault-tolerance. Installers can build extra capacity into the concentrator so that if one attachment module fails, the affected users can quickly be connected to the surviving attachment modules. Some concentrator models support hot swapping—replacing an attachment module without powering down the device.

Internetworks can be designed with redundant routes for critical data. If one router fails, the data can still get through. Bridges don't like to see multiple simultaneous routes between nodes, but many of them can be configured to compensate for the failure of one bridge in a multibridge internet. Compatibility is a touchy factor in this area, too. Different brands, or perhaps even different models of these components, may prevent proper reconfiguration following failure.

A Streaming Hub

We had an intermittent problem which was shutting down part of our network. We had a 'streaming hub.' One of the nodes of a hub went bad. It was down for about two hours. That node plugged into a workstation which was used by an expediter, who is responsible for making special health and safety labels.

> While the workstation was down, we had to do all this work manually, in order to keep shipments on schedule. Later the information had to be back-entered. The port on that hub caused another port on the hub to malfunction, which meant it was sending a stream, a reconfiguration burst (message) which was continual.
>
> The network was constantly resetting itself, or reconfiguring itself and could not service other processes. We shut the node down. We were able to isolate something on that hub because it was plugged into an intelligent hub. The solution was to replace the hub. Since we had a spare we could use, we didn't lose any more time. The actual hub in question was under warranty, so we sent it back to the manufacturer.

—Richard Sherkin, MIS Manager, Biltrite Industries

Fault Detection

Every fault occurrence is initiated by some form of detection. All kinds of system events are the raw material for fault detection. Each packet, every disk access, every retransmission—tens or hundreds of thousands of occurrences every second—make up the universe of data the fault detection function begins with. The problem is to filter this enormous volume of data to make it useful.

Some kinds of network events are not at all ambiguous. For example, all users' systems get error messages when the server is not responding or if a file transfer stops in the middle. Even if it is not clear where the source of the fault lies, it is clear that there is a fault. It is time to start troubleshooting. On the other hand, the self-correcting mechanisms of the network can mask faults. The events that indicate this class of faults require further study to determine that they are faults in the first place.

Finding No Problem

One of our networks had a VAX, and DEC engineers were telling us to use DECNET. They were recommending we use Pathworks. I was uncomfortable with this idea. The DEC engineers were unable to answer our Novell questions. They didn't seem to know how their product integrated with Novell. I didn't think this would be a good partnership. I didn't think they would come through when we needed their help. And we had already used LAN Workplace for DOS. I suggested we get LAN Workplace for DOS and they did.

The users kept complaining that their sessions would get hung. They had bought a new VAX and were going to put an extensive application on it. A PC LAN was being connected to the DEC minicomputer, plus we had some DEC terminal servers and the DEC was connected to an IBM mainframe. The users were nervous because they were converting off of another system onto the VAX. There was a lot of testing going on. The application folks were there. It was a high-pressure deal.

The LAN went in. The VAX came. We got IP up. Then the users started complaining that sometimes their sessions would get frozen. At first, it was hearsay; I never actually observed a frozen terminal. The user would complain that the terminal was frozen, but he couldn't re-create the problem.

We called the vendor and we called Novell. Novell lent us a LANalyzer and we stuck it on the network and it was fine. We tried to trap the event. We developed a form. Whenever it happened, the user would type in what their station was, what they were doing at the time, what was on the screen, what key they pressed when it happened.

The managers were really on top of this, and made sure everyone knew about it. The system was not in wide use at the time, because the network was still in the conversion phase, so only 20 users were on it. It started to shake out that most of the people whose PCs got hung used Windows for the most part, and they were running the DOS version of *telnet* under a DOS

Window. (We weren't running the Windows version of *telnet*. We couldn't get it to fit the screen and we didn't like it.)

We also noticed that the users were hitting wrong keys. Another PC this kept happening on was a Windows PC where the user had three sessions of Lotus running in the background and her computer was also a console to the phone switch running in the background—too much stuff. As we were able to identify what was going on, the events decreased, and the LANalyzer never caught any of it. But the LANalyzer was very useful because it told us we didn't have a problem. I think it was skittishness and a little inexperience on the part of the users that was the problem.

—*Jerry White, Network Manager at a West Coast financial institution*

Much fault-management activity depends on comparing normal levels of various network events to the levels encountered when users report a problem or when some other indicator raises suspicions. Thus the number of collisions on an Ethernet segment should increase gradually as new users are added, but a sudden increase might indicate a defective interface card or a user who has started running a demanding new application.

Many network management activities are therefore based on the concept of thresholds. The levels of all kinds of network events, from traffic levels to the usage of buffer space in a server, are captured when the system is behaving normally. A threshold is defined somewhere above the baseline level. Activity below the threshold level can be ignored, while greater activity should trigger investigation. Some of the best management software provides automatic capture and graphical displays of this sort of data, with red lines on a meter or a bar chart indicating a set threshold for a particular kind of event. (See Figure 4-4.)

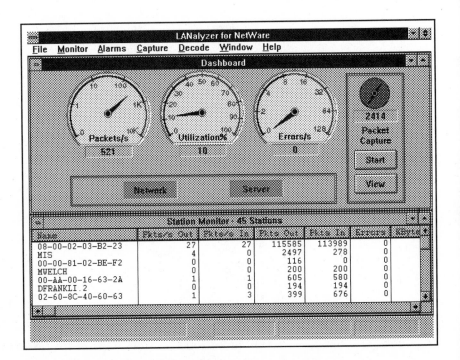

Figure 4-4 The "Dashboard" of the Windows-Based LANalyzer for NetWare

The ideal central management console would detect and display all significant faults that occurred on the entire network. It would anticipate faults whenever possible and provide warnings. It would narrow down the root cause of a fault and act to isolate it. Then the management system would take action, either diverting service from the faulty device to another one, or shutting it down and alerting the people responsible for replacing and repairing it. A system with these capabilities is not commercially available today, at least for more than the very simplest kinds of faults. But perhaps as soon as 1995, such systems should begin appearing in the market, with capabilities extending to additional kinds of devices and faults thereafter.

> ## Moving Day
>
> When we moved one of our departments to another building, we had tremendous problems trying to get the 10BASE-T up on the network. First of all we suspected the cabling, because this was in an area of the building where we suspected the

cable distances were a little bit longer than we felt would reliably support 10BASE-T. So we ran direct runs of cabling to those workstations to cut out any circuitous routing that it may have had before. That didn't work. After trying out different solutions, it turned out to be a very simple problem. The server in that area which provided routing services over to the main building had an option on the server turned off. Basically the option allows it to reply when stations request the nearest server. It was not doing that, so these stations weren't seeing anything else and we were not able to get on the network. That was a diagnostic challenge.

There were some techniques that helped us determine just where the problem was, including something as simple as running Novell's COMCHECK program, which allows workstations to send out and receive addresses from everybody else who's running COMCHECK. Once you see that, the program gives you kind of a quick-and-dirty idea that maybe the cabling wasn't the problem. You are able to see other workstations and communicate with them properly. That leads you to start looking elsewhere, to see if there's maybe a software problem.

—*Dave Fogle, LAN Development Group, ComputerLand Corporation*

The Help Desk and Fault Detection

In today's networks, the first indicator of a fault is likely to be a phone call from a user to a help desk. Symptom reports from users are useful to the degree that the network users are experienced enough to know what behavior to expect from the network, trained enough to understand what is happening with their computers, and cooperative enough to perform a few simple diagnostic actions.

The support person at the help desk is a filter for problems the users perceive. Help desk employees need to resolve quickly any problems associated with installation, configuration, administration and ignorance, and forward on to network managers or troubleshooters problems that indicate system faults or otherwise require their intervention. Help desk people must be equipped to differentiate workstation installation or application problems, network administrative issues and genuine system faults.

"Our department functions as our own network help desk. Users have our phone number, and if they have problems with local PCs or the network, we take the call. If we are not in, the phone transfers to another help desk, which assists the P.O.S. (point of sale) retail store divisions throughout the country."

—JOHN THOMAS

An example of an installation problem is a user who gets a new workstation and has trouble making Windows run properly on the network. An example of a network administrative issue is a user who is prevented from running a network application because she lacks execution rights to the directory where the program resides. In practice, distinguishing between genuine faults and installation/configuration/administration problems can be difficult and subtle.

Traditional telecom organizations often use trouble-ticketing systems in conjunction with their help desks. Each help desk call above a certain threshold of significance results in the creation of a trouble ticket. It is also possible for the management system to initiate trouble tickets automatically. Trouble tickets capture the date and time of the initial report and each of the subsequent steps taken to solve the problem. The system creates a database that is a history of trouble on the networked system.

Trouble-ticketing systems provide a number of theoretical advantages: they can measure the productivity of the network management group; they capture information about how users employ the help desk, highlighting, for example, the need for user training; and over time, they highlight components and subsystems that generate unusual levels of trouble.

The main problem with trouble ticketing on systems of networked PCs is the administrative overhead. The priorities of network management staff are often set by crises. Writing up the resolution to the problem you just fixed is rarely as important (or as exciting) as resolving the next problem.

The skills required to take user calls, 90 percent of which are likely to involve training and configuration issues, do not overlap very much with the skills of an advanced network troubleshooter. Treating help desk staff as trainees for more advanced network management jobs may lead to personnel turnover problems. The demand for multivendor-capable network managers is so great that trainees are apt to be lured away as soon as they begin to make a contribution. Many organizations contract an outside provider for partial or comprehensive help desk services. External help desk providers can offer competitive pricing because of economies of scale, especially at odd hours. They should be expected to have trouble-ticketing systems that help their customers make the best use of their services.

Help Desk Products

"Much of what we still do in network management is to have a telephone number that all systems administrators can call — a LAN support center. So if no one calls, things are OK. This is a guide to determine how serious a problem really is."

—JAMES BRENTANO

Help desk management for PC networks is an immature but rapidly growing area. Organizations interested in formally managing their help desk functions should be aware of these two products.

Remedy Corporation—Action Request System

Remedy's *Action Request System* can be tailored for three applications: network and system management, help desk management and bug fixing. The system consists of automated forms to report problems and a workflow mechanism to resolve them. It stores historical data and offers macros. It integrates readily with SunConnect's *SunNet Manager*, HP's *OpenView* and IBM's *NetView/6000*. Server software can run on Sun, HP or IBM RS/6000 platforms, while potential clients include Windows workstations as well as Unix clients. The suggested retail price is $6,500.

Blue Lance—LT Helpdesk

Blue Lance's *LT Helpdesk* manages service and support activities for large LANs. It assigns priorities and tracks user requests for service and support. The package helps prepare reports about problem resolution. It also tracks types of problems and how long it takes to solve them. End users can enter service requests directly into *LT Helpdesk* from their own DOS-based PCs. Service technicians process the requests, and supervisors manage the process.

Troubleshooting

Troubleshooting is the process of analyzing the networked system to detect the causes of faults. The best troubleshooters follow a top-down, hierarchical process that methodically eliminates potential causes until the correct explanation is found. Possible sources of the fault are systematically eliminated by repeatedly gathering data about the fault, forming a hypothesis that distinguishes between alternate causes, testing the hypothesis and drawing conclusions about the hypothesis.

"When you're troubleshooting a local area network, the number of places the problem can exist is close to infinite."

—DIANE DANIELLE

For instance, a user calls the network help desk to report that she cannot log on to a Unix host over the network. The help desk person determines that the workstation is configured correctly and forwards the problem to a network management troubleshooter. The troubleshooter confirms that the user's NetWare segment is working normally and that the Unix host is up. He forms the hypothesis that the user's IP packets are not getting to the host's segment. A specific diagnostic program, *ping*, that indicates successful IP connections, is normally installed on TCP/IP nodes. The user *ping*s the host and finds that there is no response; her node can't find the host's IP address. The troubleshooter suspects an IP routing problem. By running NetWare utility programs, he confirms that following a power outage, the NLM routing IP on a NetWare router did not come up correctly. The fault has been detected.

This example compresses the diagnostic steps in comparison with a by-the-book approach, but the basic approach begins at the top of a hierarchy—does the network support any traffic at all?—and works down through potential causes, with a sequence of tests that will cumulatively differentiate normal components and subsystems from faulty ones.

While proficient, real-life troubleshooters almost intuitively eliminate certain branches of investigation, they proceed systematically from the top down. Inexperienced troubleshooters, on the other hand, do not divide and conquer the problem. They tend to "shotgun" the process by replacing or reinstalling root-level components that might be responsible. There are times when shotgunning is, in fact, the fastest way to get the system back on track, but even in these cases, the potential sources of the problem are narrowed substantially by hierarchical troubleshooting.

"The problem for us is the scale, because a lot of third-party solutions just won't scale this big. We take a minimalist approach, 'Find it if it's down — then investigate.'"
—JAMES BRENTANO

Troubleshooting can be spelled out in detail for individual components. The value of critical devices is greatly enhanced by efficient diagnostic software and easy access to test points. A complex system, on the other hand, is unlikely to come with a troubleshooting guide, even in the unlikely event that all the components come from the same manufacturer. Effective network management groups develop more-or-less formal troubleshooting practices. Consistency in the system's components, consistency in configurations and the existence of well-documented platforms throughout the network make troubleshooting as easy as possible. But the crucial factor in networked PC systems now is rapid growth and constant change. For example, the network management group may well not be consulted before the organization merges with another organization that uses different workstations, different network cards and different routers.

Fault Isolation

Isolation means two things. First, troubleshooters must confirm that the fault they identify is the only source of trouble. An identified fault may be like a blown fuse—responsible for the symptom, but not the original source of the trouble. Before replacing a subsystem or component, it is important to be sure that some more fundamental cause will not destroy the replacement. Second, the networked system needs to be protected from further damage; faulty hardware must be turned off or disconnected, and faulty software must be prevented from running. Isolation is not always as simple as it sounds. Problems are often intermittent. It is not normally acceptable to sacrifice all the services of the networked system to the project of determining a fault precisely.

A Power Supply Problem

We had a problem with the power supply in the Compaq Systempro. It hiccuped and downed the server. We brought the server back up and looked at it—everything seemed normal. We went to our administrative PC and connected it to the System Manager board we had installed in the Systempro. We ran the system management software and looked at the log, which shows all the historical information about the Systempro. Our ±12 volts supply and our ±5 volts supply had gone out of tolerance. From that information, we decided there was a problem with the power supply. Since we were on a service contract with a Compaq reseller, we set up an appointment with their maintenance people. We notified our users, and they changed out the power supply within a half-hour time slot. The problem was solved.

—*John Thomas, Microcomputer Supervisor at a home improvement supply company*

Fault Repairing

The simplest repairs occur automatically with redundant subsystems that simply take over the job of the faulty component. Hot swaps are the second-easiest category, so long as the correct components are on hand. Most repairs require some interruption of service, though. Powering down a workstation is not usually a difficult problem, except for the affected user, but powering down non-redundant routers or servers for repair inevitably disrupts service. This is one reason network management personnel are so often on the job at 3:00 a.m.

Repair Strategy

"Mainframes are seen as big black boxes; everybody knows that it is big and strange, that it requires technical expertise. But lots of people have PCs at home and they all think they are computer experts."
—DIANE DANIELLE

If the services of the network are critical, a good hardware service strategy is essential. The key elements of a strategy are organizational and budgetary responsibility. Does the responsibility for arranging for repairs fall on the central network support organization, the users' departments or the individual users? The answer may be different for different devices: servers, hubs, cabling, internetworking equipment, telecom equipment, printers, fax servers, terminals and workstations. Who can unstick a paper jam in a big 20-page-per-minute laser printer? Whom can users call on the weekend if e-mail doesn't work? Does the organization track repair budgets across departmental lines? Who pays for 50 reams of paper that are run through the network printer with only garbage characters because a print spooler was not installed correctly?

Once a specific faulty component is identified, there is still a list of decisions to make and tasks that may need to be performed:

- Decide whether to repair the component on-site or take it away.
- Decide whether to install a substitute or hope that the repair will be completed quickly enough to do without one.
- Decide whether repair is more sensible than replacement.
- Track down a workable substitute or order a replacement.
- Install and configure the substitute or replacement correctly.

- Track the repair to conclusion, ensuring that it doesn't get hung up for some reason (for instance, the lack of software or other material available at the original site but missing at the repair facility).
- Reinstall and reconfigure the repaired component correctly.
- Confirm that repair charges are correct and allocated to the correct budget.
- Return the substitute component and document its return.
- Provide warranty documentation.

It is a common human and organizational failing to imagine that our devices have been chosen so well that they will never fail us. One form of this fallacy is to put all the budgetary resources in acquisition and none in repair and maintenance. When individual departments or users initiate acquisitions of new products, the enlightened ones remember to provide for service. It is also not in the short-term interest of a salesperson to remind the purchaser that nothing works forever, though a good one will help focus attention on the life-cycle cost of products.

Life-cycle costing means capturing the full cost of equipment over its service life. Some of the costs beyond the initial purchase or lease of a device include service contracts, repair charges, periodic maintenance, required upgrades to associated devices or software and training for users and repair staff. Particularly with PC-associated products, there is a strong possibility that these supplemental costs are charged against department budgets and remain hidden from the organization as a whole.

In a complex multivendor system, many resources need to be pulled together. No dedicated repair department—much less a particular individual—has all the reference materials, spare parts, diagnostic tools, training, practical experience and knowledge of interactions between components that are required to keep a critical networked system running effectively. In addition, people with the skills to

"In case of problems, we have a spare for everything in the file server except the motherboard: hard drives, network cards, memory modules, power supplies. For the network hubs, we keep a spare hub module and spare power supplies. For gateway PCs, we can always use other PCs as replacements."

—JOHN THOMAS

troubleshoot problems in complex systems with protocol analyzers and sophisticated diagnostic software are often not temperamentally suited to the numerous important administrative tasks that must be accomplished. On the other hand, a purely administrative employee lacks the expertise and credibility to do these jobs well.

One issue that should be easy to decide is whether the organization's employees or the employees of another company should perform repairs and maintenance. Simply comparing the fully loaded cost of homemade versus bought services will identify the right path. In many organizations, PC network repair personnel report to work at a site each day even though their salaries, benefits, bonuses, training regimens, support resources and career paths are handled through another company.

Well-communicated and widely accepted policies are the key to an effective repair strategy. If guidelines for these decisions and responsibilities for these tasks are laid out clearly, there will be far fewer occasions where faults cost too much and will hurt the organization.

Tactical Considerations

Different types of equipment require different fault repair tactics. This section addresses some of the product-specific issues that are likely to arise.

File Server Tactics

File server repairs are often the province of the on-site network support staff, rather than an off-site repair agency. As some of the most expensive components of a networked system, they are the least likely to be inventoried as backups. Because installing the operating system, applications and data on a replacement server can often take a considerable amount of time—possibly more time than it takes to

"In a distributed environment, where you have multiple file servers and multiple printers, modems, fax servers, gateways, all kinds of devices out there, it's basically a numbers game. The more things you have out there, the greater likelihood that something will go down."

—RANDY HOWLAND

repair the original server—substituting a backup server becomes an even less attractive option. However, if the internal network management organization has repair responsibility, the staff must be trained in the specific repair practices required by the servers; great skills in troubleshooting software, protocols, routers or cables cannot substitute for hardware-specific skills.

Workstation Tactics

The best tactical approach for faulty workstations is timely substitution. Users without workstations probably can't do their jobs. Even if service information and spare parts are handy, it puts a lot of pressure on the repairer and the user if a repair needs to be completed before work can resume. Swapping workstations temporarily is easy if users keep their data on the network. Restoring from tape or another backup medium does not get the user back in action as fast, and the restored data is not completely current unless the backup was made just before the failure. If users' applications also run from the network, setting up a replacement is simplified even more.

There may also be system compatibility problems. If the organization has standardized on Windows, OS/2 or System 7, backup workstations from years past may not be capable of running users' applications.

Printer Tactics

If users expect a fast laser printer that switches automatically between PostScript and PDL jobs with several sheet feed options, an old LaserJet II will not readily plug in and play as a substitute. Network printers may develop an importance to the organization equal to that of the copy machine. Therefore, they can warrant a less-than-one-day service contract. Building this repair capability inside the organization rather than buying it from outside is difficult to justify except in very special situations, just as few organizations can justify repairing their own copy machines. If users have locally attached printers, it may be prudent to preinstall print queues that can be directed to some of them if a primary network printer goes down.

Hub and Concentrator Tactics

Large concentrators are almost always modular, with replaceable components that are normally repaired only by the manufacturer. Hubs also are returned to the original maker for repair if they are repaired at all. Since these devices constitute a single point of failure, it is wise to build in redundant capacity and stock extra modules or hubs. The failure of an attachment module or a hub can be corrected in a few minutes if redundant capacity or spare components are at hand.

Bridge and Router Tactics

If internetwork links are critical, redundant bridge and router capacity is the best tactic. Many routers and bridges can automatically reconfigure traffic patterns if one component fails. Like hubs, these devices are rarely repairable in the field.

The Case of the Lost Key

There was a theft at our Houston office, and the server key [a hardware device used by Banyan to prevent unauthorized copying of its software] was stolen from one of our servers. We called Banyan, and they agreed to make us a duplicate. But when they asked for the serial number, one of the managers inadvertently gave them the wrong number—actually the number of a functioning server in Cleveland. So Banyan sent us a replacement key with this wrong serial number.

With two servers having the same keys connected at the same time, all the corporate servers started getting confused. User names and groups were falling out of StreetTalk Directory Assistance. Various services were unable to access the server name. For example, the mail service was assigning the same serial numbers to two different servers, so the mail services could not be accessed. The server name for Cleveland was switching to Houston, and the Houston server name would not show up at all on the Network Management Program (MNET).

We corrected the key problem, but still couldn't get on the network. Banyan servers are so efficient at sharing information of who's who and what's what for each server that we could not eliminate the erroneous number from the servers' memory. We couldn't delete the information on the system. It was chasing itself all over the country. So we ended up having to 'cold start' the servers throughout the system. [When a server has no knowledge of other servers over a period of time, it purges any groups associated with those servers.]

This process took an hour, with 5 people on the phone to 28 branches turning all modems off so they would not talk to each other, resetting the time to 7 days in advance, bringing the server in each location down and then back up again. Then, at night, we worked on all the corporate servers. It didn't work.

Then Banyan engineers got involved, and it turned out to be a 4-week ordeal. They went into all three servers and checked internally to see what these servers thought was out there. Those systems were cold started and checked before being put back on the network. We then added a group to all three servers, causing them to update, and the problem finally went away.

The company was affected by this—we couldn't send e-mail to the Houston branch office. Every morning sales figures are normally sent to the vice president. He could not receive them. As a first-aid measure, each day until the problem was resolved, I had to dial in to the server through a modem from a PC and create a group, which forced a broadcast to servers. Then I would connect and create a group on the corporate side, which would temporarily clear out the problem and allow e-mail to go through as well as other StreetTalk functions.

—*Alex del Rio, contract Network Manager at a home care nursing organization*

Fault Management Tools

A large variety of tools have been developed for detecting faults and analyzing their causes. There are two issues at the top of the fault-detection hierarchy: (1) the horizontal question—can data packets or frames get from their source to their destination correctly? and (2) the vertical question—is data getting serviced correctly at each node? I will refer to these as the propagation issue and the data service issue respectively.

The propagation question can be broken down by location—is it just this workstation, just the workstations on this segment or just the workstations on this side of a particular router that can't reach the server or other destination?—and by the type of traffic—is TCP/IP traffic OK while AppleTalk traffic is blocked? The data service question can be broken down by the layers of the OSI reference model that are employed by the system, and then by the particular services each layer provides.

Since the application layer is as wide open as the uses people can imagine for computers, a disproportionate share of trouble can be expected there. Networking equipment, narrowly defined, does not usually include such failure-prone mechanical devices as disk drives and printers, but for our purposes, these devices provide critical application-layer services to the networked system. Identifying a problem as an application-layer problem may turn out to be just the first step of many in the troubleshooting process.

Tools for Analyzing Propagation Problems

General-purpose electronic test equipment, such as volt/ohm/milliammeters (VOMs) and oscilloscopes, are valuable for basic tests and board-level repairs. A VOM can serve as an electrical Swiss Army knife, identifying open and shorted cables, bad fuses, deficient power protectors, faulty connectors and similar problems. While it may be capable of finding gross cable faults, it cannot indicate subtle problems. An oscilloscope can help track down interference on a cable or distorted waveforms. The problems these tools help find are not everyday issues on most networks, however.

Propagation I: Cable Testers

"There are definitely more tools available today than there were six years ago. From my perspective, however, most of the tools available today are still trying to solve the problems we had six years ago that haven't gone away. They don't help us at all with the problems that have developed over the past six years."

—DIANE DANIELLE

The key piece of test equipment for detecting and isolating physical-level faults is the cable tester. The cable plant is subject to many varieties of subtle faults including kinked, stretched, pinched and crushed cables, corrosion, bad connectors, bad terminators, reversed wires, nonstandard lengths of cable and faulty punch-downs. Cable testers identify shorted and open cables and measure the cable's impedance. They indicate the overall length of a cable segment and can generally discover the distance along the cable to a problem within a few feet.

The technology these devices often use is time domain reflectometry (TDR). TDR is similar to radar, sending out pulses along the wire and analyzing the reflections that return. Though an open cable can't support any network traffic, TDR equipment can detect the break and calculate how far away it is. Similar TDR products are made for fiber-optic cables. They generate optical impulses and analyze the reflections that return.

Good cable testers are automated so that setting up and running tests doesn't require a lot of training. Another valuable feature is the ability to interpret results, producing English messages such as "Open at 54 feet." Some can capture data for transferring to a PC or can even print certification reports directly in order to document the soundness of the cable plant. The leading cable testers work on shielded and unshielded twisted pair and coaxial cables. Some less expensive models are dedicated to token ring or Ethernet networks.

Thoughtful cable tester manufacturers provide a full range of connectors, including RJ-45, DB-9 and BNC types.

The best time to analyze and certify cables is during installation. TDR functions usually can't be performed on a live network, though some cable testers include traffic monitoring functions that can indicate realtime network events.

Microtest—Quick Scanner (Hewlett-Packard Quick Scanner)

Microtest offers a full line of hand-held cable testers, which HP remarkets with its own packaging and warranty. The Quick Scanner, at $995, uses TDR capabilities to search out common cable faults. The product is designed to be useful even if the operator is untrained, and results are displayed in English. It can analyze coaxial and twisted pair cable, measure cable length and monitor Ethernet (802.3) traffic.

Microtest—Cable Scanner (Hewlett-Packard Cable Scanner)

In addition to the Quick Scanner's capabilities, the Cable Scanner ($1,495) measures DC resistance and electrical noise. It can print cable certifications and 802.3 Ethernet traffic logs.

Microtest—Ring Scanner (Hewlett-Packard Ring Scanner)

The Ring Scanner is designed specifically for token ring cabling. It is not a TDR. It can activate token ring hubs and simulate network faults. Connected to a live network, it can monitor the data traffic level and the ring data rate for 4- or 16-Mbits/sec rings. The suggested retail price is $1,295.

Microtest—Pair Scanner (Hewlett-Packard Pair Scanner)

This model measures signal loss, detects impulse noise, and can activate a 10BASE-T hub, in addition to the functions of the other models. While it offers features specific to twisted pair installations, it can also be used on coaxial cable. Suggested retail price is $2,495.

Microtest—MT350 Scanner (Hewlett-Packard MT350 Scanner)

The most highly automated model in the Microtest line requires only that the operator identify the network type and press the AUTO button. It then captures, analyzes, displays and stores data on near-end crosstalk (NEXT) as well as the types of data the other models analyze, such as attenuation, noise, length and other fault-producing factors. The Autotest function is user-definable for the ultimate in flexibility and productivity. The suggested retail price is $3,995.

Tektronix—FiberScout Optical Fault Finder

This hand-held unit can detect user-defined faults in optical cable to within 2 meters. Despite the suggested retail price of $5,400, it is much less costly than an optical time domain reflectometer.

Tektronix—TFP2 FiberMaster Optical Time Domain Reflectometer

Models of this product with various capabilities are priced between $19,600 and $53,400.

66

Running Down the Cable

Our network problems are all cable problems. Thin-net Ethernet gave us problems, due to bad connections. As part of our upgrade, we will replace all of our networks with SynOptics and Cabletron intelligent hubs. Cabletron is more user friendly, SynOptics a bit more flexible.

We bought a diagnostic tool for cable from Beckman Instruments, TMT-I Plus [a TDR]. This has been a real time saver. We used it on one cable system we have that is a problem. It's an Ethernet system in the dietary department of the hospital. Something about that environment, the steam and heat of the kitchens, seems to contribute to cable problems.

We frequently get network errors. We used to try to track down the problem with an ohmmeter, which was very slow. Now we hook it up to the TMT and are able to identify the

> problem quickly. In one case, the T-connectors were faulty. RG-58 cable doesn't hold up well. We replaced it with UTP level 5 for 10BASE-T and solved the problem.
>
> —*Dennis Roberts, Team Leader of Network Services, Toledo Hospital*

Propagation II: Monitoring Network Traffic

Each node on a network is potentially a source of data collection for network traffic. Concentrators, hubs, routers, bridges, workstations and servers that have management capabilities can all monitor traffic that comes their way. However, Ethernet segments on coaxial cables not served by a managed hub can be a white space on the network map. This information void resulted in the development of the network monitor.

Dedicated Network Monitors

These dedicated pieces of equipment, attached to an Ethernet segment, capture data on traffic volume and type, error rates, node activity, overall utilization and other useful categories. The management agent that operates in a network monitor has a set of buffers and counters where information is captured and stored. If the agent is SNMP-compliant, the data is organized according to the SNMP Management Information Base (MIB and MIB II) specifications. SNMP-compliant agents can respond to queries and commands from any SNMP management console, ensuring compatibility with an organization's long-term plans to standardize management practices or consolidate management tools. Network monitors can often communicate outside the network cable—generally over the telephone network via a serial port and a modem—in the event of general failure. This capability can be invaluable in alerting the management staff that a fault has surfaced and in troubleshooting the problem, especially on completely inoperative coax-based segments.

Network monitors on the market today have their own management console software. This client software, running on a workstation, issues queries and commands to one or more monitors and analyzes, formats and displays the results. Typical displays include activity graphs, traffic share charts, event and error logs and maps of the network.

Network Monitor Products

The first three entries in the following list of network monitor products are combinations of dedicated hardware and software, originally designed for unmanaged Ethernet bus installations. The remaining products are software-only network monitors.

Novell LANtern—Network Monitor for Ethernet and LANtern Services Manager

The LANtern system consists of a self-contained hardware unit that attaches to an Ethernet segment and SNMP-based management software, *LANtern Services Manager*, that is installed on a network workstation equipped with Windows. Data about network activity is collected by the monitor and passed to the management console. The management console software can graph activity, filter irrelevant information, define alarm thresholds and export data for further analysis. The LANtern monitor is equipped with an RS-232 serial port for remote connections or out-of-band communications when the network is down. The suggested retail price is $4,495 for the monitor and $4,995 for the *LANtern Services Manager* software.

Hewlett-Packard—LANProbe/LANProbe II and ProbeView/OpenView Probe Manager

LANProbe and LANProbe II are HP's Ethernet standalone monitors, which capture traffic, error and other statistics and forward them to *ProbeView*, the console software, which runs on a Windows workstation, or to *OpenView Probe Manager*, the OpenView console application. These products are also equipped with a serial port for remote connections or out-of-band communications.

Intel—NetSight Sentry

Intel's NetSight Sentry is a hardware and software package that monitors numerous statistics for both Ethernet and token ring networks. The hardware is installed in a full-length slot in a 386 or higher capacity PC. The software is DOS/character-based, so the management console does not require Windows. The menu interface lets you specify thresholds for common network performance indicators and monitor all kinds of different network traffic (with tables and graphs). It can generate alarms when specific thresholds are surpassed. It also identifies network stations by name as well as by address. At $1,995 for Ethernet and $2,995 for token ring, it's competitively priced.

Cheyenne Software—Monitrix

Cheyenne Software's *Monitrix* package monitors NetWare network traffic and collects relevant statistics. It runs passively in the background with no effect on network traffic. It also tracks workstation configuration and topologies, checks connectivity and prepares reports.

Farallon Computing—TrafficWatch

Farallon's *TrafficWatch* displays internet traffic, traffic between Ethernet and LocalTalk segments, network utilization and network errors. It also filters AppleTalk traffic by protocol and analyzes AppleTalk, TCP/IP and DECNET protocols.

Farallon Computing—PhoneNet CheckNet

Farallon's *PhoneNet CheckNet* software searches for AppleTalk devices by name or type. It works across multiple zones and bridges. It's a fast way to verify network connections from any AppleTalk device. This software is included with Farallon's StarControllers and managed hub products.

AG Group—Net Watchman

AG Group's *Net Watchman* is an AppleTalk monitor software package. It tracks zones, bridges, nodes and services and can signal network changes to the manager. The package also builds graphical zone maps and highlights problems. It works across bridges and routers that connect dissimilar cable types.

AG Group—Skyline/E

Skyline/E is a Macintosh software-based traffic monitor for multiprotocol Ethernet networks. It can sound alarms when traffic is either low or high. It logs network traffic to an archive file for later analysis.

"Anytime you can be a hero on the network, that makes the job more fun."

—DAVE FOGLE

LANshark—Net Results

LANshark's *Net Results* software package monitors and analyzes VINES network activity. This includes user activity, security, server and cabling errors. It automatically compiles a historical database of VINES log files. It can also perform resource accounting and billing. Suggested retail price is $495 per server.

Trellis—Network Observer

Trellis's *Network Observer* is a software monitoring package for VINES networks. It provides basic network management features. The package monitors network performance variables and notifies the network manager about violations of programmable thresholds. It also captures network statistics in an ASCII file for analysis and graphing. Suggested retail price for a five-server license is $975.

Working with MONITOR

When our remotes lose connection to the LAN because of power failures, I have to go in on MONITOR and reset their sessions. Once we do that, they are able to connect to the Access Server. If the Access Server locks up, I have to do a hard boot on it and they have to log in again. We changed flow control, and that doesn't help.

> We were in a building that was new and still partially under construction. Someone had accidentally loosened the SynOptics cable. We spent four days checking on it before we found the problem. Two people—one from the hospital and one from our department—were working on it. They thought it was Ethernet—we were fingerpointing back and forth. One of our guys checked the wires and all of a sudden we were connected. In the future we will check the obvious first.
>
> —*Ellen Becker, Senior Systems Analyst for a large non-profit health care organization*

Managed Hubs

Most manufacturers of concentrators and hubs now build much of the monitoring capability of a dedicated monitor into the hub itself. Modular concentrators and hubs can be installed initially without management capability, and management modules added later. In addition to collecting information, managed hubs are often capable of responding to commands from a remote console. For example, a remote operator can disconnect a malfunctioning workstation or even reconfigure the hub.

As with a dedicated network monitor, the management agent that operates in a managed hub has a set of buffers and counters where information about traffic, errors and other activity is captured and stored. SNMP compliance is an important consideration for organizations with plans to standardize and unify their network management activity, as it is with dedicated monitors. Concentrators that support multiple data-link protocols—token ring or FDDI in addition to Ethernet, for example—usually require a management module for each type.

Like network monitors, hub management systems often have their own management consoles. This workstation-based software issues queries and commands to the agents in the hubs and analyzes, formats and displays the results. It can typically display a map of the overall network and submaps of portions of the network with additional detail. A common technique is to present a facsimile of the front panel of the hub or concentrator with simulated LEDs or color codes to indicate the status and activity of ports on the hardware.

Managed Hub Products

SynOptics—Hub and Concentrator Software and Management Modules

"We're comfortable we can take action locally, but because we're global, that's not good enough. When we're sleeping, our branches overseas are working. We want to make an agreement so that someone else manages remote problems, takes action and notifies us."

—ARTHUR GRANT

SynOptics Communications has several families of network management software. For enterprises with mainframe-based platforms or other network management systems, there are the NETMAP and *Lattis View* products, providing management information and control capability to IBM's *NetView*, the DEC *Polycenter* system, HP *OpenView* or IBM's *AIX NetView/6000*. For the largest, most complex networks SynOptics offers the Unix-based *Optivity* network management system, built on Sun Microsystems' *SunNet Manager* platform. For less complex networks, there are two families of Windows-based software products.

SynOptics' *Lattis EZ-View* is intended for small to medium-size networks. It runs under Windows and manages SynOptics' Ethernet and token ring hardware (SynOptics 2000 and 3000 Concentrators). It supports SynOptics' Expanded View software, which graphically displays each hub module and all its indicators down to the port level on the Windows screen. The package runs in the background on a 386 or higher-class PC. It supports IPX as well as IP, so it is a good solution for Novell networks.

SynOptics' *LattisNet Manager for DOS* is for medium-size to large networks. It supports Ethernet and token ring network hardware and offers all the functions of *Lattis EZ-View*. The package adds SynOptics' Autotopology dynamic mapping tools, which create layered maps of the entire network by network segment. Its GlobalView mapping capability is based on HP's *OpenView*. It includes a generic SNMP management capability that allows management of other SNMP devices. Hardware monitoring includes programmable thresholds for alarms. The system offers in-band and out-of-band communications to SynOptics hardware. Thus, if the network cabling fails (a common reason for wanting management features), you can still reach the management module by phone line and modem to help solve the problem. The software runs on a Windows-based 386 or higher workstation.

SynOptics' *Optivity for NetWare* is integrated with Novell's *NetWare Management System*. It provides the Expanded View and Ring View capabilities of the other SynOptics software offerings. It supports SNMP over both IP and IPX, so mixed protocol environments can be supported readily. The *NetWare Management System* runs on a Windows-based 386 or higher workstation.

Hewlett-Packard—Hub Management Capabilities

Hewlett-Packard's *OpenView* is a family of network management tools and services for local and wide area networks. It is rapidly becoming the leading platform in DOS/Windows environments. The Unix-based *OpenView* platform is also a popular foundation for other developers. *OpenView* supports SNMP and CMIP, and offers migration to the OSF's Distributed Management Environment. It supports numerous environments and networking topologies. The core software controls and manages all of HP's networking hardware, including its hubs.

HP OpenView Hub Manager/DOS is a Windows-based application that discovers Novell IPX servers and clients and maps them. In IP mode, it can discover IP devices. It can monitor SNMP devices and control HP EtherTwist hubs. It monitors traffic, produces graphs

> *"Most of the people in IBM mainframe shops want to use NetView. They're not interested in SNMP (although this is beginning to change a bit). But NetView is still primarily a mainframe tool; it doesn't help much with the management of local or wide area networks."*
>
> —DIANE DANIELLE

and trend lines, permits threshold setting and generates alarms. The suggested retail price is $4,000.

Novell—Hub Services Manager

Novell's *Hub Services Manager* is an application that "snaps in" to Novell's management platform, *NetWare Management System*. *Hub Services Manager* can collect information from and control hubs that comply with Novell's Hub Management Interface (HMI) specification, such as Intel's EtherExpress hubs. (Intel's hubs are boards that can be installed in servers or other PCs, providing managed hub ports at low cost.) HMI hub management agents must be installed on the managed hubs. The suggested retail price for *Hub Services Manager* is $995.

The PC of Death

The problem occurred at a power plant where there was 'dirty power,' due to magnetic fields. Three servers were crashing simultaneously early in the morning at 6 a.m. Our first assumption was an electrical problem because of the dirty power. The server was on the same subnet and the same LAN as the power plant. We did some detective work. We asked the question 'What happens at 6 a.m.?' Nothing obvious happens. No other servers on a big network were being affected by this.

Next assumption: There must be something on the wire, some packet on the LAN. We were looking for a corrupted packet. The Sniffer did not show anything; everything looked fine. The odd thing was another server on a different LAN, on the same subnet, also sometimes crashed.

What happened was the PC software had been corrupted; it was sending what looked to the Sniffer like a normal request for a server. The way VINES works is that you send a request to a particular server. If that server doesn't respond, you go and try another server. The PC was going out and randomly picking one server. Whatever it was that was wrong with that packet would cause that server to crash. So, the PC would pick another server. Same thing would happen again until all three servers would crash. Sometimes it would go one hop at a time through its own LAN and then, depending on the state it got to, it would also make it occur on a different server on a different subnet.

We found out what was wrong by setting up the Sniffer to stop capturing when it received an indicator that a server had rebooted. We went back and examined the trace and observed that one PC kept asking for service—VINES files. We began to suspect that particular PC workstation. We called it the PC of death. There was no way to figure out where that PC was. We had the Ethernet datalink address, but we didn't have a clue about where in the power plant the PC was located, and the people at the plant didn't know either. There was simply no way to tell.

The solution was to partition the network by disconnecting the LAN from the WAN to ensure no further damage was done. Because it is a star-wired network, we unplugged half of it to see if the problem was occurring in the plugged or the unplugged section. This all had to be done by hand because we were dealing with a 'dumb' hub that was several years old.

By a process of elimination, we finally found the PC and actually brought it into our test lab. We found we could reproduce the problem, and when we brought it into the lab and started it, it would go around killing all the lab servers. Somehow the version that happened to be running on that machine's disk drive had been corrupted, though when I copied the software off that PC, it didn't have a problem. When I copied new software onto the PC, it didn't have a problem. We reformatted the hard disk and returned it to operations. But the process of discovery was very tedious.

—*James Brentano, Network Specialist at a West Coast utility company*

Managed Routers and Bridges

Internetworking equipment—bridges, routers and hybrid products—with built-in management agents can provide information about traffic, performance and configuration to management applications. It may also be possible to reset and reconfigure bridges and routers that are built with management capability. As with the other devices that provide primarily propagation data, SNMP compliance ensures that future management applications will not supersede the installed base of equipment. Out-of-band remote management access to bridges and routers is particularly valuable when these products are installed in remote locations with no on-site network engineers.

Router and Bridge Management Products

SynOptics—Bridge and Router Management Capabilities

SynOptics' *RouterMan* software for Unix and *Optivity* automatically recognizes and displays all protocols used on routers from SynOptics and Cisco Systems. It also handles other MIB II SNMP devices. Monitoring includes router status and performance statistics with corresponding programmable alarms and alerts.

Hewlett-Packard—Bridge and Router Management Capabilities

HP *OpenView Interconnect Manager/DOS* can collect information from SNMP bridges and routers and control HP's internetworking products. The suggested retail price is $4,000.

Neon Software—RouterCheck

Neon Software's *RouterCheck* is a software package that monitors AppleTalk routers from anywhere on the network. It reports configuration and location information, reveals zone consistency problems and advises possible remedies. The package is compatible with Neon's *NetMinder* products.

"

The Disappearing WAN

We have a monitor that goes out and *ping*s and shows anything you can't reach as red on the map. On one occasion, whole chunks of the WAN were unavailable. The network was down for 4 hours that evening with the entire northern section, from San Francisco on up, unavailable.

Another symptom was that on the line from downtown to the North Bay, all the buffers on the routers were full and the routers could not accept new packets. The telecom department shut down our link to the North Bay and let all the queues drain. We turned it back on and it quickly filled up again. We found that VINES packets were filling up (we have 80 percent VINES, 15 percent TCP/IP and other lesser protocols). The nature of VINES is its interconnection; the servers talk to each other a lot.

We then disabled VINES routing to get through to other routers that use TCP/IP to talk to each other. We had a remote Sniffer in place at our headquarters in Northern California, which is where the stuff seemed to be going. It looked like it was coming from the LAN side. It showed us a PC on a LAN in Santa Rosa. The PC was stuck in some sort of loop. It was a PC software problem. It kept sending out broadcast requests at a high rate, and they all went throughout the entire company network. The problem was that in-bound you get 400 answers to each request. So, all the queues backed up in a cascade effect. When we found out where it was coming from, we disabled the VINES routing on that particular router.

We then isolated it down to one LAN. The LAN was working OK—just a little busy. It was a matter of tracking it down; we found a log-in name to go with the network address. Then, we contacted local people who knew where the user's office was. We found it, took it off the network and brought it down to our lab. We don't know if it was the VINES software or some application. It was a VINES call, but something had gone wrong with Windows or *Word* and left it in an unhappy state.

> When we ran it down in the lab this didn't happen. So it was something about the state that the machine was in at the time. Our topology made it worse because we're set up to be very efficient at routing. In that case, the very efficiency of it, the fact that all 400 servers got it and could answer back quickly, probably made it worse, not to mention the fact that it was 5 p.m. and there wasn't much traffic.
>
> There aren't any tools to deal with that problem except to know what you should be seeing and how that's different from what you are seeing.
>
> —*James Brentano, Network Specialist at a West Coast utility company*

Data Service I: Network Operating System Server Monitoring Functions

On many networked PC systems, file servers and the network operating system software that runs on them are the heart of the entire installation. Because servers are used heavily, reconfigured often and built around mechanical components, such as disk drives and fans, a substantial fraction of networked system fault detection paths quickly lead to the server. The network operating system's built-in utilities are a critical tool for fault-detection and fault prevention. Some of the more useful types of information they can provide include the following:

- The operating system's CPU utilization—the CPU becomes a bottleneck to overall system performance if the CPU usage approaches 100 percent
- The configuration and activity of disk drives (considered as physical devices), especially write errors and bad disk blocks
- The configuration and activity of server volumes (considered as logical components), including file space limitations

- The usage and limits of server RAM for different tasks, including cache buffers and other critical functions
- The presence and activity of special drivers, libraries and utility software, such as alternate protocol stacks, database facilities or management tools
- The details of file usage, including who opens and closes them, locks and unlocks them, creates and deletes them

In addition to gathering information, server monitoring software formats, displays, logs and reports what it finds. Graphs of activity levels and utilization share may be the only practical way to observe important symptoms of trouble. Alarms or alerts can initiate recovery activity before there is a catastrophic breakdown. In addition to warning messages that appear on server consoles or workstations, alarms can take the form of e-mail messages, computer-voice phone calls or pager messages. The alarm mechanism can be harnessed to initiate automatic execution of programs or batch files to begin the recovery process or to help diagnose the fault.

Network Operating System Monitor Utilities

Novell—NetWare MONITOR NLM

The MONITOR NLM is the primary native mechanism for viewing server activity. The program executes on the server and displays output on the server console. It plays an important role in configuration management and performance management as well as fault management. The main screen displays statistics about key indicators of server activity such as processor utilization, the number of connections, the number of open files and the usage of cache buffers. The primary subsections provide information about connections, disks, LAN drivers, operating system components, file and file lock activity and critical server resources. MONITOR can provide many details about one thing at a time. Its displays are character based, showing numbers in fields rather than graphical representations of trends or comparisons of related factors. Knowledgeable users can discover much of what they need to know about a server from MONITOR, but they must know just where to look, and they must interpret the raw numbers themselves.

Frye Utilities—NetWare Management

The Frye Utilities for Networks (FUN) consist of several utilities for NetWare that make a manager's life simpler. They include *NetWare Management, NetWare Early Warning System* and *LAN Directory. LAN Directory* is discussed in Chapter 5, Configuration Management.

NetWare Management provides a summary of all server activity on one screen. Navigating to detailed screens of information is much simpler than with MONITOR and other NetWare utilities, requiring only function key strokes. Comparing data between nodes is simplified, too. The program also provides sophisticated report generation capabilities for server conditions. It is a DOS/character-based application that can run on any PC compatible with 640KB of RAM. The suggested retail price is $495.

Frye Utilities—NetWare Early Warning System

Frye's *NetWare Early Warning System* (*NEWS*) is a NetWare server management package that not only monitors server errors and other events, but can also fix some problems. When the server violates thresholds set by the network manager, *NEWS* can execute DOS commands and batch files automatically. This creates tremendous capabilities for automating routine administration and management tasks. *NEWS* can also notify network managers locally by NetWare message (the 25th line of the screen) or MHS message, or remotely by phone, fax or pager with the appropriate hardware. Remote managers can dial in with a touch-tone phone and get voice updates.

Monitoring the Network

When we were adding a 10BASE-T hub, everyone was saying 'The server is down,' and I didn't believe them. I knew that file server had two network cards on it. I walked to the console and saw that it was alive. The server wasn't hung. I got into MONITOR and selected 'LAN Information.' From there, I selected the Ethernet segment and saw there were many errors in the generic statistics. For example 'Transmit-Retry Failures' was high and it wasn't supposed to be. When I selected the token ring card, everything was normal. The server was available on the company internet and I could get to it through the token ring side. So I used MONITOR to let me know that the problem was on the Ethernet side, it wasn't in the file server. It was in the cable. One of the workstation cables had a short, which was causing the entire hub to have problems. The fact that I could get into MONITOR at all was an indication that the server was OK. I didn't need a cable tester to tell me there was something wrong with the cable.

MONITOR is very helpful for just finding out the general health of the network. If people complain the network is slow, the first place I go is MONITOR. That tells me what the CPU utilization is, what the traffic is in the network, whether a disk drive is up or down.

—Jerry White, Network Manager at a West Coast financial institution

Data Service II: Server Monitors

Server monitors provide information about the server hardware that is not captured by the network operating system. For instance, they can capture the voltage put out by the system's power supply, the operating temperature and details of drive-array controller activity. They use a plug-in board or built-in sensors to gather measurements and statistics, which are passed to the software component of the monitor. A console program running on a workstation formats, displays and prints the information. A valuable added feature is provision for out-of-band communication when the server or the network is down.

If the server monitor is designed to meet network management standards, any standard management console on the network can capture information and manage the server. As in other classes of management products, SNMP-based products are more common than those based on any other standards.

By analyzing the information provided by a server monitor, a remote support technician may be able to identify the need for a specific spare part and have it delivered to the server site without first traveling to the site and disassembling and troubleshooting the server. This capability can be extremely valuable when server downtime may cost thousands of dollars an hour.

Server Monitor Products

Compaq—INSIGHT Manager and Server Manager/R

Compaq offers management software that complements its hardware line. The Server Manager/R is a combination hardware and software package that includes an EISA System Manager interface board, which gathers environmental and electrical data from the server and its subsystems and also supports remote control activities over a serial communications line. It works with Compaq drive-array controllers to analyze drive performance at periodic intervals, to manage RAID performance and to detect impending problems. It also tracks DC voltages at the power supply and on the EISA bus to warn of possible trouble. Server Manager/R is intended for remote servers not readily accessible to network management staff and for critical servers that must run 24 hours a day. Server Manager/R works with VINES, LAN Manager, LAN Server and SCO Unix systems; in fact, it can continue to function when the network operating system is not running at all on the server. The Server Manager Facility/R is the Windows-based remote console software for Server Manager/R.

INSIGHT Manager is a software-only package that provides over-the-network management capabilities with NetWare servers. Both *INSIGHT Manager* and Server Manager/R help diagnose and prevent faults, improve security, monitor performance and manage configuration. *INSIGHT Manager* is integrated with Novell's *Net-Ware Management System* and uses SNMP by defining a MIB for Compaq servers.

Data Service III: Protocol Analyzers

Protocol analyzers are the shop vacuums of network information gathering. They suck up more or less all the activity on the network—thousands of frames or packets each second; hundreds of interdevice messages, confirmations and replies; all of the error-preventing and setup-maintaining traffic that is ever-present on a LAN. This primary protocol analysis function is called capturing a trace.

Some protocol analyzers include a special-purpose network interface device that is more sensitive than a standard network interface card. Some kinds of network events that could be the source of faults are forever invisible to a normal network interface card, and therefore to a software-only protocol analyzer. This specialized hardware can account for several thousand dollars' difference in cost between software-only and software-plus-hardware protocol analyzers.

Fortunately, protocol analyzer software can filter the incoming flood of data by any relevant factor: particular nodes or servers only, particular kinds of packets only, protocol-specific traffic only, and combinations of these factors. The traffic of interest can then be decoded, packet by packet, to display each time-stamped step with a full English (or in some cases, hexadecimal) account of what it is accomplishing. The display sequentially shucks off each protocol (the outer envelopes surrounding the application-level data), proceeding from lower layers up, until it gets to and presents the kernel of data that the network is responsible for transporting. (See Figure 4-5.)

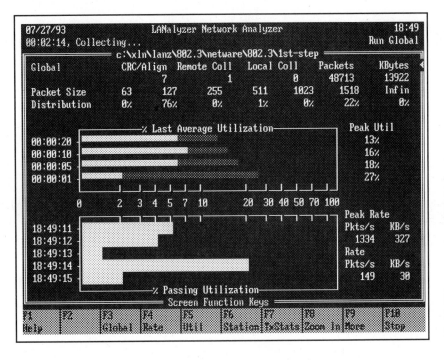

Figure 4-5 Novell's LANalyzer Collecting Statistics

In addition to capturing and displaying traces of network traffic, protocol analyzers summarize and format the raw information about that traffic. Counters and graphs can show the volume of particular events or types of traffic. The time difference between a message and its response, often a critical clue to internetworking problems, can be displayed or graphed. A captured data stream can be injected back onto a reconfigured or repaired network to confirm that a problem has been corrected.

The biggest problem with protocol analyzer traces is interpretation. Even a filtered, formatted summary of troublesome network data requires a skillful and experienced operator to reach the correct conclusion. The information may only be meaningful in comparison with baseline information from a time of normal operation. Some manufacturers address the problem of interpretation by including expert system technology. Their products automatically perform sequences of tests and measurements and produce English diagnoses of a problem, based on built-in rules and inferences. Other manufacturers offer the more modest capability of saving and repeating test sequences for specific problems. These products often come with prerecorded scripts for commonly encountered faults.

"I think there's a big ad push for LANalyzers, Sniffers and cable scanners. All those tools are valid and important and the organization should have them and know how to use them. It's been my experience that, most of the time, common sense will help you isolate the network problem, rather than the LANalyzer."

—JERRY WHITE

One area of concern to users of protocol analyzers is the breadth of protocols that are supported. A protocol that seems esoteric and rare today may be a crucial part of the network tomorrow because of a new partnership or merger, or just because a new application needs to link up with the rest of the network. Some protocol analyzer producers supply additional protocols as extra-cost options. As the network operating systems and other protocol-determining components on the network are upgraded, it is crucial for the protocol analyzer to keep in step. For instance, if the network is upgraded to support AppleTalk Phase II, the protocol analysis tool should be ready to handle it too.

One area of controversy among the makers of protocol analyzers is the need for realtime analysis. Some protocol analyzers have separate capture and analysis phases. They collect and capture network activity in one phase and filter and decode it afterward. Other producers argue that instant feedback is inevitably faster and more responsive, allowing operators to identify faults and performance inhibitors with minimum delay. For the most common network problems, neither method offers overwhelming advantages.

Protocol Analysis Products

Novell—LANalyzer for NetWare

This inexpensive software-only product currently supports Ethernet segments with any version of NetWare network operating systems and AppleTalk Phases I and II. It addresses the problem of data interpretation by providing a Windows-based "dashboard interface." Graphical representations of meters, gauges and idiot lights present the default overview of network activity. "Red lines" on gauges can be set up to indicate thresholds that are cause for concern. Filters can be selected by clicking with a mouse on a particular address, protocol or activity. Trends can be graphed or saved to a file for comparative analysis and data can be exported to a spreadsheet.

Despite the accessible face *LANalyzer for NetWare* presents to a user, it can perform full seven-layer decodes of NetWare and Apple-Talk traffic. By taking advantage of some of the features of a graphical user interface to link highlighting in multiple windows, *LANalyzer for NetWare* makes reading a packet trace about as interesting and enlightening as it can be made.

LANalyzer for NetWare is not designed to analyze networks with non-NetWare servers or even those with non-Ethernet segments. Its ability to capture activity on the network is limited to the network interface card on the workstation it is installed on. But it does offer great capabilities to those networks that conform to its mission. The suggested retail price is $1,495.

Intel—NetSight Professional

NetSight Professional is a software-only protocol analyzer that performs realtime seven-layer decodes on NetWare, VINES, LAN Manager and other networks. It can decode TCP/IP, IPX/SPX, SNA, OSI, AppleTalk Phase I and II and XNS traffic. It can filter traffic by location and by protocol type. *NetSight Professional* is also capable of generating specific kinds of traffic. It tracks protocol use, errors, conversations and network utilization by workstation. It includes many simulation features for capacity planning. It also reads and analyzes trace files captured by other protocol analyzers. token ring and Ethernet versions are available. *NetSight Sentry*, Intel's network monitor offering, is included with *NetSight Professional*. Suggested retail price is $7,995 for the Ethernet version and $8,995 for token ring.

Intel—NetSight Analyst

NetSight Analyst is a NetWare-specific protocol analysis tool. It can filter packets, decode them and transmit traffic. Since it is a compact software-only tool, a single *NetSight Analyst* diskette can be taken to a user's workstation and executed there. The suggested retail price is $995.

Network General—Sniffer

The Sniffer is one of the market-leading industrial-strength protocol analyzers. It can be purchased as a combination of a special high-sensitivity network interface card and protocol analysis software to be installed on an MS-DOS-compatible portable PC that has an available ISA slot. It can decode a selection of protocols as wide as or wider than any other protocol analyzer.

The flagship Network General product for PC networks is the Expert Sniffer, a software update to the Network General Sniffer. It automatically identifies many common network problems in realtime at all seven decoding layers. The package also recommends solutions to problems. It automatically checks the network configuration in realtime so it learns about the features of a specific network.

Network General Distributed Sniffer System

Network General's Distributed Sniffer System is a family of products for Ethernet and token ring LAN segments, and bridged or routed internetworks. The system consists of hardware (the Sniff-

"I can diagnose 80 percent of the problems we have with the network that are hardware-related. But I don't have the facilities or the background to solve the communication protocol problems we have. Even if you have a Sniffer, you have to take a sophisticated course in how to use it and how to interpret what's coming across."

— RICHARD SHERKIN

Master console and Sniffer servers) and software. Applications include expert analysis, protocol interpretation, traffic generation and network monitoring. SniffMaster Consoles provide the user interface and management while Sniffer servers actually perform monitoring tasks, even at remote locations. The system uses SNMP.

Novell—LANalyzer

The LANalyzer was the first PC-based protocol analyzer and remains one of the most popular products on the market. Like the Sniffer, it is typically purchased as a combination of software and a special ISA network interface board that is installed in a portable PC.

"When you have a theory of what the problem might be, you pursue that, sometimes to the exclusion of other possibilities. The trick is to go through this logically and find out what's the most likely problem, then work on trying to eliminate that, and go from there."

—DAVE FOGLE

LANalyzer's Automated Troubleshooting System is a set of prerecorded tests for the most commonly encountered network problems. This suite of applications draws on the experience of past users to simplify testing. The suggested retail price for an Ethernet or token ring LANalyzer is $12,500. A combination package is available for $19,980.

Hewlett-Packard—Network Advisor

Hewlett-Packard's Network Advisor is a high-end, hardware-based, intelligent network analysis tool. It's a luggable PC with a special high-performance network interface. Ethernet, token ring and FDDI interface modules are all available. It monitors network traffic, discovers and maps the network, finds faults and proposes solutions. It handles all popular protocols and decodes in realtime. You can get three different decoding styles: network stack decodes, protocol decodes and protocol layer decoding. The Advisor comes with several predefined filters and lets you build and add your own. It offers simultaneous reception and transmission. It comes with several network-specific tests that isolate common problems, including cable testing. Its rules-based artificial intelligence offers the user the experience of several of HP's troubleshooters. Perhaps its most important feature is that it learns what is normal for your network while everything is functioning routinely. This is a big help when things go wrong. Its biggest drawback is that you cannot add to the knowledge base yourself—you have to wait for updates from HP. Suggested retail prices start at $19,382.

Hewlett-Packard—4972A

Hewlett-Packard's 4972A protocol analyzer was one of the first such devices in the testing industry. It's designed for more sophisticated users than is the Network Advisor. It is more helpful for engineers than it is for network managers. Its programmability makes it very flexible. HP offers a wide range of software applications for the unit that solve specific problems. For example, HP offers a NetWare protocol interpreter and several tools for dealing with TCP/IP networks. Suggested retail price for the base system is $21,000.

Wandel & Goltermann—DA-30

Wandel & Goltermann make some of the world's most sophisticated protocol analyzers for telecommunications engineers. The DA-30 is a multiport dual LAN/WAN analyzer that is roughly the size of a small suitcase. Its different modules test bridges, routers and gateways for Ethernet, token ring, FDDI, X.21, V.35, V.36 and V.24 systems. Since it has two active analyzers, it can analyze both sides of a bridge or router at the same time on the same screen. It also performs all the normal protocol analysis functions like data capture and analysis with filters and triggers, protocol decoding and network loading. The DA-31 is a similar unit with a single analyzer (instead of the dual system in the DA-30). The company also offers a line of ISDN simulators and test equipment. Suggested retail prices start at $24,000.

AG Group—EtherPeek, TokenPeek and LocalPeek

AG Group's *EtherPeek*, *TokenPeek* and *LocalPeek* packages monitor network communications and analyze traffic on Ethernet, token

ring and LocalTalk networks. These Macintosh software-based protocol analyzers decode all major network protocols. You can set up
filters and triggers. The packages also retransmit captured network
traffic to test networks under various loads and to simulate future
growth. AG Group throws in *EtherHelp*, *TokenHelp* and *LocalHelp*
software for sending data to remote sites in order to capture data for
remote troubleshooting.

Neon Software—NetMinder

Neon Software's *NetMinder* is a software-based network analyzer
for Macintosh systems. It comes in two versions—LocalTalk and
Ethernet. It checks media, finds conflicting software and spots traffic bottlenecks. Features include pre- and postfiltering, error detection, statistics monitoring, triggers and alarms. It handles a variety
of other protocols besides AppleTalk. Neon includes software for
capturing network traffic at remote sites. Both systems offer detailed help about protocol decodes and what they mean.

Management Tools

There are things about managing a network that lots of people
just ignore. They don't recognize them as being issues. On the
other hand, a lot of effort is being spent to make it easier to manage the wire. Sniffers and LANalyzers, for example, are very
helpful when you're developing network software or are trying
to solve certain types of network problems. But they are very
technical tools and are useful only in the hands of skilled technicians. I have this theory that Sniffer-type products may be the
most frequently put on the shelf products in the market. People
buy them but never use them because they don't know how to
use them. We are seeing some progress being made in the development of expert systems or, at least, easier ways of looking at
a network so that the average administrator can figure how to
solve a network problem. But we have a long way to go.

—*Diane Danielle, industry columnist and President of
Danielle Associates, a network consulting firm*

5 / Configuration Management

Configuration management involves identifying the components of the network, verifying that they have been set up correctly, tracking them as they attach and detach, and changing their installation parameters as the network grows and changes or as problems are identified. Comprehensive configuration information is crucial to fault troubleshooting; the process can't even begin without a substantial amount of basic data about what is connected. In fact, many reported faults turn out to be improper or deficient configurations of perfectly sound components. Reliable, comprehensive configuration information and control capability are also the essential foundation for performance management, security management and accounting management.

The two principal components of configuration management are gathering information and exercising control. Much of the information that configuration management requires is readily accessible to a management application that knows where to look. This chapter begins by considering some of these sources of information and discussing the ways they can be pulled together and overlaid to provide more-or-less unified views of the networked system. It also examines the actions a management application can take to modify or correct configurations on the network. Finally, it considers some of the broader organizational aspects of network configuration control and discusses the tradeoffs involved in striking a balance between user initiative and efficient management.

Configuration Information

Perhaps the greatest challenge to network management is the difficulty of pulling together configuration information from many diverse, nonsynchronized sources. The following list includes the principal information resources:

- Network maps
- Physical inventories
- Directories
- Native network operating system utilities
- Network operating system query and reporting tools
- Hub, router and bridge management tools
- Product-specific configuration programs
- Workstation configuration tracking tools

Information provided by these sources includes overlaps and redundancies. Network maps, for example, may be produced by hub managers, by inventorying systems or by a universal management development platform.

The configuration sites that need the most intervention from network managers are, in rough order:

1. Workstations
2. Printers
3. User administration (access privileges, new passwords, etc.)
4. Servers
5. Cables, punchdown blocks, patch panels and terminators
6. Hubs/concentrators
7. Routers and bridges

Network Entities and Their Attributes

Configuration information consists of sets of attributes about network entities. This book uses the abstract word "entities" for this discussion because networked systems include many diverse sorts of components. The configuration management task includes, but is much broader than, an inventory of hardware devices and links on the network.

Objects

"Object" would be a preferable term to "entity" were it not already employed otherwise. In standards documents, vendor literature and textbooks, an object means a package of data and rules for behavior that can function as a reusable component of a software application. Object-oriented programming concepts and object-oriented design are fundamental to the descriptions of network management standards. In SNMP or CMIP parlance, objects are abstractions—data values combined with rules for accessing and manipulating them—rather than the physical or logical components of the network. The term "managed objects" is often used (imprecisely) to refer generally to network resources, hardware or software. But rather than mislead readers into thinking that this discussion is about developing software, this book uses "entities" to refer to these components.

Network entities also include software processes (programs, drivers, libraries, protocol stacks); logical entities, such as volumes, directories, queues and files; and customer entities, such as users, groups and enterprises. It is a logical entity, the drive volume, that runs out of space and aborts a network operation, not the physical disk drive. The failure to assign appropriate rights to a customer entity—the user—can prevent the user from executing an application that unsuccessfully attempts to create temporary files in a particular directory. The improper installation of a graphical user interface such as Windows, a software entity not normally thought of as a component of a network, can prevent a workstation from connecting to the network at all.

"An increasing number of people are starting to support SNMP, but not everybody. Some people are still building proprietary systems for control."

— DIANE DANIELLE

Much information about network entities is stored in various places on and off the system prior to any explicit configuration management activity. Physical inventories—paper-based or electronic lists of the organization's assets—can be one starting point. Another primary source is the network operating system software, which can supply information regarding customer entities and logical entities. Workstations always contain substantial information about their own configuration, though it may not be readily accessible to a configuration management system. Gateways and special-purpose servers—database servers, communications servers, fax servers, print servers, message handling servers, e-mail servers and the like—keep track of their own configuration information, which may not be available to a network management application. Such devices as hubs, routers and bridges can also maintain their own local configuration databases; when they do, they are marketed as intelligent or managed devices. If these databases (and access to them) comply with SNMP or CMIP standards, the information can be gathered by a management application that supports the appropriate standard.

Standards and Configuration Reporting

The premise behind the drive for standardization is straightforward: if all the component manufacturers were to agree upon a list of the necessary pieces of configuration information, how to represent this information and how to communicate it, then it would be easy to develop automated network-wide management tools. On networks that employ IP (the Internet Protocol), there is today a widely accepted standard called SNMP, for Simple Network Management Protocol, for components of the network defined narrowly. In other words, hubs, routers and bridges often have SNMP management capabilities. But not all SNMP implementations require IP; Novell and other PC network-oriented manufacturers can send SNMP packets over IPX as well as IP.

"A problem we've run into is that when you're administering protocols like TCP/IP, every workstation has a unique TCP/IP address. You also have a wide area network that's going to route based on a TCP/IP address. So if you move a workstation from one building to the next, you clobber the users' ability to get out of the building and electronically communicate with anyone else."

— RANDY HOWLAND

SNMP defines management information bases (MIBs) that provide structures for managed entities—the network components—to store and communicate management data. The most current implementation is called MIB II. A remote monitoring MIB (RMON MIB) also has been adopted to extend the kinds of information that can be provided to a management application by remote networks. (The details of MIB specifications are primarily of interest to programmers developing management software, but more detail can be found in Appendix C. Many SNMP management console applications include a MIB browser capable of inspecting the MIB. Access to these specifications is also useful for those who need to employ these browsers.)

SNMP network management is a distributed application in the sense that multiple processes running on many devices must cooperate. The management console runs the overall management process and queries and controls the MIB, which is normally distributed among the management agents. Managed entities run management agent processes to communicate with the global management application.

Management agents require substantial computing resources, which explains two prominent facts about today's market. First, network components with management agents are substantially more costly than those without them. And second, the vast majority of PC network nodes lack the power and the resources to sustain SNMP management agents. It could even be argued that network management standards apply only to networks in the narrowly defined sense; in other words, these standards don't really apply to workstations and servers.

PCs that lack sufficient resources to be SNMP agents are even less suitable candidates to be agents for CMIP (Common Management Information Protocol, the OSI standard). CMIP is implemented at all seven layers of the OSI Reference Model, with overhead galore. In practice, however, with no more than a handful of commercial implementations, the question of whether or not to use CMIP does not come up very often.

Attempts to define lower-overhead implementations of CMIP include CMOL (Common Management Over Logical Link Control) and CMOT (Common Management Over TCP/IP). CMOL applications talk directly to the Logical Link Control sublayer of layer 2, the data link layer. CMOT applications pass management traffic to TCP/IP at layer 4 and at layer 3. Very few implementations of either of these hybrid standards have been announced.

Standard SNMP (or CMIP) agents can only be truly useful with an effective front-end management application. It is possible to send out individual queries and interpret the cryptic replies that come back from agents. Some management software includes a MIB browser capability for non-native management agents. If there were one specific fact you needed to know, such as whether a piece of equipment was in service, these tools could be valuable. More often than not, however, trying to do configuration management with a browser or a series of queries would be about as futile as bailing out a sinking yacht with a thimble.

No Single View

We have a graphical representation of all the routers that make up the wide area network so they can be monitored. But in a local area network sense we don't monitor things as much in realtime at this point.

Right now, because of the size of the company, some departments can't even fathom the number of nodes we have on the network. There's no way to get a single view of the entire network.

—*Randy Howland, Network Manager for a Fortune 500 technology company*

Network Maps

Servers, bridges and routers maintain dynamic tables of their connections. A sufficiently clever management program can infer the topology of the network's nodes from these tables and display it as a logical map of the network. In many cases, the logical network map display is the home screen of the management application—it is the first thing you see when you load it and it is the starting point for moving to more detailed views. The producers of unified management platforms provide maps and automatic node discovery as essential resources to software developers. Many standalone management applications draw their own maps and discover nodes, too.

Maps can be extended along two axes. First, the logical map, which shows only an abstract view of the network, can be integrated with geographical maps, building plans and office layouts to show the physical locations of particular devices. The physical network map can greatly simplify troubleshooting and performance problem-solving. For example, a source of electrical interference, such as an elevator motor, would be visible on a floor plan that incorporated the physical network.

Second, the map can be integrated with the records for each physical node, including such information as the English name of the device (rather than a string of arbitrary alphanumeric characters) and its make, model and serial number; a workstation user's name; the name of a local person responsible for resetting or unjamming the device; the hardware installed (e.g., network interface card type and configuration, amount of RAM, CPU type and speed, hardware interrupt assignments, disk drive types and capacity); and software configuration details.

"I used to joke that I needed a TSR, a terminate-and-stay-resident program, just to keep track of computer moves."

— DIANE DANIELLE

Maps that successfully integrate other applications, such as those provided by the integrated management platforms discussed in Chapter 9, Network Management Platforms, permit the network manager to identify events and problems, zero in on them intuitively and make any needed changes.

Physical Inventories

Managing the network requires information about the physical locations of particular devices (many of which are distributed throughout an office, a building or a campus), what has been installed inside them and what is attached to them: Which wiring closet has the concentrator that connects a particular workstation? Who has the keys to the office at a remote location where a router operates? Does the Macintosh router have an uninterruptible power supply? Who can reset the fax server in building D after the file server crashes?

Network administration, just as much as network management, requires this kind of information. Adding new users, modifying an office's layout or moving a department all depend on reliable physical configuration data. Furthermore, while keeping track of the organization's physical assets is not itself a network management problem, when all the computing resources are networked, the ability to maintain this record in one place can be a valuable side effect for the organization's overall asset tracking needs. The problem of gathering this kind of information automatically, though, has not yet been solved.

Workstation Configuration Management

Workstations—the most numerous group of nodes—pose the greatest problems. Some DOS utility programs, such as *Norton Utilities*, *PC Tools*, Quarterdeck's *Manifest* and automatic inventorying software, can report the total amount of RAM, the microprocessor type and speed, the hard disk size and type, the BIOS type and version, the generic network interface card type, the generic video type and the contents of the primary configuration files. These products work by interrogating the operating system and the hardware setup information; they are therefore aware of the software that interfaces to other devices, but not the devices or boards themselves. Thus a Brand X network interface card that used a 3Com 3C509 driver would be indistinguishable from the real thing, as far as the inventorying software was concerned. In general, these methods cannot report the make and model of the workstation, whether a printer or a modem is attached, or the existence of other kinds of cards or peripherals (fax, scanner, video capture, audio). Many of the most important producers of workstation components belong to the Desktop Management Task Force, which is attempting to specify uniform methods for reporting the details of the desktop environment to management applications.

"We wanted to have a homogeneous network. We knew we would not have a lot of time to spend on the network, so we wanted to reduce problems by insisting on compliance. I purchased all the machines."

—JOE ESTRADA

Network Printer Configuration Management

Network printers are another common node type. The state of automated information gathering is particularly dismal here. There is no easy way—that is, no standards exist—to report over a wire such important facts as how much memory is installed in the printer, which fonts are available, whether the printer can interpret PostScript, whether it is bogged down processing a large bitmapped image rather than experiencing a hardware failure, or even whether it is correctly connected to the server.

This problem results mostly from the prevalence of parallel port connections to printers in the Intel-based PC world. Parallel ports are still almost entirely one-way links, capable of putting out data rapidly but providing little or no return information beyond basic receipt confirmations and perhaps an out-of-paper indicator. Makers of large printers oriented toward network installations have begun proprietary attempts to alleviate this problem. Multivendor committees are working to spell out standards for printer configuration information, but at this writing, Hewlett-Packard, the most important manufacturer of printers on PC networks, has not elected to participate in one widely supported attempt. Some printers can detect PostScript or PDL jobs and switch their processing automatically. Direct network connections, either built into the printer or added on like Intel's NetPort, can support two-way communication of printer status and error messages.

Organizations can minimize the problem of keeping track of physical configurations if they rigidly control the acquisition of workstations and printers, specify acceptable platforms and keep them secure from freelance upgrades. Of course, the converse problem is that without freelance upgrades, the organization may not make the most of its network investment, and users have less of a stake in the system.

Sharing Printers

We had a problem with print functions on the networks. Originally we set up our print function using a Novell function, RPRINTER, which allows you to set up remote printer servers. We made two mistakes:

First, we decided that because every one of the seven secretaries in the building had a LaserJet, we didn't have to buy any more and we could share all of these amongst different work groups. The secretaries and the engineers, however, are two distinct work groups, with different priorities and expectations. The result of this error was that an engineer would print something, then walk over to the secretary who was trying to work and ask 'Where's my printout?' The secretary might have something printing out as well, and it became an annoying problem for both groups.

The second problem was that RPRINTER services were not reliable. For example, the printer function uses a print server and takes jobs, queues them up and sorts them out. For some reason, one server would lock up. Then someone had to reboot, reinitialize the print server and ask the clients to resubmit their print jobs. We worked on this problem with Novell and ComputerLand continually. Our ComputerLand SE talked to Novell, but it never did work right.

Our solution to the problem was to call other branches of the company and ask what they were doing. We found that one of our sites was using a product called NetPort from Intel, which receives print jobs from clients on the network and does not require a server or setting up any procedures using PSERVER. You just plug it in and hook it up to the queues on the network, and it's very reliable. Now we are able to maintain a network print function using only three of our LaserJets very satisfactorily.

—*Joe Estrada, Support Services Manager for a chemical manufacturer*

Network Device Management

Hubs, concentrators, bridges and routers can generally be purchased with management capability. As networking devices in the narrowly defined sense, SNMP management capability is widely implemented on these products, although some producers stick with their proprietary management information formats and transport mechanisms. (Nonstandard management capability requires proprietary software from the producer of the device to provide any value.) SNMP's mechanisms can supply the attributes of physical devices required for configuration management. Manufacturers usually produce their own management consoles to present information returned from the managed entities. Despite the uniformity of data and querying techniques that SNMP ensures, these console applications are often proprietary in the way they accumulate and format management information. The SNMP standards provide for extended MIBs that include proprietary categories of information, which could prevent producer B's management agent from working with producer A's management application. The impetus for a universal management platform and user console is the result of this situation. (See Chapter 9, Network Management Platforms.) Novell, Hewlett-Packard, Sun or IBM could become fair brokers for the other vendors with their platform architectures and development kits.

Cable Configuration Management

Configuration management with respect to cables is almost entirely a matter of physical inventory. Some organizations require that the lengths, endpoints, terminators and cross-connections of the cabling plant be documented, maintained and kept accessible. Unlike other kinds of management applications, software designed to track cables cannot somehow query them, though there can and should be links between cable-tracking applications and network management consoles. Cable management applications typically stand alone as a database or combine a CAD-type application—including floor plans and office layouts—with a database of cable attributes.

Physical Inventory and Mapping Products

ISICAD, Inc.—Command

ISICAD's *Command* software is useful for physical network management. There are two versions: *Command 2000* runs on DOS-based PCs, and *Command 5000* runs on an HP-9000 Unix workstation. The package started out as a cable management database and CAD package to plan cabling installation and track costs. It manages physical networking items down to the smallest devices. For maximum usability, it must be incorporated with HP's *OpenView* or Cabletron's Spectrum management systems. The packages also include help desk management utilities.

Farallon—NetAtlas

Farallon's *NetAtlas* creates logical maps of AppleTalk internets by recognizing about 200 AppleTalk devices. It also stores this information in a database that can be sorted by name, address, type, zone, system, finder and version number. Since it compares maps generated at different times, it can also track network modifications.

Neon Software—LANsurveyor

Neon Software's *LANsurveyor* is a network management package for Macintoshes. It draws logical maps of AppleTalk networks. It can be used as an interface to SNMP devices on the network. The program tests network responsiveness, illustrates problems and monitors network traffic. It also offers realtime troubleshooting features.

Directories

The network directory is a database of users and services on a network. It is the starting point for any kind of network administration as well as for configuration management. It is an essential feature of any network operating system, though it may not be called a directory by the producer of the NOS.

Among PC network operating systems, the best directory services belong indisputably to Banyan's VINES. VINES was designed from the beginning to work with multiserver, multisegment networks. The VINES directory is therefore replicated in each VINES server. This replication permits users, administrators and management applications (with appropriate rights) to view all the resources of the wide area network from any point. StreetTalk, the VINES directory services application, serves as a kind of phone book for the enterprise-wide network.

NetWare, with its roots in capital-L Local Area Networks, lacked multiserver directory services until the release of version 4.0. (NetWare Name Service does not provide directory services, though it is a useful administrative tool for synchronizing users on multiple servers.) Instead, each NetWare server has a database called the bindery, which maintains records of users, user groups, file servers, print servers and other NetWare "objects." Before NetWare performs services, it verifies the client's access rights and confirms passwords, if necessary, via the bindery. Utilities and management applications that report NetWare statistics about file usage, traffic or almost anything else of interest must look to the bindery for their operation.

Novell produces an optional extension to NetWare called NetWare Name Service. NetWare Name Service is especially useful as an administrative tool that permits the system administrator to define multiserver domains to which clients can have uniform privileges. Thus users log in to a domain with a single password and can be connected to multiple servers, rather than being required to log in to each server individually, with a password for each. The Name Service Database is replicated and synchronized on all the servers in a domain. NetWare Naming Services is not a directory service, though it addresses some of the problems that result from Novell's roots in single-server LANs.

In an interesting strategic move, Banyan has introduced a product called Enterprise Network Services (ENS). ENS is essentially an implementation of StreetTalk directory services for NetWare networks. It runs on a standalone directory server CPU and facilitates interoperation with VINES networks as well as functioning as the NetWare global directory.

The current version of LAN Manager, version 2.1, supports multiserver domains but does not have a global directory service. Apple-Talk supports the definition of zones, which provide some of the functions of domains to Macintosh networks.

The International Standards Organization X.500 committee has been working for some years to establish universal directory specifications. Network operating system makers will attempt to migrate toward these standards in the mid-1990s.

Network Operating System Tools

Many of the configuration parameters that must be managed effectively are located within the network operating system. The tools for controlling NOS configurations may be supplied with the NOS itself, or developed by independent software companies.

Native Network Operating System Utilities

NOSes provide tools to administer and inquire about users, groups, drive volumes, directories, files, printers, print queues and other logical entities they create and maintain. These administration and inquiry operations often consist of changing or fetching information in the directory (bindery) or another system configuration file. These utilities typically perform one operation at a time, making them unsuitable for reporting most kinds of summaries and overviews. They are the socket wrenches of configuration management, just right for certain operations but limited for more general ones.

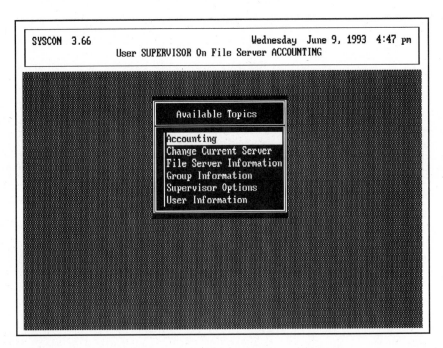

Figure 5-1 Main Screen for SYSCON

NetWare

SYSCON (and NETCON)

SYSCON is the primary user administration tool for NetWare. It runs on DOS (or OS/2) workstations. NETCON is the special version of SYSCON used when NetWare Name Service has been employed to create domains. It can be used to set volume, directory and file access rights for users and groups. It performs password administration. It permits the definition of login scripts—lists of executable actions—much like a DOS AUTOEXEC.BAT script, which is performed each time a user logs in to the server. It can limit user access to particular workstations (i.e., network addresses) and to particular times of the day.

User accounts can be set to expire on particular dates. Local work-group managers can be created by giving them the rights necessary to administer a subset of the network, such as the ability to create new user accounts and change passwords for a specific group.

Figure 5-2 MAKEUSER Main Menu

```
MAKEUSER  3.61                        Wednesday  June 9, 1993  5:09 pm
File Server: ACCOUNTING
```

```
         Available Options

        Create New USR File
        Edit USR File
        Process USR file
```

MAKEUSER

MAKEUSER is the express version of SYSCON, for times when multiple similar user accounts need to be created at the same time.

MAKEUSER executes on a DOS workstation. It uses a script file with special commands that establish rights, define group membership, create login scripts and so forth. When multiple accounts need to be created, MAKEUSER saves administrators a tremendous amount of time compared to the alternative of setting each account up by visiting all the SYSCON submenus one after another.

USERDEF

USERDEF permits the creation of user templates with default access rights, group memberships, login scripts and so forth. Like MAKEUSER, it executes on a DOS workstation. These templates can be used to override users' existing access and membership profiles. USERDEF provides an efficient mechanism for assigning a collection of user rights to a particular user.

Figure 5-3 USERDEF Main Screen

MONITOR

The MONITOR NetWare Loadable Module (NLM) is the primary native mechanism for viewing server activity. The program executes on the server and displays output on the server console. It plays an important role in fault management and performance management as well as configuration. The main screen displays statistics about key indicators of server activity such as processor utilization, the number of connections, the number of open files and the usage of cache buffers. The primary subsections provide information about connections, disks, LAN drivers, operating system components, file and file-lock activity and critical server resources.

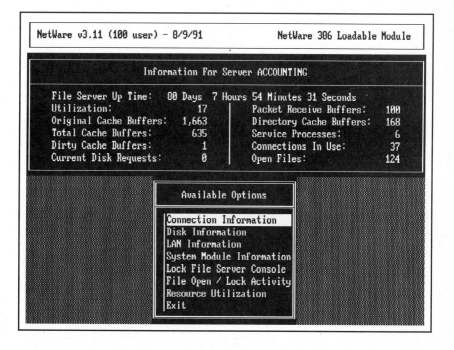

Figure 5-4 MONITOR (Accessed Via RCONSOLE)

MONITOR can provide many details about one thing at a time. Its displays are character-based, showing numbers in fields rather than graphical representations of trends or comparisons of related factors. Knowledgeable users can discover much of what they need to know about a server from MONITOR, but they must know just where to look and they must interpret the raw numbers themselves.

> ### MONITOR on the Case
>
> I take care of day-to-day administration, going into LAN security and setting print configurations. I monitor who's actually connected, because occasionally the application software gives us a message that tells us another user has locked the case.
>
> Sometimes people forget to back out of a case when they've looked at it. Then the nurses who are about to do surgery can't retrieve the case. That's when I use Novell. I have to go into MONITOR to see who was logged in and what files they were viewing. When you have 60-odd people using a system, you have to track them down. At least I can see which people are into which files. I can call them on the phone. I'm now asking the application vendor to modify the program to display user IDs.
>
> —Ellen Becker, Senior Systems Analyst for a large non-profit health care organization

VOLINFO, CHKVOL

These DOS workstation utilities produce statistics about available disk space. VOLINFO displays a screen that regularly updates the information; CHKVOL produces a one-shot report on the screen.

RCONSOLE, ACONSOLE

RCONSOLE (Remote CONSOLE) is a workstation program that allows a network manager to view the server console from any workstation on the network. The server must run two NLMs named RSPX and REMOTE to enable remote console operation over the network. ACONSOLE (Asynchronous CONSOLE) supports remote console viewing over RS-232 serial lines with a modem. It requires communications support from the RS-232

NLM as well as REMOTE.NLM in order to function. With these remote console facilities, network managers can view MONITOR, load and unload NLMs, execute server utilities and perform other console operations without traveling to the server's local console. The local console can even be disabled.

PCONSOLE
This is the main utility for defining, examining and manipulating print queues and print servers. It executes on a DOS workstation and is an important tool for uncovering network printing problems.

PRINTCON
PRINTCON is a DOS workstation utility for defining print job configurations. The process that prints a job looks to these configuration profiles for information about which file server, print queue and print server to use, how many copies to print, whether to produce a banner to separate the job from others and other settings.

Testing Software Through CompuServe
I have been looking for good configuration management software. I want something that is Windows-based. I have obtained trial packages by logging on to CompuServe. Here you can download LAN management demonstration programs. Third-party manufacturers offer them. I tried a few. One of them, *LANimation* software, temporarily obliterated my network connection to my server. It had done something to my entire Ethernet. I had to reboot the workstation. Fortunately, I was working in a controlled environment, so no damage was done.

—*Richard Sherkin, MIS Manager, Biltrite Industries*

Network Operating System Query and Reporting Tools
This class of product, at its simplest, adds elaborate report generation capabilities to the basic network operating system utilities.

Thus attributes and specifications that NOS utilities let you see one at a time can be sorted, summarized and printed out. More ambitious products of this type integrate with inventory and workstation configuration-tracking programs.

Network Operating System Query and Reporting Products

The LAN Support Group—BindView Plus

BindView Plus is a kind of report generator for the NetWare bindery and other internal NetWare configuration files. It can perform security audits, report on disk space utilization, identify insecure passwords and create documentation of how the network is configured. The suggested retail price is $395 for the first server and $195 for subsequent servers.

The LAN Support Group—Traveling BindView Plus

Traveling BindView Plus is the portable version of *BindView Plus*. It can be carried from server to server to query and report from the internal NetWare configuration databases. The suggested retail price is $1,495.

Blue Lance—LT Stat

Blue Lance's *LT Stat* documents the NetWare bindery objects and other parameters. Most of the data is also available in NetWare utilities, but this product organizes all of it in one place. It tracks server installation settings, server performance, disk utilization, trustee and effective rights for users and groups, login scripts and duplicate files. The package also offers reports on all these items. The suggested retail price is $295.

NC Group—LMD II

This documents LAN Manager networks. It tracks servers, user accounts and shared names, and provides audit logs in xBase files. The stored data can then be used to provide various reports.

Hub, Router, and Bridge Management Tools

The hub, router, and bridge management schemes (often compliant with SNMP standards) that were discussed in Chapter 4, Fault Management, can provide and modify any configuration information a central management application might need.

Product-Specific Configuration Programs

One class of configuration tool is specific to particular devices or software entities. These are the ordinary setup or configuration utilities used to install hardware and software. The more tightly a device or program is tied to the native device, the more crucial the setup routine may be. For instance, special device drivers for HardCards or SCSI drives may have side effects with network configurations. File compression utilities and add-ons like *Stacker* can substitute one drive assignment for another and make other utilities unpredictable. Windows sometimes demands a great deal of tinkering with its configuration before it works properly on a network. In many cases, these configurations can be changed by modifying setup profiles with a text editor. It is rare that the ability to change these configurations is integrated with other configuration management tools.

Reconfiguring Network Printers

With Novell, there are print queues associated with a print server, and our refinery uses Intel's NetPort. When I got here, I had to reconfigure it because it was unstable. Printers were losing connections and users were losing print jobs sent to the NetPort. The problem was a combination of NetPort and queue problems in the file servers themselves.

I spent about two months troubleshooting, working via trial and error. I came in on Saturdays, when there were no users with printing needs. I talked to Novell, and investigated the level of firmware on NetPort. It turned out that the symptoms were caused by the old version of firmware on NetPort.

To diagnose this, I used NP Admin, one of Intel's configuration utilities. It's a tool that queries the unit to find the revision level. The utility pulls data down from individual NetPorts and lets you look at it individually on screen. I found that the version of the firmware was 2.10, an older version. I then upgraded this NetPort over the network using NP Admin. The second half of solving the problem involved Novell tech support. They referred me to Novell NetWire on CompuServe to download an update of PCONSOLE. I used PCONSOLE to delete and reconfigure the queues, because some of the queues were created using the older version. Because they didn't interface properly with the bindery, the system lost sync between the queue and NetPort, creating problems.

I created new queues, upgraded and reconfigured. This stabilized the printing process, and so far, there have been no more complaints from users.

—Lawrence Sachartoff, networking consultant for an international petrochemical firm

Workstation Configuration Tracking Tools

There are two commonly used methods for gathering workstation configuration information. One is the universal login script, which runs a reporting utility on the workstation every time it is logged on to the network. This utility updates the configuration database on a central server. The other method is the resident reporting utility, which is loaded and active on the workstation all the time, and therefore available to be polled by a server application.

Products that track workstation configurations generally create and maintain a proprietary database stored on a server. Information in one of these databases is formatted for the application that creates it. As time passes, it becomes more and more important for this information to be integrated with other configuration information.

Software configuration details are often the most crucial information the network manager needs. For managing workstation configurations centrally, it is essential to know the following:

- The workstation operating system, its version and its location (on a local drive or on the network, in an expected or unexpected place)
- Operating system extensions and their versions, locations and parameters (e.g., CD-ROM extensions, sound capabilities, local drive device drivers, memory management facilities, disk compression facilities, terminate-and-stay-resident or other pop-up utilities)
- Windows (or another user environment) and its version, location, setup parameters and extensions
- The network shell, its version and its location
- The protocol stacks, their versions and locations
- The applications, their versions and locations
- Application configuration details—printer drivers, database libraries, serial and parallel port usage, font capabilities
- The availability and location of diagnostic utilities.

Windows Configuration Problem

Here's what happens if you allow Windows to select the size of its swap file. In my department, a user would go to another workstation and log in and get this nice blue screen that said 'Your swap file is corrupt.' We had it configured so that the only thing kept on a user's C drive was the swap file. Everything else was on the file server. The problem was that Windows files were stored on the server, under the user's account, and the information about the swap file was also stored on the server. So, if you logged on to a PC that didn't have the same swap file as the one you were just on before, you would get this blue screen with the error message. We solved the problem by giving everybody a temporary swap file. Then the message went away.

—Jerry White, Network Manager for a West Coast financial institution

Workstation Configuration Tracking Products

Frye Utilities—LAN Directory

LAN Directory inventories hardware and software on both DOS and Macintosh NetWare workstations. It gathers information through periodic polling and at login time based on login scripts. It examines hundreds of individual configuration items for each workstation, including information about disks, RAM, CPU, BIOS, IRQ usage, video, ports and configuration files. *LAN Directory* also includes a flexible, powerful report generator. The suggested retail price is $495.

The LAN Support Group—BVequip

BVequip is a workstation inventory manager, collecting more than 200 configuration statistics on DOS workstations and the software on their local drives. *BVequip* integrates with the report generator in *BindView Plus*, so reports can be customized to draw on configuration statistics as well as user privileges and network usage. It is limited to NetWare LANs.

Cheyenne Software—Monitrix

Cheyenne Software's *Monitrix* tracks workstation configurations and performs automatic inventories, including tracking asset IDs, purchase data and depreciation. The program also gathers statistics that are valuable for fault and performance management. It runs as an NLM on a NetWare server. *Monitrix* also generates a map of the internetwork. Suggested retail price is $895.

Magee Enterprises—Network H. Q.

Network H. Q. tracks DOS and LAN workstations on NetWare, LAN Manager, VINES, and more networks. It has DOS and Windows interfaces. It includes a powerful, flexible report generator and can export data to *dBASE* .dbf files. The suggested retail price is $595/server for unlimited users and $395/server for up to 100 users.

Horizons Technology—LAN Auditor

Horizons Technology's *LAN Auditor* is a package for tracking network inventory on NetWare, VINES and LAN Manager networks. The package has both DOS and Windows interfaces. It keeps track of hardware and software in a database. It finds hardware parameters for PCs including processor type, logical and physical disk sizes, memory, and interrupts, and software on local and network drives by publisher, name and version, all without manual entry. User queries into the database are simple. The suggested retail price for 50 workstations is $495.

Brightwork Development—LAN Automatic Inventory

LAN Automatic Inventory, or *LAI*, creates a hardware and software inventory of the network. One novel feature is its ability to flag changes in the inventory database, making discrepancies, new workstations or missing workstations obvious. The suggested retail price is $695/server.

Technology Works—GraceLAN

GraceLAN is a Macintosh-specific inventorying tool. It displays applications that are running and produces a map of the network, too. The suggested retail price is $495 for 50 Macs and $1,195 for an unlimited number.

Funk Software—AppMeter

Funk Software's *AppMeter* is a server-based software metering program that lets network administrators tailor software use to suit

"When I first started my job, I spent a week going through all the records, sifting through 14 years' worth of POs. I determined how many copies we owned and how many we were using. Then our department purchased a product called AppMeter, *which allows us to control software usage on the network by metering the software application for a limited number of users."*
—JOHN THOMAS

their licenses and situation. They can strictly limit software use or generate exception reports when too many users access an application.

This is very handy when it comes time to justify paying for additional license fees. It also controls over-buying. The package logs all application use and provides a variety of reports in both tabular and graphical form. It also checks each application for virus contamination every time it is used.

On Utilities

Frye Utilities are the greatest. They give you a lot of information, which integrates SYSCON and MONITOR in a console together on one screen. I use that especially to monitor disk space. If the system gets low on disk space, Frye is the only way to go in and find out who the hogs are.

I send them nasty notes. One was to my boss, who had backed up one of his drives onto the system. Since we don't have e-mail, I went to his terminal and taped a note to his screen. He agreed to comply with my request.

—Jerry White, Network Manager for a West Coast financial institution

Configuration and Control

Finding out what is present on the networked system and how it is set up is a major portion of the configuration management job. But there is another important aspect of the job—control. It includes ensuring proper initial configuration, changing incorrect or outgrown configurations quickly and efficiently and preventing frivolous, ignorant or unintentional disruptions of configurations. There are two dimensions of configuration control. The first is the organizational dimension—the cultural and policy-based control that underlies how a networked system is employed in the organization. The second is the technical dimension—the tools that can change configurations in practice when change is called for. These tools are in most cases the same ones that report configuration information.

Organizational Control

Configuration control is a sensitive political issue with respect to user workstations. In most organizations, the users are not interested in access to server, router and hub configuration parameters except in extreme cases, such as where they feel they are not well taken care of and can do better themselves. (Even then, their interest would most likely be limited to administering adds, moves and changes, rather than diagnosing faults or tuning performance.) However, personal computer workstation users have often invested much time learning to use their software and customizing their computer environment to get their work done efficiently. (Some have also invested time and effort to make their computers produce funny noises, print silly messages and display surrealistic icons.) One of the most important battle lines in organizations with networked PCs is defined by the users' need for freedom to configure butting up against network management's need for efficiency.

"We are still very much dealing with the technical issues of making product A work with product B and product C. We are constantly essentially solving vendor problems."
—DIANE DANIELLE

The issue of control harks back to the discussion of totalitarian and anarchic networks in Chapter 3, Planning Networked Systems for Management. At one extreme, it is possible, albeit difficult, to install networked PCs that have neither local floppy drives nor local hard disks (so they cannot be rebooted and reconfigured); deactivated serial and parallel ports (so they cannot be reconfigured through those routes); and locked cases (to prevent anyone from changing this restrictive setup or installing a drive). In this extreme system implementation, workstation users would be presented with a menu that had only their applications on it. They would never see a DOS prompt or a Windows Program Manager display. New applications, approved by Control Central, would be installed on the server and added to the menus of users who needed them. Users' data could be restricted to specific directories and groomed periodically for backup and deletion to control the use of disk storage space and ensure that attention is paid to security concerns. With no local drives, all software updates could be performed at the server. Software execution could be metered precisely, so investment in software licenses could be maximized with full conformity to the intellectual property laws. Managing such a network would be about as simple as it gets.

Extreme uniformity, though, is often accompanied by extreme inflexibility. In the totalitarian network just described, all the work done with PCs would be absolutely dependent on the network. The PCs could not operate at all without the network to boot the operating system, load applications and furnish data. Furthermore, any new tools or techniques that could improve productivity would be installed centrally, most likely with relatively cumbersome approvals and sign-offs. Users would perceive that their opinions carry little weight and their suggestions would be discounted—much like the experience of mainframe users.

Standardizing Configurations

The first thing network administrators need to do is standardize as much as possible. I can't emphasize that enough. The job is definitely really, really difficult if you don't standardize. However, it's easier to say 'standardize' than to do it, simply because most vendors these days have about a 3-month product cycle.

It used to be that IBM would come out with a PC, say an 8088. Two years later, there's a 286, and a couple of years later there's a 386. So generally speaking, during those time frames, machines essentially looked the same. But today, I can buy a machine from vendor A and discover, 6 months later, that it's been discontinued and I can't buy it any more.

> I recommend standardizing as much as possible, within the limits of what's turning into a really strange industry cycle. I wish we could get back to the Detroit-style model cycle, where there's only a major change every 2 or 3 years. It would make life easier. Standardizing definitely helps.
>
> —*Diane Danielle, industry columnist and President of Danielle Associates, a network consulting firm*

Uniform Configurations in the Organization

This section discusses some of the specific tradeoffs that affect the configuration of user workstations. All other things being equal, a network manager prefers uniformity to diversity. With a multiplicity of network entities and sources of information about them, every exception to uniformity must be considered a potential problem; it may have some sort of adverse interaction with any other entity on the network.

Say a user or department installs a particular network interface board that costs less than the organization's standard board. There is no difficulty until the day those users need TCP/IP as well as IPX. They find that there are no drivers for the board that support multiple concurrent protocol stacks. The only alternative is to buy new network interface boards and dump the old ones. The network manager graciously refrains from saying "I told you so."

Workstation Hardware Uniformity

The proliferation of brands and models of PC workstations doesn't have to present a major problem to network managers, provided that the machines use the same (or compatible) buses and run the same operating system. However, repairs and substitutions can be performed much more readily if there is a uniform hardware platform. Diagnostic programs and setup utilities are usually hardware-specific, so keeping track of up-to-date copies of these tools may be difficult if there are many brands of workstations.

Some useful configuration features may only be available on particular brands. For instance, Compaq began, in 1991, to write the serial numbers of its PCs in system ROM, permitting an inventory application to collect that information automatically over the network, which saves the effort of manual recording.

The most promising middle course is to designate a small number of workstation platforms as the standard for each distinct functional class of systems. For example, a company might designate an entry-level Intel platform, a high-performance Intel platform, an entry-level Macintosh platform, a Macintosh publishing platform, a Macintosh notebook with a docking station and a Sun engineering platform. An approach like this accommodates reasonable diversity, but minimizes the burden of too many models and too many manufacturers.

Documentation

Documentation is important. I write up a LAN standards document for the LAN administrators, which I add to and update monthly. It's usually a 20-page document that describes how a workstation looks, how a file server is supposed to look, and so on. I am working with another site manager to incorporate that document into a global network plan that anyone in their company can use as a resource. Now I want to take that one step further and have a network diagram that would print out all the information for me.

—*Jane Shea, Sr. Technical Analyst, AmSys Telemanagement*

Local Drives

Security-conscious organizations often prefer workstations without floppy disk drives. Some are concerned that data may be taken away illicitly, though in most networked environments there are easier ways to transfer files than on floppy disks. Others want to prevent rebooting the workstation, so that users can't get to a DOS prompt and perform impermissible actions. Some manufacturers allow the floppy drive to be boot-inhibited or write-inhibited if desired.

"Sooner or later, most large corporations are going to see that they've got a lot invested on the desktop and that it doesn't make sense to have forty different people buying from fifteen different vendors."
— DIANE DANIELLE

Local hard drives are normally bootable after the system is reset or the power is interrupted. With a local hard drive, data stored locally can be accessed when the network is down, but it probably is not backed up centrally as reliably as data stored on the file server. Similarly, locally installed applications run when the network doesn't run, but copies may violate the organization's license agreement with the producer. Portable computers need local drives today, although the wireless networked devices of the future may be feasible without local storage.

Today, a well-managed network of PCs should be sufficiently reliable to serve as a central application and data source for most workstations. A few applications, such as PC-based databases with files that are tens or hundreds of megabytes in size, may need the performance advantage of a local drive. Some purists may contend that universally installed local hard drives are tantamount to the admission that the network doesn't stay up. On the other hand, the Windows environment likes to see local configuration files and swap files, so it may not yet be time to do away with individual hard disk drives.

Minimum RAM, Video and Processor Capability

Workstations at the lower range of capability recommended for a particular operating system or application are responsible for more than their share of problems. It may not help the network management cause substantially to make sure that all the hardware configurations are identical, but it certainly helps if they are all above a certain threshold.

Asynchronous Links

The problems that serial communications introduce to the network are notorious. Every asynchronous communications application permits modifying the communications parameters of the serial port and the modem. Windows and other environments are subject to unpredictable failures when asynchronous sessions are run. Dial-out capabilities make security-conscious organizations nervous—users might send confidential information out over the wire. Dial-in capabilities make security-conscious organizations terrified—dedicated crackers with sufficient time can usually break into systems that lack elaborate protection.

If asynchronous communications are necessary, it is best that they be centralized. The network management group is better off taking responsibility for a central communications server than hoping nothing goes wrong with users who have installed their own copies of *Carbon Copy* or *Timbuktu* and dial in from outside.

Configuration and the Roving User

Once you've got multiple hardware platforms, you have to face the question of whether the software runs on all of the platforms. If it doesn't, is it smart enough to know, or is it simply going to crash? In addition, too many vendors of 'LAN' software suggest, or insist, that the manager install part of the package on the server and the user install the rest on the local hard disk. But on a lot of LANs many of the desktop computers don't have local disks. And even when they do, software installation is usually not the user's responsibility.

You also run into what I call the problems of the roving user. If someone moves from one department to another, you might move the computer with them, you might not. When cubicles are switched, for whatever reason, the computer gets moved around. People go to a different department, they get a different computer.

Another aspect of the roving user problem is that people sometimes want to run applications at someone else's workstation. John decides to go over to Mary's desk to show her how to do something. Except that John's been working on this high-end slick 486 machine with all the bells and whistles, and Mary's got this 8088. So John logs on to the network and the things that ran just fine on his machine here don't work any more.

LAN administrators have to think about those things, have to plan for them, have to figure out what the consequences are, and look for software that they can manage in this environment.

—*Diane Danielle, industry columnist and President of Danielle Associates, a network consulting firm*

Workstation Software Uniformity

If there is reasonable hardware uniformity among desktop workstations, the temptation to define a standard system software configuration is very strong. The reason is that on DOS/Windows machines, simple deficiencies, such as the failure to increase DOS environment space, can make the workstation inoperable. Not maximizing the use of memory resources is one of the primary reasons for fragile Windows sessions on the network. TSR (terminate-and-stay-resident) utility programs can have unpredictable side effects. A possible compromise position with users who customize their workstation configurations is to ask them to reboot with the standard configuration before they ask for help.

One of the thorniest problems network managers face is the addition of new workstation operating systems to the network. In 1990, running Macintoshes and Intel-based PCs on the same network was almost impossible to do well. In 1991, Windows conversions occupied big chunks of network managers' working days. In 1992, OS/2 was preinstalled on many IBM models, many of which had to be connected kicking and screaming to networks. In 1993, Windows NT will doubtless torment its share of network managers.

Peer-to-peer network operating systems, such as Apple's System 7, Windows for Workgroups, Windows NT, NetWare Lite and the like open the door for individually or departmentally installed subnets, which could mean heavy administrative requirements and unpredictable side effects on the broader network. The networking features of these easy-to-use products are under the control of individual users, who are unlikely to be disciplined in their implementations of these programs without the advice of the organization-wide network management group. Ease of use does not necessarily mean ease of management; it may, in fact, involve the opposite.

New workstation operating systems require their own network interface board drivers and their own configuration utilities, as well as their own user applications. All the ways the new environment is different are not always apparent at the outset. For example, Macintosh workstations are assigned node IDs when they attach to the network; a particular Mac may not have the same ID number from one session to the next, unlike DOS/Windows PCs. As a result, destructive activities cannot be traced to a particular workstation when they originate on Macintoshes.

Never Enough Storage Space

I think the type of management problem that's constant is file server storage space. No matter what size hard drive you have on the network or how much storage space you have set aside, it's never going to be enough. So you constantly have to monitor that and let people know when they are taking up too much disk space or try to rearrange things so that the storage is a little bit more efficient and people aren't duplicating files. There are quite a few tools out there now for doing that kind of management: File Wizard is a good one that will rank your users by the amount of storage that they have. It has some automated capabilities for archiving files that haven't been used for a long time. It will let you get those kinds of files off the server, but still give you quick access to them. There is also Frye Utilities that lets you see what's going on in the network and monitor storage requirements or storage space to make sure that you are not running out.

—*Dave Fogle, LAN Development Group, ComputerLand Corporation*

Local Applications

When the network operates 100 percent reliably, there are many advantages and no serious disadvantages to running applications from the server. The organization's aggregate disk space occupied by applications is minimized. There is no uncertainty or legal risk regarding the proper number of software licenses to purchase. Upgrades are easy. It may be possible to automate software distribution.

If the network is unreliable, however, local applications may be the better choice. If the network goes down, personal productivity applications can still run on local drives. A few megabytes of disk space is cheaper than several hours of an idle worker's salary.

Application Uniformity

Every application interacts differently with the components of the network. The issue of whether to force users to standardize on particular applications is broader than whether multiple applications make life difficult for network managers. One successful moderate position some management groups have adopted is to support only the approved list of applications, but not to get alarmed if users run an alternate application. Any problems isolated to that application and its configuration are the user's responsibility.

There should, however, be some limits to this laissez-faire position. It is usually inappropriate for users to initiate peer-to-peer networking, a new and different database server, e-mail or host connectivity applications.

Local Subdirectory Organization

When a workstation configuration could be contributing to a problem, it is valuable for the help desk operator to know where on the local hard drive to find the relevant configuration files for the operating system, the network shell, the graphical user interface, the applications, the printers and any other peripherals. If the user community is in the habit of doing its own configurations, enforcing standard directory layouts and file locations is likely not worth the effort. If applications and data are all kept on the server, access rights can easily impose conformity with the standard directory structure.

Automating certain network processes, such as software distribution and virus scanning, may be easier with uniform directory organization.

Server Uniformity

Using a standard server platform offers the same sort of serviceability advantages that can be achieved with workstations. There is an additional benefit that has to do with comparing the behavior of two servers. When something anomalous happens to a server, it is reassuring if another identically configured server keeps working fine. And if the anomaly affects multiple servers, it is immediately apparent that some common component—the network operating system, the network interface board, the disk interface board or something else—is the root cause.

Standardizing Servers

People have become so completely reliant on their network that we have to do a better job of providing backup services. We try and standardize our servers, but as the company has grown and our technology changed, we have upgraded our server specification. We're no longer buying 386, we're buying 486 processors. We're no longer buying 240 or 600megabyte drives, we're buying one gigabyte drives. We've had to purchase all those components and keep them in stock in case of a failure.

—Jane Shea, Sr. Technical Analyst, AmSys Telemanagement

Hub and Concentrator Uniformity

The principal advantage of a uniform hub implementation is that a single management application can handle them all. The improved ability to stock or quickly source spares when there is only one type of hub is also important. Uniform documentation practices in the wiring closet also pay off quickly.

Router and Bridge Uniformity

Routers from one manufacturer often have difficulty interoperating with other routers. There is no option to support diversity in these cases. As much as possible, it is important to define specific configuration practices with bridges and routers so that the environment is familiar to the network manager who has to fix a problem.

Good Configuration Practice

In general, any new installation on the network—a fax server, a shared CD-ROM drive, a video conferencing application—is an opportunity to specify a configuration platform. A good network management team can document a platform with a minimum of fuss and find the configuration specifications again when the next installation comes up.

Configuration Management Through Documentation

One of our problems is configuration management in the VINES area. We have 430 servers, so when we want to do a software upgrade from Release 4.11 to Release 5.00, it takes several months to get all the servers to that level. We redocument and rewrite instructions because it's more efficient for us to have documentation that's aimed specifically at our users. Much of our configuration management comes from our documentation. We publish a handbook, which we call a cookbook. Our cookbook gives answers to setting up servers. It's written by a tech writer who works with specialists on the various areas. We run through the draft and go through the steps in our labs to confirm the instructions are clear.

—*James Brentano, Network Specialist at a West Coast utility company*

6 / Performance Management

Performance management consists of the activities necessary to evaluate and improve the speed, responsiveness, flexibility and adaptability of the networked system. The distinction between proactive fault management and performance management is hard to pin down precisely. Proactive fault management typically uses performance data and trends to anticipate and correct problems. However, the time horizon of performance management is often measured in weeks and months, while that of fault management is minutes and hours.

Evaluating performance is closely related to planning. Performance information propels any planning to expand the existing system and develop new projects. Performance can often be improved by

"One advantage of duplexing is that you can also increase network performance when you are not having hardware failures. A workstation makes a request for a particular file. It's kind of a race to see which drive can answer first. So you can see some fairly good performance increases just by duplexing."

—DAVE FOGLE

reconfiguring components, and these performance-tuning activities can be the most cost-effective way to improve user satisfaction. Conversely, measuring performance improvements may be the only way to configure the network correctly. Configuration management capabilities are necessary to support performance management, and vice versa. Faults are identified and fixed. Configurations are optimized. Performance is measured and improved. The most visible and critical aspect of performance is the speed of completing a particular action. Efficiency, the best use of network resources, is another readily measured aspect of performance. Dependability and flexibility, also crucial aspects of performance, are harder to measure. Dependability means that responses to users are predictable and uniform, but a low average-response-time statistic may disguise intermittent but annoying, or even unacceptable, delays. Flexibility is the openness of the system to future options, including new network components and links, but also including new organizational missions, policies and structures.

This chapter first talks about response time in relation to network applications and some of the ways response time can be measured. It then compares the data transfer rates of various networked system components, to help concentrate on the most likely bottlenecks that limit performance. After a short discussion of efficiency, the chapter addresses some of the tools that can help analyze the overall performance of the network. It then considers some of the device-specific measurement tools for servers, hubs, routers and workstations. Finally, it considers the option of simulating a network for performance analysis.

Performance monitoring is an essential part of supplying high-quality network services to users. Unfortunately, it can easily fall to the bottom of a network manager's to-do list, which is probably crowded with fault- and configuration-related tasks that are more urgent. Until performance deteriorates to the point where it turns into a fault, it rarely gets adequate attention. What is called for is thoroughly automated performance measurement. Performance-capturing tools should be set up to update historical files automatically at regular intervals, so that the comparative data is available when there is a performance problem to solve.

In discussing performance on PC networks, the terminology that managers of traditional voice and data networks use can lead to confusion. One of the first performance criteria that is spelled out in a contract for telephone company network services is service level or availability. Guarantees of greater than 99 percent availability are widely offered. PC network service failures—down networks, server crashes, cable problems—are generally considered the responsibility of the fault-management function. One reason this is done is that when the network is down, there is probably no entity to capture the elapsed time the service is not available or to otherwise monitor the PC network services. Mainframe and telephone company networks, in contrast, usually have around-the-clock monitoring capabilities. Network managers certainly should maintain logs of server and network downtime and analyze them to calculate the service level or availability of the network. However, the performance management tools discussed here will not help that project.

Response Time Within Real Applications

The most important measure of PC network performance is response time. Response time can be analyzed into different phases—time between keystrokes, time between screen updates and other actions. However, this kind of detailed data is hard to acquire and probably irrelevant, anyway. PC users expect near-instantaneous response to keystrokes and pointing actions, and they have next to no tolerance for noticeable screen repainting as opposed to instant refresh. (Exceptions might be PC users doing terminal emulation on a slow mainframe, PC users who have experience only with slow mainframe applications or PC users who knowingly put heavy loads on their systems, such as statistical analysis or CAD.) The best way to measure response time is also the easiest in practice: time real applications.

Criteria for Acceptable Response Time

Different user applications will have different criteria for acceptable response time. The following describes some of the informal, but commonly accepted, standards that are applied in practice.

Word Processors, Spreadsheets and Desktop Publishing

Typical user productivity applications on the network, such as word processing, spreadsheets and desktop publishing, have an implicit standard of comparison for loading the program and data—the performance of a local disk drive doing the same task. Data transfer rates over Ethernet or token ring networks are usually close enough to those of local hard disk controllers that small file transfers over the network do not take noticeably more time than the equivalent local operation. When big files, such as bit-mapped images or 10,000-row spreadsheets, are shipped over the wire, the difference may be apparent and hard to tolerate. LocalTalk and the wide area links slower than 1.5Mbits/sec are annoying and inefficient for remote program loading and large file transfers.

Single-Process Databases

PC-based database operations (that is, non-client-server databases such as *dBASE IV, FoxPro, Paradox* or *Fourth Dimension*) may be held to the same local-hard-disk standard as productivity applications, but an apples-to-apples comparison is difficult if the server has the only drive with enough space to do the job. These database management programs are primarily customers of disk input/output services, so small performance penalties on each operation can add up to unacceptable overall performance. On the other hand, long-running database operations may be done almost as batch operations. In these cases, the difference between a half hour and an hour can sometimes be ignored. The advent of workstation operating systems with preemptive multitasking will minimize the problem of long-running jobs. If users can use their systems for other tasks while the database chugs away, they will be more forgiving of relatively slow completion times.

"Vendors who write inventory software to help you determine, over the wire, the types of computers and configurations you've got are faced with the almost insurmountable problem of the sheer stupidity of these machines. Vendors can report only what they can query, what the computers can report back. And it is not nearly enough."

—DIANE DANIELLE

Client-Server Databases

Users of client-server database applications probably don't know what performance to expect because so many of these applications are new. Response time will probably be compared to that of analogous mainframe or minicomputer applications. Users will probably not be happy if they have to trade off quick action for an elaborate graphical front end.

Terminal Emulation

Terminal emulation users expect service no worse than an actual terminal would provide.

E-mail

E-mail users expect instantaneous local message delivery but usually forgive up to an hour or two for store-and-forward processes to move messages across the country or farther. Dependability is particularly important for store-and-forward applications like e-mail. Users are often willing to trade off some amount of average delivery time if the variability of delivery times can be reduced.

Custom Applications

Custom applications are compared to analogous mainframe applications to assess acceptable response times.

Printing

Network printing jobs are processed from queues. If the printer itself is fast and there are a few simple anti-hogging policies in place—for instance, jobs longer than 50 pages must be run after hours or at lunch time—print queue waits of a few minutes are usually acceptable. Users' expectations can best be managed by enabling them to look at the queue, see their jobs listed and gauge the wait they can expect.

Measuring Response Time and Factors Affecting It

The simplest method of measuring response time is manual: take a stopwatch and time a typical operation. If the test operation can be performed from a DOS batch file, a timer utility like the one in *Norton Utilities* or the DOS TIME command can be inserted into the batch file prior to the operation being timed and after it to capture the elapsed time automatically. These utilities typically return the elapsed time to the standard output device, so the data can be redirected to a file for additional analysis. Some applications—particularly programmable database systems—have internal timers that can capture elapsed times and store or print them.

In the PC world, manufacturers often optimize their equipment to respond well on widely used benchmarks or performance-measuring tools.

One commonly used program that can benchmark a series of operations and report the results is distributed freely over Novell's NetWire forum on CompuServe. PERFORM3, like its predecessors PERFORM2 and PERFORM, measures maximum available bandwidth across a network based on varying file sizes. The program can be used on any network with Intel-based workstations and servers, including VINES, LAN Manager, LAN Server and PATH-WORKS. By substituting components one at a time and comparing the results, managers can find the most efficient way to improve performance. Changing configurations to measure performance this way can be a lot of work, particularly where the server or its subsystems may be involved, but there is no real alternative to piece-by-piece substitution. If you are performing major reconfigurations to run a benchmarking program like PERFORM3, it doesn't take much added effort to time an actual application or two with each setup as a reality check.

The more elaborate a benchmark test is, the more likely it is to be biased toward some particular feature, unintentionally or not. In the PC world, manufacturers often optimize their equipment to respond well on widely used benchmarks or performance-measuring tools. Independent testing organizations have sprung up in response, attempting to establish impartial tests that do not favor particular products. One such group is the Transaction Processing Council, which has defined a series of benchmarks identified as TPC-A, TPC-B and so forth. These tests measure transactions per second on a complete system. The term "transaction" is used here in its technical sense, as a multiphase operation that can be rolled back to the starting point if any phase is disrupted before the entire operation is complete. Unlike many benchmarks that test only a single component of the network, the transaction benchmarks exercise all the components of a distributed system.

Bottlenecks on the Network

Just as a chain is only as strong as its weakest link, a network can respond only as rapidly as its slowest component. The most high-powered, state-of-the-art components are wasted if anything on the path from user to service and back is inherently slower than they are.

Figure 6-1 provides a rough performance comparison of several common network components. These comparisons are imprecise and not fully commensurable because different components do different jobs with different kinds of overhead. CPUs do many other things besides moving data; routers and bridges operate on packets, not data as the user sees it, and the kilobytes per second of data they process depends on the amount of data in each packet; Ethernet, token ring, ARCnet and LocalTalk act on data frames, which can include varying quantities of user data per frame, and are typically not utilized at anywhere near the theoretical maximum capacity. One added reservation is that some of these components are expected to serve only one process at a time, while others are shared among hundreds or thousands of processes.

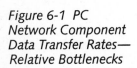

Figure 6-1 PC Network Component Data Transfer Rates— Relative Bottlenecks

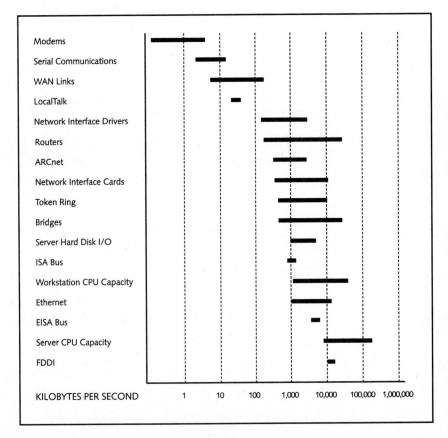

Because many components on a network are shared, traffic analysis can provide valuable clues to the choking that occurs at a bottleneck. The best solution is often to partition a user or a group so that they have exclusive use of the bottlenecking service. If a particular group has an application that generates a lot of traffic but doesn't demand a lot of server resources, a bridge that keeps that group's traffic local may provide great performance improvements for other users. Alternatively, a switched Ethernet hub module may help isolate users with high demand for bandwidth. If the high demand involves file or database resources, an additional server may be required.

There are circumstances where simply looking at bottlenecks one at a time does not uncover a response-time problem. These situations occur when interactions between multiple components cause problems greater than the sum of their parts. Deadlocks—where component X is unable to conclude an action until component Y releases a resource, but component Y can't release the resource until component X concludes its action—are one example of such a problem. Another is the broadcast storm, where retransmissions of broadcast packets multiply to the point where these transmissions swamp the network's bandwidth.

Solving Perceived Response-Time Problems

While effective fault troubleshooting starts at the top of a hierarchy of possible causes and works down, performance measurement can maximize its effectiveness by starting at the detail level and working up. Thus user perception is the best starting point for performance management. The theory of bottlenecks identifies likely suspects that may be causing a slowdown, then specific tests and measurements serve to confirm or disprove these hypotheses.

Historical Performance Tracking

Keeping statistics about the past performance of the network is often a great help in identifying performance problems and opportunities. Testing theories of where slowdowns are occurring can be very simple with good historical data. For instance, a router may be common to a set of applications that are experiencing slow response. A check of the history indicates that the router successfully forwarded 1,000 packets per second 6 months ago, and is now forwarding 5,000, which is close to its maximum specified capacity. As any device approaches its capacity, it becomes a bottleneck for additional traffic. The root cause may be a new application, a new set of users, a faulty device or an improper configuration. The historical data points in the right direction to find the ultimate solution.

Many performance-monitoring products capture performance trends over time. These trends can be long-term, such as the gradual increase of traffic on a segment over a number of weeks, or shorter-term, such as the daily traffic peaks that result from all the users coming to work at the same time and loading their applications from the network.

> *"You have to be able to build a base line, which means you need history. If you can keep track of different things over time, then when something goes wrong you can look for a change in the pattern that may explain what's happening."*
>
> — DIANE DANIELLE

Efficiency

At a time when most organizations are rapidly extending their PC networks, not much attention is paid to efficiency, particularly in the purely local network components. With constantly increasing demands for capacity, it still has not been a high priority in most organizations to seek out components or subsystems with excess capacity. The history of the PC marketplace has many examples of formerly scarce and costly resources declining in cost to the point of near irrelevance. Local network connections, with connectors at each workspace that lead to a wiring closet with a managed hub, and network interface boards for PCs have repeated this pattern. Servers, routers and wide area links, on the other hand, still have high costs for incremental performance, so efficiency improvements (and better price performance) will be achievable if the organization has excess capacity and will not soon grow into that excess capacity. Network carrying capacity is a kind of inventory. Planning for the ability to add capacity just in time can lead to significant savings.

Traffic-Monitoring Tools

Local area network traffic information can be captured and analyzed on a server equipped with monitoring software (that runs on the network operating system), on a workstation equipped with monitoring software (that runs on the workstation operating system), on a dedicated segment monitor or on a managed hub or concentrator. Wide area network traffic information gathering requires managed bridges or routers. The statistics and graphs of interest for managing performance are often the same ones used for fault management. The distinction between the two purposes is that performance management is more concerned with quantitative values: How much traffic? Precisely how many errors? Fault management is often more concerned with qualitative results: Is the traffic getting through? Are there a lot of errors?

Traffic-Monitoring Products

Novell—LANtern Network Monitor for Ethernet and LANtern Services Manager

The *LANtern* system consists of a self-contained hardware unit that attaches to an Ethernet segment and SNMP-based management software, *LANtern Services Manager*, that is installed on a network workstation equipped with Windows. Data about network activity is collected by the monitor and passed to the management console.

The management console software can graph activity, filter irrelevant information, define alarm thresholds and export data for further analysis. The LANtern monitor is equipped with an RS-232 serial port for remote connections or out-of-band communications when the network is down. The suggested retail price is $4,495 for the monitor and $4,995 for the *LANtern Services Manager* software.

Hewlett-Packard—LANProbe and ProbeView

LANProbe is HP's Ethernet standalone monitor, which captures traffic, error and other statistics and forwards them to *ProbeView*, the console software, which runs on a Windows workstation. The LANProbe is also equipped with a serial port for remote connections or out-of-band communications.

Intel—NetSight Sentry

Intel's NetSight Sentry is a hardware and software package that monitors numerous statistics for both Ethernet and token ring networks. The hardware is installed in a full-length slot in a 386 or higher-capacity PC. The software is DOS/character-based, so the management console does not require Windows. The menu interface lets you specify thresholds for common network performance indicators and monitor all kinds of different network traffic (with tables and graphs). It can generate alarms when specific thresholds are surpassed. It also identifies network stations by name as well as by address. At $1,995 for Ethernet and $2,995 for token ring, it's competitively priced.

Intel—LANDesk Manager

Intel's *LANDesk Manager*, a Windows-based network management package, includes tools for remote node management, traffic monitoring, hardware and software inventory tracking, application monitoring, and virus detection and removal. The package monitors

NetWare servers, runs NetWare management utilities and keeps track of queue activity. The suggested retail price is $995.

Cheyenne Software—Monitrix

Cheyenne Software's *Monitrix* package monitors NetWare network traffic and collects relevant statistics. It runs passively in the background with no effect on network traffic. It also tracks workstation configuration and topologies, checks connectivity and prepares reports.

Farallon Computing—TrafficWatch

Farallon's *TrafficWatch* displays internet traffic, traffic between Ethernet and LocalTalk segments, network utilization and network errors. It also filters AppleTalk traffic by protocol and analyzes AppleTalk, TCP/IP and DECNET protocols.

AG Group—Net Watchman

AG Group's *Net Watchman* is an AppleTalk monitor software package. It tracks zones, bridges, nodes and services and can signal network changes to the manager. The package also builds graphical zone maps and highlights problems. It works across bridges and routers that connect dissimilar cable types.

AG Group—Skyline/E

AG Group's *Skyline/E* is a Macintosh software-based traffic monitor for multiprotocol Ethernet networks. It can sound alarms when traffic is either low or high. It logs network traffic to an archive file for later analysis.

LANshark—Net Results

LANshark's *Net Results* software package monitors and analyzes VINES network activity. This includes user activity, security, and server and cabling errors. It automatically compiles a historical

"You can never have too many tools. If your network is slowing down and if you've got a couple of networking boards in there, you want to see whether one is bogging down. That will characterize not necessarily the network traffic but what's happening inside the system."

—DAVE FOGLE

database of VINES log files. It can also perform resource accounting and billing. Suggested retail price is $495 per server.

Trellis—Network Observer

Trellis' *Network Observer* is a software-monitoring package for VINES networks. It provides basic network management features, monitoring network performance variables and notifying the network manager about violations of programmable thresholds. At the same time, it captures network statistics in an ASCII file for analysis and graphing. Suggested retail price for a five-server license is $975.

Dayna Communications—NetScope Console, NetScope Probe

NetScope Probe is a hardware monitor that connects to an Apple-Talk segment. *NetScope Console* runs on a Macintosh and collects information from Probes. It can produce graphs and reports on traffic, errors, bandwidth utilization and device usage. The suggested retail price for both components is $899.

Frye Computer Systems—The Frye Utilities for Networks: NetWare Management

NetWare Management provides a summary of all server activity on one screen. Navigating to detailed screens of information is much simpler than with MONITOR and other NetWare utilities, requiring only function-key strokes. Comparing data between nodes is simplified, too. The program also provides sophisticated report generation capabilities for server conditions. It is a DOS/character-based application that can run on any PC compatible with 640KB of RAM. The suggested retail price is $495.

Hewlett-Packard—OpenView Resource Manager/DOS

OpenView Resource Manager/DOS provides realtime trend analysis on traffic data collected with HP's special instrumentation scheme, EASE (Embedded Advanced Sampling Environment). The program can identify Top Talkers, Communication Pairs, other heavy users, and errors and their sources. A Windows-based product,

"Networking tools will allow network administrators to concentrate a little more on proactive sorts of network management tasks, such as trying to optimize network performance, making your users happier, rather than just having to react to a hardware failure. The tools take a little stress out of the job."

— DAVE FOGLE

OpenView Resource Manager/DOS produces graphs as well as reports and data for export. It is integrated with *HP OpenView Hub Manager* and *HP OpenView Interconnect Manager*.

Network General—Watchdog LAN Monitor
The *Watchdog* can monitor network traffic and errors on Ethernet segments and token rings. It is shipped with a special network interface board. It gathers performance statistics, generates alarms, performs test functions and generates reports. The suggested retail price for the Ethernet version is $1,995; for the token ring version, $2,695.

Trellis Communications Corp.—Trellis Exposé Network Manager
Trellis' *Exposé Network Manager* is a server-based network management system for VINES networks. It monitors network performance and displays the results on Windows-based client workstations. *Exposé* provides interactive mapping, alarms for performance threshold variances, trigger management, and reports about traffic and bandwidth. Perhaps its best feature is that it can respond to some network fault conditions and take remedial action through scripts. The suggested retail price is $1,495 per server.

Protocol Analyzers and Performance Measurement

Decoding protocols is necessary for only the toughest performance problems. Bottleneck and traffic analysis, the foundation of much performance management, usually does not care about the contents of data higher than the network layer, layer 3. The dedicated hardware of some of the high-end protocol analyzers is probably likewise unnecessary. One of the software-only products may be the most cost-effective solution if performance analysis is the principal goal.

Apart from decoding, filtering and measuring traffic, protocol analyzers often have the valuable capability of generating traffic on the network. This traffic can be nonsense, with no object other than to load the network to a certain level. It can also be a particular sequence of packets captured previously, perhaps a pattern that led up to some kind of problem. (Chapter 4, Fault Management, includes descriptions of some of the market-leading protocol analyzers.)

dBASE vs. SQL Performance

We asked our consultant to do a performance analysis on our network throughput. We were in the process of gradually moving reporting functions to a SQL server. We executed a report against an old-style *dBASE* application and a new SQL server application. We measured the network throughput and noticed there was a consistently high level of data traffic on the *dBASE* application. Using the SQL database server we had to wait for the reply to come through once the query was sent. We were watching the screen, waiting for traffic to come across, and there was hardly enough to measure. Client-server was new at the time and the analyst had never witnessed this kind of performance. The test confirmed our migration plan. We scrapped the old *dBASE* files and migrated to SQL, which resulted in an immediate reduction in traffic.

—*Richard Sherkin, MIS manager, Biltrite Industries*

Server Performance Factors

On many networks, the file server is upgraded reflexively when a performance problem arises. The justification for this reflex is that the disk I/O subsystem of the server is typically the slowest component of network file service. Slow disk I/O can be counteracted to some extent with mass quantities of RAM, serving as a disk cache. The second-slowest component of the server is usually the network interface board. If the capacity of the network interface is a bottleneck for performance, installing another interface and dividing the network into two (or more) segments may balance the load better. In many situations, the processor so outperforms the disk system and the network interface that big improvements in the processor speed or type produce minimal improvements in overall performance. Upgrading the server CPU before adding RAM, upgrading the disk drive subsystem or increasing the number and performance of the network interfaces is begging for disappointing results. By itself, the number of processor MIPS (millions of instructions per second) is a poor predictor of server performance.

"I don't expect server mirroring to provide a performance increase. It is generally the drives that are the limiting factor of the bottleneck in any network."

— DAVE FOGLE

While only the most exceptional workstation applications use the full capacity of the ISA or AT bus architecture, servers are likely to need the additional capacity afforded by EISA, Micro Channel Architecture or one of the other high-speed buses.

Maximizing the performance of a server involves monitoring performance as the configuration is changed. This process, commonly called tuning the server, has as much to do with the network operating system as it does with the server hardware. The network operating system has dozens, if not hundreds, of parameters that can be set to get the most from a server. An additional advantage of using common server platforms throughout the organization (discussed in Chapter 5, Configuration Management) is that the tuning efforts expended on one server can be carried over easily to others.

Server Monitor Products

Novell—NetWare Services Manager

NetWare Services Manager consists of the console software and the server agent components of Novell's *NetWare Management System*. The *NetWare Management System* is a platform for developers to produce management components that work together and support network management from one central console. *NetWare Services*

Manager can provide such data as RAM utilization, NLM (NetWare Loadable Module) usage and printer queues.

Compaq—Server Manager/R and Insight Manager

Compaq offers management software that complements its hardware line. The Server Manager/R is a combination hardware and software package that includes an EISA System Manager interface board, which gathers environmental and electrical data from the server and its subsystems and also supports remote control activities over a serial communications line. It works with Compaq drive array controllers to analyze drive performance at periodic intervals, to manage RAID performance and to detect impending problems. It also tracks DC voltages at the power supply and on the EISA bus to warn of possible trouble. Server Manager/R is intended for remote servers not readily accessible to network management staff and critical servers that must run 24 hours a day. Server Manager/R works with VINES, LAN Manager, LAN Server and SCO Unix systems as well as with NetWare; in fact, it can continue to function when the network operating system is not running at all on the server. The *Server Manager Facility/R* is the Windows-based remote console software for Server Manager/R.

Insight Manager is a software-only package that provides over-the-network management capabilities with NetWare servers. Both *Insight Manager* and Server Manager/R help diagnose and prevent faults, improve security, monitor performance and manage configuration. *Insight Manager* is integrated with Novell's *NetWare Management System* and uses SNMP by defining a MIB for Compaq servers.

Hub and Concentrator Performance Factors

Hubs don't become bottlenecks on the local network; they are an integral part of the physical/data link topology and operate at the full capacity of that subsystem. Hubs provide many advantages for ease of installation and reconfiguration, for fault identification and isolation, for fault tolerance and more. But they are essentially transparent to the speed dimension of performance.

Hubs and concentrators are well placed to monitor traffic, though. Management agents can be justified in hubs for performance tracking as well as for reporting and controlling configurations and for isolating faults.

Hub and Concentrator Monitor Products

SynOptics—Hub and Concentrator Software and Management Modules

SynOptics Communications has several families of network management software. For enterprises with mainframe-based platforms or other network management systems, there are the *NETMAP* and *Lattis View* products, providing management information and control capability to IBM's *NetView*, the DEC *Polycenter* system, *HP OpenView* or IBM's *AIX NetView/6000*. For the largest, most complex networks, SynOptics offers the Unix-based *Optivity* network management system, built on Sun Microsystems' *SunNet Manager* platform.

For less complex networks, there are two families of Windows-based software products. SynOptics' *Lattis EZ-View* is intended for small to medium-sized networks. It runs under Windows and manages SynOptics' Ethernet and token ring hardware (SynOptics 2000 and 3000 Concentrators). It supports SynOptics' Expanded View software, which graphically displays each hub module and all its indicators down to the port level on the Windows screen. The package runs in the background on a 386 or higher-class PC. It supports IPX as well as IP, so it is a good solution for Novell networks.

SynOptics' *LattisNet Manager for DOS* is for medium to large networks. It supports Ethernet and token ring network hardware and offers all the functions of *Lattis EZ-View*. The package adds SynOptics' Autotopology dynamic mapping tools, which create layered maps of the entire network by network segment. It includes a generic SNMP management capability that allows management of other SNMP devices and is compatible with HP's *OpenView*. Hardware monitoring includes programmable thresholds for alarms. The system offers in-band and out-of-band communications to SynOptics hardware, so if the network cabling fails (a common reason for wanting management features), you can still reach the management module by phone line and modem to help solve the problem. The software runs on a Windows-based 386 or higher workstation.

Optivity for NetWare is integrated with Novell's *NetWare Management System*. It provides the Expanded View and Ring View capabilities of other SynOptics software offerings. It supports SNMP over both IP and IPX, so mixed protocol environments can be supported readily. It runs on a Windows-based 386 or higher workstation.

Hewlett-Packard—Hub Management Capabilities

Hewlett-Packard's *OpenView*, a family of network management tools and services for local and wide area networks, is rapidly becoming one of the leading platforms in DOS/Windows environments. The Unix-based *OpenView* platform is also a popular foundation for other developers. *OpenView* supports SNMP and CMIP, and offers migration to the OSF's Distributed Management Environment. It supports numerous environments and networking topologies. The core software controls and manages all of HP's networking hardware, including hubs.

HP OpenView Hub Manager/DOS is a Windows-based application that discovers Novell IPX servers and clients and maps them. In IP mode, it can discover IP devices. It can monitor SNMP devices and control HP EtherTwist hubs. It monitors traffic, produces graphs and trend lines, permits threshold settings and generates alarms. The suggested retail price is $4,000.

Novell—Hub Services Manager

Novell's *Hub Services Manager* is an application that "snaps in" to Novell's *NetWare Management System*. The *NetWare Management System* is Novell's management platform. *Hub Services Manager* can collect information from and control hubs that comply with Novell's Hub Management Interface (HMI) specification, such as Intel's EtherExpress hubs. (Intel's hubs are boards that can be installed in servers or other PCs, providing managed hub ports at very low cost.) HMI hub management agents must be installed on the managed hubs. The suggested retail price for *Hub Services Manager* is $995.

Router and Bridge Performance Factors

Bridges and routers are basically microcomputers with very limited missions: Grab packets, identify their destinations, look up the destinations on an address table and blast the packets out the correct port. Bridges are substantially simpler than routers: They look only at the MAC address on the outermost layer (layer 2) of the frame, and decide to forward it or ignore it. Routers have to strip off the layer 2 envelope and read the network-layer address (layer 3). They may have to choose one lookup table out of several based on the protocol type. They may also have to take into consideration such factors as the minimal number of intermediate hops, or the relative speed or expense of different routes to the destination.

General-purpose microcomputers can be pressed into service as routers. Probably the most widely used software is the Novell *Multiprotocol Router*, which is a NetWare NLM. Any NetWare server can function as a router, but a special no-file-service-client version of NetWare 3.11 can support the router NLM in a standalone setting. This configuration provides a relatively low-performance but inexpensive routing solution. High-performance CPUs and network interface boards pay off in this application. Most of the action is in the processor, in the memory, and in and out of the network interfaces.

Bridges can often do their jobs at the full carrying capacity of the medium access scheme. If they can in effect keep up with the wire, they are not a major bottleneck.

Dedicated routers have been built using Motorola 680X0 processors, special RISC processors and other high-powered chips. They often cost in excess of $5,000 if they are not to present a bottleneck to heavily loaded Ethernet or token ring segments. Prices are much higher for high-performance multiport routers and those that connect to wide area links.

Router and Bridge Monitor Products

SynOptics—Bridge and Router Management Capabilities

SynOptics' *RouterMan* software for Unix and *Optivity* automatically recognizes and displays all protocols used on routers from SynOptics and Cisco Systems. It also handles other MIB II SNMP devices. Monitoring includes router status and performance statistics with corresponding programmable alarms and alerts.

Hewlett-Packard—Bridge and Router Management Capabilities

HP OpenView Interconnect Manager/DOS can collect information from SNMP bridges and routers and control HP's internetworking products. The suggested retail price is $4,000.

Workstation Performance

Today, the incentive for workstation upgrades derives from the way applications perform locally, rather than any network-related performance. The slowest 1984-vintage clone can process data faster than a typical Ethernet or token ring board can deliver it. Properly configured workstations do not strongly affect the timeliness of network service delivery.

Workstation network interface boards (or their driver software) can constitute a bottleneck on high-performance workstations. Properly configured, the fastest network interfaces may have several times the carrying capacity of the slowest interface boards of the same medium-access type.

Some workstation system information tools, including *PC Tools* and *Norton Utilities*, calculate a single performance number for a workstation. They also have performance measurement utilities for network activity. These utilities read and write data to the network drive and calculate the rate in kilobytes per second. Running one of these programs on two successive network drives, one of which was connected through a bridge, could provide evidence whether the bridge slowed access or not.

Redundancy

On a local area network, where we've provided services the way we're trying to, there's enough redundancy that if a modem goes down, chances are we may not know because there are other modems operating—people still get the service. If a certain gateway is down, you may not notice it. So in some cases it makes it difficult to know everything that's happening in real-time. But this hasn't been a problem because we've designed the architecture in such a way that certain small delays do not significantly affect the end user's workstation.

—*Randy Howland, Network Manager for a Fortune 500 technology company*

Management Traffic and Its Effects on Performance

Much like a medical doctor, network management must resolve first of all to do no harm. This refers not so much to performance measurement or other management activities that go wrong—although injecting large artificial loads onto the network with a protocol analyzer during working hours should not be done lightly—as to the more insidious growth of management traffic as a fraction of total network traffic and as a performance drag on users. For instance, an automatic inventory program that runs as part of every user's login script may easily add a minute or two to the time it takes the user to get to the first application. An antivirus scan may take even longer.

Summarizing Management Data

The problem of too much management traffic is often most noticeable when a network at a remote site is managed by a console connected to it by a wide area link. Shipping all the raw management data across a low-bandwidth, high-cost line may not be the best use of the network's resources. It makes more sense to somehow summarize the information locally and send only summary information to the console.

One product that takes this approach is the *Network Control Engine* from SynOptics Communications, an SNMP-based option for SynOptics' System 3000 concentrator products. It processes and summarizes management data locally and forwards only the most necessary information to a remote console.

Simulating Networks

Users on production networks are unsympathetic to experiments that go wrong. Dedicated test networks are a luxury that very few organizations can afford. Even with a test network, connecting and configuring equipment, installing software and getting everything to work together is time consuming and largely unproductive in the most restrictive sense of the word. A simulated network could help prove an initial concept, identify potential bottlenecks and determine optimal configurations without disrupting the working network. The ideal simulation would include sufficient detail to permit changing the same parameters as on the real components, but would of course never have hardware failures or bad cables.

Simulation Tools

Internetix Inc.—LANSIM

LANSIM, by Internetix Inc., is a software simulator of LAN performance and response. It can simulate various topologies and protocols. With other Internetix tools, it can accept actual network traffic captured from a protocol analyzer to model the simulated network's response to real events. The suggested retail price is $9,200.

7 / Planning for a Secure Network

Systems that include PC networks face security threats from multiple directions. The security of the network, narrowly defined, is important, but ensuring the integrity of the cable plant, routing devices and wide area links is only a portion of the overall problem. Servers and workstations are subject to power outages, theft, viruses and other kinds of disasters not strictly confined to traffic between servers, workstations and hosts.

It is the job of a security plan to prevent all these security threats, if possible, and to remedy them when prevention fails. A good security plan outlines the procedures needed to protect network hardware from theft and downtime and to protect network data from theft and tampering. It should also not prevent people from doing their jobs efficiently.

Why Write a Security Plan?

"All of the network operating systems have security features now. They all have password protection and file access controls. What most of them have lacked, however, have been the robust auditing features that have been common on mainframes and minicomputers for years. Controlling access is not enough. It's critical to be able to find out who did what when and where."

— DIANE DANIELLE

Entropy is always at work, continually increasing the probability that some point of vulnerability will turn into a disaster. In thinking about security, the most obvious first question is, "How much has the organization invested in the LAN hardware and software?" The answer to this question often determines how supportive management will be of any security plan. If the network hardware represents a major corporate asset, spending to ensure security makes sense; it should be easy to convince expense-conscious managers to pay for protection.

The next question is, "How valuable is the data stored on the LAN?" The answer to this question has as much impact as the first. Oftentimes the answer is, "Our organization (or department) would die if we suddenly lost all our network data." Data is generally far more valuable than the machines that store it. Insurance commonly replaces stolen or destroyed hardware; stolen or destroyed data is another matter entirely.

When asking both these questions, paranoia is an asset. Err on the side of caution. If you think something poses a threat to the network, plan for that eventuality. Base the response on the probability of the threatening activity. For example, Pacific Rim residents might want to take more precautions about earthquakes than people in Indiana—yet Indiana is not totally immune. A small, close-knit firm with only a few employees might not feel the need to limit file access, while a large network probably demands strict access control.

How to Write a Security Plan

The first step in writing a security plan for a network is a threat analysis. Decide what types of security problems—threats—exist for the network; then decide what to do about them in advance. On the surface this sounds more like a job for a crystal ball than one for a network manager, but careful thinking and planning are what it takes to prevent security problems and avoid disaster. Furthermore, a good security plan is like carrying an umbrella when you leave the house in the morning—it often prevents rainfall!

Once you decide what you are protecting from what, write a security plan based on the following issues:

Authentication

Verify that users are who they say they are and where they say they are. Authentication also means preventing anyone else from impersonating a legitimate user. Even if you don't have anything to steal, you don't want a bogus user tying up your disk space. You also don't want a valid (but possibly angry or crazy) user to perform some sort of mischief while using someone else's account, thus casting blame on an innocent user.

Sometimes authentication may also involve larger issues, like electronic signatures. For example, the government's electronic data interchange plan requires that vendors accept orders and subsequent payment electronically. It is important to authenticate the order and the payment by something more than a simple ASCII text string that anyone can counterfeit.

Access Control

Make sure that only the right people have access to the right data and that the wrong people do not, even though they may be valid users. For example, in an engineering environment, it may be necessary for everyone to read specifications stored on the network, but only specific people are allowed to change them.

Connection Integrity

Maintain valid connections for users and prevent connections by invalid users. This is largely governed by the security of the cabling and all associated hardware.

Backup and Recovery

These processes constitute life insurance for the network administrator in the event of a disaster or accident. If you have no backup strategy, you have no recovery strategy.

To provide security in all these areas, every LAN administrator has the following resources:

- Hardware physical security features
- Network operating system security features
- Application software security features
- Disaster planning
- Personnel

In all these areas, the plan should include as much prevention as possible—it is inevitably more powerful than remedies. Unfortunately, it is impossible to prevent a sufficiently determined intruder from gaining access to a network. The key is to place enough barriers between the network and the intruder to stifle the intruder's determination. Nor can network managers prevent disasters that might befall the network—even insurance policies refuse to cover acts of God. But it is possible to be prepared to deal with emergencies when they happen.

"Because of our background with PC networks, we have a different attitude toward security than the mainframe guys. Our attitude is, 'Unless we tell you not to, go ahead,' and their view is 'Unless we say you can, you can't.' It's a matter of control."

—JAMES BRENTANO

A well-designed security plan integrates all these goals and resources into a security system for the network. Decide how to employ the network features in the above list to authenticate users, control file access, assure connection integrity and restore lost data. Leaving out any one of the possible tools leaves holes in network security. A matrix like Table 7-1 can help close the holes. It lists the solutions provided by network assets to problems with authentication, access control, connection integrity, and backup. Write down all the threats to the network and examine them in light of the matrix. Most threats have a solution somewhere in the matrix.

After writing the best possible security plan for the network, take a second look at the plan. Carefully consider the costs. Every item in the plan involves tradeoffs of some sort. Security costs cannot always be measured in dollars. Consider the impact of security both on the local area network and on the people who use it. The ultimately secure network stores inaccessible data on untouchable, impregnable hardware. This is neither practical nor desirable. Revise the security plan in light of available dollars, current hardware and, perhaps most important, the users. A security plan you cannot afford, or that prevents users from doing their jobs, is more harmful than helpful.

Sticking With the Plan

After writing the plan, be sure to stick with it. An unimplemented security plan is no better than none. The plan may need modification as the network and the organization grow, but add it to the list of things that need to be managed for the network. A well-maintained security plan should be part of the total network management strategy.

Table 7-1 Security Issues vs. Security Resources

	Authentication	Access Control	Connection Integrity	Backup & Recovery
Physical	Limit server access Additional special hardware Virus protection with diskless workstations	Secure cable runs fiber-optic cabling to prevent electromagnetic or physical interception	Limit additional physical local and remote connections to the network Install cabling properly to minimize problems later	Local backup copies locked away
Network OS	MONITOR SECURITY SYSCON SECURE CONSOLE Network address tracking	Passwords Directory and file trustee rights	Use up-to-date versions of workstation network software	Rudimentary services
Application		Passwords Encryption Redundant files Virus protection software	Timed backup files on local drives	
Disaster Planning	Limit server access		Redundant hardware Spare parts	Off-site backup storage Locked storage for original OS and application software disks
Personnel	Establish and maintain user accounts Establish supervisor-equivalent users Establish custodian for all the keys and the ultimate password	Train users about passwords		Automatic backup procedures

Back-Door Security

I once visited a company installation and noticed a back door propped open by a rock. I could read a sign on the inside of the door while driving by in my car, 'This door to remain shut at all times. Emergency exit only. Alarm will sound.' It was during the summer in an area where summer heat is a real problem, and someone had apparently opened the door for additional ventilation.

I attached my driver's license to my lapel with two paper clips for a fake badge and walked in the open door. I found myself in a computer room with an adjacent tape library. Acting as if I belonged there, I walked into the tape library, ran my finger along the tape racks and picked out two tapes at random. I tucked them under my arm, left my briefcase next to the computer power supply and walked back out the door.

I attached my real badge, and entered the building by the main entrance. After introducing myself to the shift manager, I handed him the tapes. I told him, 'I just swiped these and left my briefcase in the computer room. It has a tag on it that tells anyone finding it to report it to you for a reward. Nobody challenged me. Has anyone called yet?' The shift manager called the computer room and asked if anything strange had happened or if anyone noticed anything out of the ordinary. All replies were negative.

The open door may have been necessary to keep the hardware working in the heat, but failing to compensate by increasing security was a big mistake. The proper solution would have been to improve the air conditioning. Had I been a nut with a real bomb...

—*Fred Vincent, Security Auditor for a public utility company*

Auditing Security

A periodic security audit is essential to maintaining a viable security plan. A security audit is an evaluation of current security practices.

It consists of physical inspection and a review of security procedures to make sure they still match the needs of the network. An impartial but knowledgeable person is necessary to conduct the audit. It should not be performed by the same people who wrote the security plan—they are too close to the system and too sure that it is perfect. The frequency of the audits depends on the circumstances, but an annual review is a good start.

In a NetWare installation, an audit requires running the SECURITY program to see who has supervisor equivalence. It also requires using SYSCON to see which users have access rights to which data. The final step is to evaluate the results in light of users' actual needs and take any remedial action. As we'll see later, both these programs should be part of the normal operation of the network.

NetWare 3.x manuals mention future features to track which users read and write which files on the server. These features function in NetWare 4.x. They are a boon to network security managers who track problems associated with data file access.

Physical Security

Physical security involves protecting network hardware from all sorts of physical threats. Some physical security features provide authentication. Others provide access control. Others provide disaster control by preventing accidents. In terms of threats, physical security means that a security threat masquerading as a janitor cannot use the network after hours, and a clumsy janitor cannot knock over a server with a runaway industrial vacuum cleaner.

If the building or department is protected by its own security system—guards and alarms—find out who controls the system.

Decide what it can do to help protect the network. For example, the security provider may be willing to have existing patrols check the server room door or install motion detectors near critical hardware. Make sure the security people know how to reach the network manager in an emergency. Integrate network security into the building security system.

In terms of authentication, physical security means that only authorized users have physical access to the LAN hardware. This prevents hardware and software theft and data tampering. The security plan should specify the measures needed to prevent problems and to remedy problems when they occur.

Preventing Data Tampering

From a physical security standpoint, data tampering is relatively easy to prevent. The physical defense against data tampering is to lock up file servers. It is possible for interlopers with sufficient knowledge to change the supervisor's password on Novell 2.x and 3.x file servers, tamper with anything they want on the disks, restore the password and walk away leaving little trace that anything had changed. All it takes is a disk sector editor on a bootable DOS floppy and physical access to the file server. The required knowledge and technical skill is quite small and is common among Certified NetWare Engineers. Luckily, the process leaves tracks—it resets the file server up-time in the main MONITOR screen on the server console.

The Server

The key is to prevent physical access to the server. Keep it in a locked room or closet and control the key. Clean this area yourself. Don't allow the janitorial staff access to this room and don't allow

Exotic physical authentication devices, much like those you might expect to see in a James Bond movie, are available.

anyone else to store anything in it. Be inflexible and unreasonable about this. Don't allow any unaccompanied visitors. The fewer people who can touch or see your servers, the better. A running computer is a real temptation to many employees after hours. Some may want to see if it has the latest video game on it. Some may try to tamper with it maliciously. Eventually, someone will accidentally bump it or spill something over it. If it is locked up, they can do none of these things, whether accidentally or maliciously. One company kept boxes of stationery and photocopy paper in the server room because the server room was next to the copy machine. This made sense until the paper deliverer and four boxes of paper on a hand truck had an argument with a file server. The server lost.

There are other prosaic but effective methods of deterring access to the server. If the server boots without a keyboard, disconnect the keyboard, but make it look like the keyboard is still connected. Use the server's setup routine to tell it that it has no floppy drives and internally disconnect the floppy drives. This prevents use of a sector editor even if an intruder can touch the server. Make use of the server's setup and boot passwords. In any event, lock the server case and control the keys. If you fail to do this, you might as well invite people to steal your data. These steps involve tradeoffs that become evident if the server malfunctions—you will have to reattach the keyboard and enable the floppy drive to perform repairs or maintenance.

Another way to prevent an intruder from fouling up NetWare drives is to refrain from installing a small DOS partition on the hard drive. Use only NetWare partitions on all hard drives. This renders many DOS-based disk sector editors useless. It also means booting the server from a floppy. Don't leave the boot floppy in the drive. Store it in a locked cabinet and keep a spare copy of it in another site in case the original gets damaged. It is also a very good idea to keep the original NetWare OS disks under lock and key.

Additional Hardware

There are more extreme security measures available than just a locked room. Several vendors make physical authentication readers that require some kind of a key, often a credit card-sized gadget, to be inserted into a slot in the reader. The SecureCard reader from Datamedia Corporation, for example, installs much like a floppy drive. Until the SecureCard key is inserted and the proper password entered, the server cannot boot. These devices may also be used to prevent unauthorized access to workstations. The SecureCards offer programmable levels of security. For example, some cards can be set up to disable local floppy drives or communication ports, while others permit their use.

There are also more exotic physical authentication devices available, much like those you might expect to see in a James Bond movie. Retina scanners, thumbprint readers and handwriting analysis systems are all real technologies. These biometric devices are very expensive and time-consuming in actual use, but they effectively exclude all but the most determined intruder.

On the workstation side of the network, diskless or disk-optional workstations can prevent data theft and the introduction of viruses. They also prevent use of other unauthorized software (e.g., software-based protocol analyzers) on the network. There are also software locks that can inhibit the use of local disk drives and communication ports for the same purposes.

Remote Connections

Wide area network links also expose the network to potential unauthorized access. Most wide area routers have effective security features built in. Many even offer encryption to prevent the interception of data as it travels through the phone system. After proper installation and configuration, security for these devices is the same as it is for local users. Those who are really worried can also pull the plug and disconnect WAN routers outside of normal hours when they can be monitored.

Some routers and bridges offer programmable security features. These features include limiting traffic between specific network addresses and setting up one-way traffic. While such features are more commonly used to improve network performance through traffic management, they can also prevent sensitive data from leaving the network via the router.

Protocol Analyzers and Local Cabling

"The flip side of a protocol analyzer like Sniffer is that anybody with one can read anybody else's mail, unless it's encrypted."

—James Brentano

The only other place a threatening human (or a natural disaster) can intercept or disrupt data is while it is in the cable between the server and local workstations. The threat from humans, at this point, is usually limited to such things as password interception or other eavesdropping with a protocol analyzer. Encoded passwords solve the first problem. From a security standpoint, protocol analyzers can be a real weakness. There are software-based protocol analyzers (Chapter 4, Fault Management) that can turn any decent PC with a good network interface card into a very capable device for watching network traffic. Because they can function passively, they may be difficult to observe. The good news is that most nontechnical intruders will not understand how to use them. Diskless (or floppy disk-deactivated) workstations are the principal defense, although a firm policy prohibiting unauthorized software could help provide appropriate disciplinary tools for anyone found using such a package.

Hardware-based protocol analyzers are simpler to spot because they are bigger than a floppy disk and require a new physical connection to the cabling system. Network managers may want to consider eliminating superfluous T-connectors in a thinnet system, or removing unused twisted pair wiring from the hub. This process may be as simple as pulling extra cable up above the ceiling tiles. Some buildings already have motion sensors in the ceiling plenum that alert the security patrol if someone tries to tamper with such a connection.

Threats to Local Cabling

Nature is a more common threat than people. Cables installed above suspended ceilings or in walls often sit right next to AC power lines or near fluorescent light fixtures. Fluorescent lights all have high-voltage transformers that often produce electronic noise. The LAN cabling can act like an antenna that picks up the noise, causing interference with the data in the cable. Voltage anomalies in the AC lines produce the same problem to a lesser extent. Prevention and remedy are the same in either case—keep the LAN cabling away from the source of the problem.

Cable Eavesdropping

To add another problem to the list, the only cabling that is immune to data interception without a physical tap is optical fiber. It is also immune to electrical interference. During the Cold War, federal agents caught more than one spy sitting outside a defense contractor with an antenna aimed at the contractor's building. In one case, the eavesdroppers managed to pick up traffic from shielded coaxial cabling.

Cabling is not the only network component capable of radiating interceptable signals. Computers, video displays, even loose or corroded connectors can produce electromagnetic fields capable of being picked up half a mile or more from their source with relatively unsophisticated and inexpensive equipment. A security audit with equipment that can pick up these weak electromagnetic fields could reveal any vulnerability in this regard. The Department of Defense solution—equipment that meets the government's TEMPEST standard everywhere—will certainly be costly and cumbersome.

Encryption Devices

Encryption devices and software can make it nearly impossible to eavesdrop on a network. This is an extreme measure, and is not without pitfalls. Should something happen to cause difficulties in the network, a legitimate remedy would be to use a protocol analyzer to identify the trouble. Encoded traffic would render the analyzer useless and prevent diagnosis of the problem.

Application-level encryption offers the advantage of leaving the protocol information at the lower levels unencrypted. Thus protocol analyzers could still perform their functions.

Security in Corporate Computing

Setting security standards for passwords and access control is determined by the corporate audit department. We provide training to the users as to standards. The biggest gap for us is in the area of encryption. We send a lot of stuff by e-mail, and all these monitors are passive. You can put up a star network and every queue is theoretically on the net. The subnet I'm on involves three floors of this building. There are hundreds of cubicles. You can put a laptop Sniffer on any one of those and you see everything that crosses the wire. If you want to know what the manager is saying, you can just look at the manager's e-mail. It's both difficult and expensive to handle this problem, so nothing is being done about it as of now.

—*James Brentano, Network Manager at a West Coast utility company*

Peripherals

Some network-ready printers and fax servers require the use of unencoded passwords. The question is whether the use of the device offsets the risk to network security. Network-ready printers also offer an additional location where someone with a protocol analyzer

"We also did an internal audit of our file services. The system does not limit access rights to software. The problem is that access is not that hard."

—JAMES BRENTANO

could tap into the network cabling. For example, in old Wang OIS systems, workstations were often designated as word-processing-only units. This prevented the workstation from getting to all the system functions at the next higher menu level. Because the printers used the same cabling, but could not be assigned word-processing-only status, someone could bypass this limit by connecting a workstation to the printer cable.

Newer systems may not have similar problems, but prospective data thieves might decide to use notebook computers with network adapters on a printer connection instead of in someone's office. If they were to use offices, the normal occupants might notice any slight change. Printer areas are ideal for eavesdropping—as they're common space, no one notices if anything is a bit different, and there's always power in case the portable's batteries run low.

Preventing Theft

Theft is a major problem wherever electronic equipment is extensively used. It's relatively easy to steal a PC one piece at a time. It is even easier to steal software—one shirt-pocketful at a time. Prevention must be the primary strategy for dealing with theft because any remedy involves prosecution and recovery, very messy processes that may well cost more than the value of the stolen articles.

There are only two types of people who can steal hardware or software—employees and others. Unfortunately, employees steal more from employers than do outsiders. Many consider it an unofficial fringe benefit. Theft is almost always an inside job. Guards at many companies are not there to protect the workers from outsiders, but to deter theft by insiders. One policy that could reduce theft and increase productivity is to allow employees to borrow computer equipment to work at home. Some sort of checkout procedure and modifications to normal inventory practices could prevent this program from increasing inventory shrinkage. One of the online inventory programs discussed in Chapter 5, Configuration Management, may simplify this process.

Copying Software

In the area of software theft, the company must set a good example by abiding by software license agreements. How can anyone expect employees to live by rules the company violates? And if it is caught violating license agreements, the company, including the network manager, may be liable for hefty civil fines—$10,000 per occurrence. All it takes is a phone call from an angry employee who knows about illegal software use, and the federal marshals will be all over the place. It is in the organization's best interest, practically as well as morally, to obey the law.

A current, accurate hardware and software inventory is a very powerful defensive tool. How can you know something is gone unless you know you had it? Periodic inventories not only spot theft, but deter it as well. There are several software packages available to help track this database. (See Chapter 5, Configuration Management, for possible solutions.) Network administrators also find these programs to be helpful management tools when it comes to upgrading workstation software and configuration files.

Hardware Theft

To deter hardware theft, take reasonable precautions such as actually using the case locks on all the workstations and controlling the keys. In public areas, it may also be necessary to use cable locks, which are available in most office supply catalogs. They come with lugs that can be glued on to, or sandwiched between, the case components of computer hardware. You fasten a cable to the lug, and then lock the cable to something massive, like a desk. Unfortunately, these devices can affect morale, making users feel as though they were in a cheap hotel room where the TV remote is nailed to the nightstand.

Keys

Hardware locks are recommended as reasonable solutions to many physical security worries. Having locks on the server room door, the software storage cabinet and the server case won't do any good if the keys are readily accessible. These keys should be controlled with at least the same diligence applied to keys to everyone's offices. Server room keys are often found in the department secretary's top right desk drawer, which isn't much more secure than hanging the key on a nail right by the door.

At the same time, people other than the network supervisor may need to work with the server after hours. If all the keys are secured in an impenetrable vault, a minor emergency could turn into a major problem. This is another security tradeoff. The secret is to control the keys in a way that helps secure the network from intruders without impairing network operation during maintenance or an emergency.

Software Security

Every network can implement at least three levels of software security: the security facilities built into the operating system (such as log-in passwords); add-on utilities that provide supplemental security features (such as antivirus programs); and application-level security (such as *WordPerfect* passwords). Most software security is preventive—designed to prevent security breaches rather than to repair the damage after a breach has occurred.

Remedial action is a bit more difficult. It often consists of procedures to follow in the event you suspect a security violation. Start with written procedures about adding users and setting up passwords and account restrictions. Also consider procedures for deleting users when people leave. A disgruntled former employee could wreak havoc with the network. Definitely set up procedures for changing any passwords used by former employees. You may also want to establish procedures about how often to run the SECURITY program and whether to use SECURE CONSOLE, MONITOR and other security features. The best time to develop such a plan is before it is really needed.

Care and Feeding of Passwords

Being serious about network security implies being equally serious about protecting passwords. NetWare's default password requirements are minimal, but its additional options offer very good security. Setting the minimum length for passwords to at least five characters, requiring unique passwords and forcing periodic password changes will at least keep interlopers guessing.

"Passwords in our organization last 16 to 17 weeks, for security reasons. We did an audit and found 2,000 accounts with no password. We made a list of the accounts, sent out a memo and got compliance."

—JAMES BRENTANO

Users need training about proper passwords. Helpful tips include not using their names or birthdays or words written on nearby signs. The best passwords are completely random. Foreign-language passwords are often good. One user, an American white man, habitually invents passwords in Thai because he speaks it fluently and finds his passwords easy to remember. Other coworkers would have a very tough time guessing his passwords, and most Thais would probably not guess that he would use Thai. The objective is to make it hard for someone else to guess the password.

Above all, train users not to write the password down. It is surprising how often a user's password is written on the pullout shelf in the desk. Teach users to change passwords immediately if they discover someone has found out their password.

Expiring Passwords

Our help desk received about 20 calls in one period reporting that users had let their passwords expire. We had to re-enable each user and set up new passwords for them. This really should not have happened, as our system provides users with three chances to renew their passwords by typing in a new one before the old one expires. Users get a message and a query asking if they want to create a new one, but somehow the users were not getting the point.

After this incident, I put out a memo in the company newsletter about the importance of renewing passwords before expiration, and that seemed to work.

—*John Thomas, Microcomputer Supervisor at a home improvement supply company*

Recovering Lost Supervisor Passwords

The last thing to say about passwords is that they sometimes get lost. This can pose a real problem for networks with only one supervisor. Suppose the network supervisor falls overboard while on a cruise or, more mundanely, changes the supervisory password and then forgets the new one. Either way, the network now has a password unknown to the network users. There are several possible solutions to this problem. The first is to call the secondary supervisor. The second is to find a systems engineer who knows how to change the password using a disk sector editor.

The third is to find a password utility that decodes passwords. These utilities are less of a security threat than they might seem. Most packages have built-in protection against illicit use. *NTPASS* from AccessData works like this: You order the package because you've lost the password. It arrives. The documentation says to call tech support for the package. You provide them with the serial number of your copy of NetWare and a key from *NTPASS*. Tech support then provides a code over the phone that lets that specific copy of the software unlock the copy of NetWare with that specific serial number. To find out passwords for other servers, you must purchase a separate package for each copy of NetWare.

Perhaps the simplest way to safeguard the password is to write it down and seal it in an envelope and store the envelope in a safe. Split the combination to the safe between two people.

Account Management

The flow of people here is fairly significant.We end up with a high volume of account maintenance, and we want to make it easier for all those people who need to do local area network administration. We want to manage fewer accounts and fewer servers, but still provide maximum benefit to all the workstations on the network.

One of the hardest things is to manage the number of accounts any one individual requires and the number of passwords. A typical user here would have an account on the IBM mainframe for *PROFS*, plus another mainframe account on MVS. There may also be a local area network mail account, a file server account and an account on the Sun SPARCserver. In some cases, unique account names are necessary and all the passwords have to be managed. We end up changing accounts as a daily routine.

We have so many accounts for a given individual that there's no way to keep up with it. It takes me about 30 minutes every 2 months to work on an account that kicks off and says, 'You have to change your password.' Then I have to go through and change every account that I have access to. There's a list of about 20 different accounts in various places, and whenever there's a password change, we have to go through and change them all.

—Randy Howland, Network Manager for a Fortune 500 technology company

OS Preventive Facilities

Network operating systems all offer some sort of software security, and an organization's security plan should address the use of each feature. The following sections discuss several of the security features NetWare offers. As with hardware security, most of these features are preventive, and a few are remedial. Passwords help authenticate network users; trustee rights and file attributes limit access to files, even for valid network users; and NetWare comes with rudimentary backup and restore abilities (though Novell has wisely simplified development of backup systems by other developers). Together, these features provide a good preventive mechanism to many authentication and access control problems. Most security in NetWare is available through SYSCON (the system configuration utility). Other preventive measures can be implemented via MONITOR, SECURITY and SECURE CONSOLE.

Standard NetWare Utilities

SYSCON

SYSCON offers several security options under Supervisor Options on the main menu. It looks like Figure 7-1. These functions are only available to supervisor-equivalent users. The menu looks very different to ordinary users.

- **Default Account Balance/Restrictions** allows the supervisor to set an expiration date on a user name. This is very handy if there are temporary users. It also sets up user accounts so that they require passwords, sets a minimum length for passwords, requires unique passwords at each change, forces periodic password changes and limits the number of grace log-ins. (A grace log-in is a log-in with an expired password.) If supervisors change a password because they fear it has been compromised, they should also limit grace log-ins for the new password. The default is six grace log-ins.

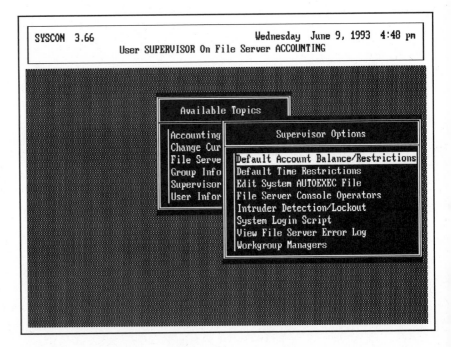

Figure 7-1 SYSCON
Main Menu, With
Supervisor Options

- **Default Time Restrictions** limits the time of day and days of the week when users can log-in to the server. These options can limit undesirable operation after hours.
- **Edit System AUTOEXEC File** allows the supervisor to edit the AUTOEXEC.NCF file. Since this file contains the commands that start the server, it might be a good idea to check it periodically, but it has no other direct relationship with security.
- **File Server Console Operators** specifies which users are file server console operators. Such users can access the FCONSOLE utility. Among other things, FCONSOLE allows users to down the server from a workstation.
- **Intruder Detection/Lockout** monitors log-in attempts with an incorrect password. The default threshold is seven incorrect attempts, but it can be changed. The detection

feature is programmable in two additional ways. The supervisor can specify the period during which the system counts incorrect attempts and then resets the counter to zero. Supervisors can also set how long the account stays locked after reaching the maximum number of incorrect attempts. For example, you can specify that the system locks accounts for ten days if there are more than five incorrect log-in attempts in a two-day period.

- **System Login Script** sets up the default log-in. It is very useful for providing access to printers and files based on group membership.

- **View File Server Error Log** lets the supervisor look at and clear the server error log. This is another good place to check for alterations to the bindery (the database that stores passwords and other user data). It indicates each time the bindery was opened or closed.

- **Workgroup Managers** lets the supervisor administer workgroup managers. A workgroup manager is an assistant supervisor with limited supervisory rights for creating, deleting and managing user and group accounts.

If a supervisor wants to perform these options for individuals instead of for all network users, the User Information option on SYSCON's main menu can often do it. User Information lets you set up account restrictions, set passwords, specify full names, write log-in scripts, determine managers, set group membership, assign security equivalences, designate file and directory trustees and limit disk space restrictions for individual users.

MONITOR

NetWare also provides a software server console lock through the MONITOR utility. Once locked, the server console requires a password to unlock it. MONITOR also displays the time the server has been up and running. This is handy for those who worry about an intruder downing the server, changing passwords and restarting the server. Check this number at the start of every shift. If the server has not been restarted for a valid reason, such as a power outage or maintenance, then there may be cause to worry.

SECURE CONSOLE

Supervisors can also use the SECURE CONSOLE command to secure the server against improper access. It prevents loading any loadable modules that might provide unauthorized access to server data or system files. The exception is that NLMs can still be loaded from the SYS volume SYSTEM directory. The SECURE CONSOLE command also makes it harder to change the system date and time.

SECURITY

The NetWare SECURITY program is also helpful. It runs from a workstation and has many of the same reporting features discussed above relative to SYSCON, but it does them for all users at once. It is also simple to pipe the results into a DOS text file to generate a concise security report. This report forms a part of every security audit. SECURITY also spots several kinds of problems, such as passwords that match user names, short passwords, inactive accounts and supervisor equivalence.

Supervisor equivalence means that a user can do most supervisory functions on the network. Be careful how this power is distributed. It is prudent to have at least one user other than the network administrator with supervisor equivalence. The supervisor equivalent can function as a secondary supervisor when the primary administrator is not present. Every such user should have two accounts on the file server—the supervisory equivalent account and another account with normal access controls. The user should not use the supervisor-equivalent log-in name unless it is necessary to perform a supervisory function.

Secondary supervisors should habitually use their normal accounts. Imagine what could happen should a supervisor equivalent accidentally introduce a virus to the network. The virus could have unlimited access to the network drives. Use of a normal, non-supervisor log-in would limit the virus to the user's disk space.

File Usage Tracking Products

Blue Lance—LT Auditor

Blue Lance's *LT Auditor* was one of the first auditing products developed for NetWare LANs. It tracks network software use by user and network location. The package monitors log-in activity so that you always know who logged in to the network and from which workstation—a big help during security audits. It monitors file use so that you know who's doing what and for how long. *LT Auditor* reports on all bindery changes, maintains equipment and software inventory and enforces software license agreements. The suggested retail price is $695.

Farallon Computing—LANtrail

Farallon's *LANtrail* software provides audit trails for all NetWare server activities. It tracks executed programs by user, file access of all sorts by users, and any changes to network security. *LANtrail* stores all this data in a compressed log file to minimize disk space impact and to prevent tampering. The package includes report generation features.

LANshark—File Service Analyzer

LANshark's *File Service Analyzer* tracks file services on VINES networks for auditing. It tracks each access of each file and provides file descriptions, detailed user information, inactive file reports and disk use reports.

Virus Prevention Software

Software virus detection and removal packages can greatly enhance a network manager's peace of mind. Antivirus programs scan new software distribution disks for signatures of known viruses. A signature is a recognizable pattern of bits specific to the virus. Some antivirus packages can remove specific viruses. The biggest difficulty is that antisocial or misguided people invent new viruses daily (so peace of mind may not be totally appropriate). No package can spot them all. The best that can be hoped for is periodic updates from the antivirus vendor. Those who are worried about viruses should invest in a good package and use it religiously. Before buying, make sure you understand what the updates will cost. Some vendors include free quarterly updates. Because this class of products changes so rapidly, a book such as this one, with its relatively long lead time, is not the best source for product descriptions. The personal computer and networking periodicals regularly provide up-to-date information on the virus wars.

The Propagating Virus

I manage tape backups in case of disk failure on the server. We had a virus incursion that caused us to revamp our procedures. Whenever users booted they had the option to invoke a virus check on their workstations. Most of them say 'No,' because they don't want to be bothered. A virus got in from a contractor and propagated across multiple servers. Once it was discovered, we ran two virus checks per server. We used *Netscan* (from McAfee) and ran two passes across the net. This took about 16 hours. We found eight or nine instances of the 'Keypress' virus on the servers, which we remedied using the *Clean* utility (also from McAfee). Once we cleaned out the virus, we made the virus check mandatory through the system log-in script on workstations. To do this, we put *Netscan* on each server as an NLM checking all incoming files.

—Lawrence Sachartoff, Sr. Technical Analyst for an international petrochemical firm

Application Security

Most network application packages offer some security features. Word processors and spreadsheets usually offer document password protection. This is particularly useful when most access control is based on NetWare groups. People using these features can protect specific files in shared directories. Management utilities may offer multiple levels of password protection that allow some users to manage more than others. Some database packages offer installation on redundant machines. Each approach represents a response to specific threats against the data governed by the application.

Disaster Planning

The final part of a well-designed security plan is to plan for the unpredictable. Many network managers think that a good data backup is all there is to a disaster plan. While it is certainly important to a disaster plan, data backup is not all there is. A spare parts plan, UPS installation, data backup and storage procedures are all facets of dealing with minor emergencies.

What happens when a major catastrophe clobbers the entire network? It will happen to some of those who read this book. Don't be sure it will happen only to someone else.

The Backup System

The first part of a disaster plan is a good method of backing up the data stored on the network. If the data is not stored somewhere unaffected by the disaster, you can't get it back. Many systems today, such as those from Palindrome, Cheyenne and Gigatrend, offer backup as a natural extension of data management. Many systems offer disk grooming to migrate old or unused files to offline storage (e.g., tape) as an independent feature—as opposed to making a copy of network data just for emergencies. All offer tape library management by keeping track of what data went onto what tape when.

There are several factors to consider when deciding on the backup system. As much as some manufacturers in the tape industry would like us to believe that speed is the overriding factor, it is far from the only one. The primary criterion is really data recovery performance, that is, how long it takes to get back a file accidentally deleted by a careless user. This is by far the most common use for a backup data set. The only time speed is important is when there is too much data to back up during off hours, or when there are no off hours.

The next criterion is the backup system architecture. In the networking world, there are three distinct architectures: server-based, workstation-based and backup station-based. All involve tradeoffs between performance and cost. The typical system consists of a SCSI interface card, a cable, some software and some sort of tape drive. There are three common types of tape drives in the networking world—8mm, 4mm DAT and QIC (quarter-inch cartridge). Each offers different capacities and performance. With the availability of DAT cartridge changers, there is a tape system to handle the backup and recovery need of any size network.

Backup and Corporate Confidentiality

Our legal department is concerned about e-mail because the company is involved in litigation. They wanted to know about the feasibility of erasing mail throughout the company after a certain period of time. I can't do this easily, partly because of the way the software is set up, partly because there's a trade-off between our abilities. On the side of consistency, data management and protection, you want to guarantee that mail messages are not lost and that you have backups. This conflicts with those issues. Backup tapes sent to outside storage can stay there for weeks or months; it's random.

—James Brentano, Network Manager at a West Coast utility company

As far as daily operational security is concerned, the only risk of data interception during backup is by an intruder with a protocol analyzer. All the data will eventually run this risk unless the network uses a server-based system for each individual server. Tape station and workstation systems both require that all backup data traverse the network cabling, as do server systems that back up more than one server.

Additionally, the backup system must be able to back up and restore all the data on the network. This sounds obvious, but it becomes a real problem on mixed-platform networks. Any backup system can handle DOS files, but if some file servers store Macintosh files, then the backup system has to handle the data fork and the resource fork (the format required by Macintosh files) when backing up and restoring the data. It may also have to handle Unix files. It is prudent to see these capabilities successfully demonstrated before purchasing the system.

Finally, it may be wise to implement a system that backs up local workstation hard drives in addition to server disk systems. Such an arrangement is preferable to having network users copy their C: drives to the network disks. This process appears to be a security hole because workstations must be left on to be backed up. The backup vendors have found ways to do the job without having the workstation logged in to the network until it is time to start the backup. With Gigatrend's system, all that is necessary in a NetWare environment is to load a TSR (terminate-and-stay-resident) program and leave the workstation running. At backup time, the tape station sends a peer-to-peer message to the TSR that starts the local backup to the tape system. At the end of the backup, the TSR resets the workstation.

All decent backup systems offer unattended operation, allowing administrators to set them up and walk out at day's end. Large networks with multiple gigabytes of data may need a robot changer to switch tapes. In good systems, the tape station does not even need to be logged in to the network. Some, however, may require that a password be kept in an ASCII text file that starts the backup. Usually backup systems need a supervisor-equivalent account. If these two conditions exist, then there is a massive security hole.

Using the Backup Data

During daily use, backup systems offer three types of operations: full, incremental and differential backups. A full backup copies everything. An incremental backup copies files that have changed since the last (full or incremental) backup. Differential backup copies files that have changed since the last *full* backup. Incremental backups are the fastest, but in case of a disaster they may take more time to restore. This is because it is necessary to start with the last full backup and then restore every incremental backup performed later. Several vendors offer support for various backup strategies that schedule different backup operations to ensure maximum data protection.

When integrating a backup system into a disaster plan, assume that some sort of disaster will eventually destroy the network—and plan how to recover. This is one time when prevention doesn't do much good. Ordinary mortal network managers can't usually prevent floods, hurricanes, riots, earthquakes, boiler explosions, huge fires (and water damage), terrorist bombings or wars. But they can be ready to recover from them. Managers need three things to recover from a disaster: all the files from the file servers, a network to install them on and the people to install the hardware and restore the data.

Any effective disaster plan requires an off-site backup of some sort. Service bureaus can handle this process over telephone lines during off-peak hours. The tradeoffs are the cost and the need to trust data to another company. A simpler way is to take backup tapes away from the office periodically. This may be as simple as having the network administrator take the backup tapes home every other night, or the organization's plan may specify a more formal procedure such as putting the tapes in a bank vault. Just be sure the vault is not in a place subject to the same catastrophe that destroys the server.

Replacing Lost Hardware

The ability to replace destroyed hardware depends on the severity of the disaster and the urgency to rebuild. If the disaster is limited to an organization's office, as a fire might be, then an order to a nearby reseller may solve the problem. If the disaster is widespread, and dozens or hundreds of other businesses are all in the same difficulty, then a local PC supplier may not be able to handle calls from everyone. It might be a good idea to cultivate a relationship with a national organization, or at least a supplier whose source is some distance away. At any rate, make sure that insurance covers replacement with comparable equipment and not current value for depreciated hardware.

When dealing with insurance companies, the complete inventory is valuable (assuming it wasn't also destroyed). Store a copy along with the off-site backup tapes, listing all the features of all the hardware. Such items as extra memory are easy to overlook, but hard to justify to the insurance adjuster unless there is an inventory. Six extra megabytes of RAM in all your Windows workstations will cost about $300 to replace at $50/MB; if you have 100 workstations, that's $30,000. Also keep a complete phone log of company personnel who might help after a disaster and the phone numbers for hardware replacement sources.

Missing People

Replacing missing personnel after a disaster may be the hardest job of all. Should friends or coworkers be hurt or lost in a disaster, it could be very difficult just to carry on, let alone rebuild a network.

In a less extreme case, transportation system failures or sudden illness may keep key personnel away from the office for extended periods. Take a minute while writing your security plan and think the unthinkable—plan what to do without crucial networking people, including yourself. Every person vital to the network should have a backup person. The disaster plan is one way to formalize such procedures. On a lighter note, this thinking comes in handy when vital personnel go on vacation or leave the company.

Lesser Environmental Difficulties

All network managers are exposed to smaller day-to-day hassles that probably don't deserve to be called disasters. While they may not have the widespread impact of a deadly fire, hardware failures and environmental problems can still cause their share of heartburn. Disaster plans have to cover them as well.

Hardware Failures

Hardware failures are a fact of life; sooner or later a hard drive is going to break or a network interface card is going to stop working right. Buying hardware from reputable vendors and manufacturers offers some preventive protection in this area.

There are three potential remedies for hardware failures: redundant hardware, a good spare parts plan and a great technical service provider. Some data recovery service bureaus claim to restore data from damaged disk drives, but it would be costly and dangerous to count on these services for every case.

Redundant Hardware

Redundant servers are possible with NetWare 4.x. Novell has demonstrated online and standby file servers. In one demonstration,

Novell had two parallel file servers, one online, the other a standby, cabled together with a high-speed link. They dropped an immense anvil from the local village smithy on the primary server. As you might expect, this destroyed the server pretty thoroughly. Despite the shrapnel, the backup server kept the network running. Novell had a large collection of machines on hand, and repeated the demo time after time.

For those of us still running NetWare 3.x, many vendors offer hot-swappable disk drives in drive arrays. This means that the network manager can remove and replace a failed drive while the server and the network keep running. The remaining drives then reconstruct the missing data on the new drive. Other than initial costs, the only tradeoff is that these drive arrays with parity for protection are generally not as fast as other arrangements.

It is also possible to have redundant bridges or routers in the network. Generally these devices have a very long time between failures, so they are not usually of as great concern as disk drives. The most common failure item in a network is probably the workstation. Every network has redundant workstations in a sense. The trouble is convincing two operators to share one PC.

Spare Parts

A good spare parts plan might not prevent downtime, but can minimize it. For example, many file servers are designed around a card cage. With such a design, it is possible to install a motherboard and cards in a second card cage and keep it as a spare in the server room. If the server fails due to anything other than a disk drive or power supply, a technician can swap the guts and card cage in less than 10 minutes. The server can be up and running again very rapidly. Technicians can then repair the card cage without desperate users and irate managers breathing down their necks.

Similar strategies apply to cabling and associated devices. If the network has many routers, you may want to consider stocking a spare. The same is true for workstations and network interface cards. The number and types of spares depends on the number and types of workstations cabled to your network.

Technicians and Their Organizations

The final method of dealing with hardware failure is to have a good relationship with a highly capable service technician, backed by a service organization with superior logistical capabilities. Find one who can fix things when hardware problems exceed the network staff's experience. Finding such a person or group is often difficult because the complexity of networks is growing faster than the number of skilled technicians. This is an excellent argument for additional training for network managers.

Environmental Problems

Environmental problems may be the most common threats to network security, because they affect connection integrity. The three major environmental factors that affect hardware are temperature, humidity and power quality. Every piece of hardware in a network has a specification sheet somewhere in the manual that gives maximum operating thresholds for temperature and humidity.

Air Conditioning

Since servers should be installed in a locked area to prevent unauthorized access, the area should also be air-conditioned like the rest of the office. Keep a thermometer in the server area. It is a good idea to control the air conditioning for the server area with the same thermostat as the network administrator's office if they are in the same control zone. If it is too hot for the human, it is definitely too hot for the machine. If the network is in a building with computer-controlled climate, be sure the facilities engineer arranges a proper environment for the hardware.

There is a problem with locking a server in a small closet with an uninterruptible power supply (UPS). In the event of a prolonged power outage, the UPS makes sure the server keeps running. In a small closet, now without air-conditioning due to the power loss, heat can build up rapidly. Be sure to set up the shutdown time so that it happens before the temperature gets too high. Make sure the server closet is well ventilated.

Baking Servers

We've got our facilities doing certain things to cut costs, such as cutting back air conditioning at nights. That poses problems for us as network managers. Now we've got our servers sitting in a room and they essentially bake overnight. When employees come back in the morning, the air conditioning is on. So we're going to have to deal with that as seasons change. The facilities problem is something that has evolved along with the rest of the network. We didn't anticipate climate problems like this.

—*Randy Howland, Network Manager for a Fortune 500 technology company*

Power

Power is probably the biggest environmental problem for PCs. Protect every server with an uninterruptible power supply and good-quality power conditioning equipment. A $7.95 power strip from the local discount store is not good enough. Regrettably, price alone is not a sufficient indicator of quality, nor are vendor advertisements. Check trade magazines and user groups for recommendations. The UPS should be capable of keeping the server running for at least 10 minutes. It should not shut down the server immediately because most power outages are quite brief. It should also have some local intelligence and communication ability. At a minimum, it should be able to shut down the server properly without panic in case the outage lasts more than a few minutes. Modern UPSs support software with all kinds of excellent monitoring, management and control features. The UPS should also boost AC voltage during a brownout.

If you have a functioning, but nonintelligent, UPS that cannot communicate with the server, then you need a product available from Computer Aided Business Solutions. It consists of an optically isolated cable that connects a server serial port to a wall outlet and a NetWare Loadable Module (NLM). The NLM checks the server serial port periodically, and if it discovers there is no power, it shuts down the server.

Some vendors (notably EFI and Emerson) have started building UPSs that support Simple Network Management Protocol (SNMP). EFI contends that the SNMP Management Information Base (MIB) for the UPS should include temperature. This MIB permits network managers to monitor the UPS remotely, and indirectly to monitor the air conditioning as well.

Include periodic testing of the UPS in the security plan. Batteries eventually fail, so don't count on an old, untested UPS to protect your server. A good rule of thumb is that an increase of 10 degrees in ambient operating temperature decreases useful battery life expectancy by about 25 percent. That is another good reason to make sure there is a decent server environment.

People

The final environmental concern is the human operator. Train users in a few do's and don'ts. Be sure they report to the network manager or the help desk when things seem strange. Make sure they know about security procedures so they can help enforce them. This does not mean network managers should foster a Big Brother atmosphere and have everyone watching everyone else (although in some circumstances that may be appropriate, too). It merely means raise the security awareness level among users.

On the mundane side, encourage users to keep coffee and other drinks away from workstations and network hardware. Teach people not to cover ventilation grills in PCs and monitors. A user often unwittingly covers a monitor with a paper and shortens its life expectancy dramatically. Some environments may also need anti-static devices or carpeting.

A Final Word

Security should be an integral part of the network management plan. The driving forces behind good security are common sense about accidents and paranoia about malice. Locking up servers is common sense because it prevents accidental damage by the guy who delivered the copier paper with a hand truck. It is also paranoia because it deters tampering, maybe by the same guy in the dark of night. Just because you're paranoid doesn't mean they are not out to get you.

8 / A Note on Accounting Management

Drawbacks of Network Accounting
Disk Space Accounting Products

On a network, accounting means keeping track of the use of system resources by users. NetWare, for example, allows you to set up charges for disk space use, connection time, memory use and other network resources. It then charges each account the set rates.

When you set up an account, you can enter a starting balance. As users employ network resources, the accounting package deducts the appropriate charges from the account balance. Eventually the account balance reaches zero and the account must be credited again. Accounting techniques may be a useful way to assign the costs of a network shared by multiple cost centers.

Not many people use NetWare's accounting package. It is hidden as the first option under SYSCON's main menu. There are valid reasons, though, for installing accounting. The best may be to change user behavior. If users are storing excessive garbage, limiting their access to disk space may be too harsh a solution. Charging for it is a bit more subtle. Accounting may also be a way to control use of one department's LAN by another department.

Drawbacks of PC Network Accounting

Because the costs of PC network resources are low—and declining quickly—many network managers are inclined to give accounting mechanisms low priority. The cost of one megabyte of disk space is rapidly approaching one dollar at this writing. Accounting at this level may make about as much sense as accounting in detail for local phone calls or for nails at a construction site.

Accounting in detail for resource usage will most likely crimp the performance of the server significantly by using CPU cycles, occupying disk storage space and generating traffic on the server I/O subsystem. The return on investment may be much lower than it looks at first because of the potential need for more equipment and the possibility of performance degradation.

Finally, there are fundamental difficulties in measuring network resource usage. Many applications, including printing from any program, many database activities and most kinds of e-mail, create transient files that wait for servicing in queues or go away after a session. These essential files may be enormous, but exist only for a few minutes. They typically are beyond the awareness or the control of a user, even a very sophisticated one. Accounting may be unworkable on networks that support these activities.

Disk Space Accounting Products

Many of the configuration and administration utilities listed in Chapter 5, Configuration Management, can report on disk space usage.

LANshark—SPACEcheck

LANshark's *SPACEcheck* software is a disk management tool and auditor for VINES networks. It assigns disk space to users and groups, monitors disk space use, manages violations and tracks user log-ins and file accesses.

> ### Accounting for Disk Use
>
> We have 10 nodes on a Novell network for medical staff, 175 nodes on an IBM PC LAN for billing. Out of the total user population, ten doctors use Sound Blasters to listen to their voice mail. The physicians using this voice mail continued to store old messages, which contain large chunks of voice in them. So their disk space usage was accumulating. To circumvent the problem, I had to establish disk space limits, which is part of the Novell operating system. There's a built-in accounting feature to set up parameters. If there are too many messages, the users get a 'disk full' error. I sent an e-mail notice explaining that this means they have to erase their messages.
>
> —*Dennis Roberts, Team Leader of Networking Services, Toledo Hospital*

PART THREE

The Evolving Discipline of Network Management

9 / Network Management Platforms

Network devices require management tools to detect faults, monitor and tune performance, change configurations and plan capacity. Vendors have always offered these tools, ranging from simple utilities to sophisticated management systems; typically, however, each tool was specific to a particular vendor. For instance, the network operating system had its own set of management utilities. Similarly, each brand of router, bridge or gateway had its own management utility or system.

Multiple management tools led to multiple management consoles, user interfaces, alarm systems and management databases. Users have had to learn how to use all these different utilities and systems. They often had to run them on different platforms; some, for example, run under DOS, and some under Unix. Worst of all, there was no way to get a unified view of the network. Devices that were in reality interconnected had to be viewed as separate, isolated systems for purposes of management.

Fortunately for network managers, the emergence of the *management platform* represents a major step away from fragmented network management and towards integrated network management. A management platform is a single software environment for running multiple management applications from different vendors. The key to the power of the management platform is that all the management applications running on the platform share a single console, user interface and alarm system and often share a database. A single, consistent user interface makes it much easier to learn multiple management applications. The shared map and alarms provide an integrated view of the network. The shared database makes it possible to gather statistics for analysis—and to produce reports—reflecting the same kind of integrated network view.

However, management platforms are not a panacea for fragmented management. For one thing, each platform supports a limited number of management applications. In any complex environment, it is quite likely that there is no management application for some critical components of the network, such as the network operating system. Thus, multiple management systems are still the rule. However, the management platform can significantly reduce the number of management systems required. In addition, the user may be able to customize the management platform to cover network components that lack specific management applications. Such customization is usually based on the *generic SNMP* capability, discussed below.

Fragmentation also remains because, other than three or four shared management resources (map, alarms, user interface, database), management applications run "side by side" on the management platform—independent of, and not communicating directly with, one another. For example, if a router is having a problem that affects a file server, the two corresponding management applications do not usually exchange information that might help pinpoint the problem.

Some management platforms do offer an "alarm correlation" feature that makes it possible for the platform to generate a single problem report from multiple related alarms. In effect, the management application is making a guess about the cause of the alarms. For example, if the system receives a major alarm for a router and a major alarm for each device on the far side of the router, the management application may report only the router alarm, since the other alarms probably stem from the fact that those devices have been isolated by the failed router. The user normally has to enter the rules by which such deductions are made.

Elements of a Management Platform

A management platform consists of software running on a central management station. It may be divided into a management server, where the data collection and processing is done, and one or more viewing stations. The central management station communicates with agents, which consist of software or firmware, usually running in the managed device. Agents may also run in computers, usually somewhere near the managed device. Agents do the moment-by-moment monitoring of devices, and forward raw data, statistics and alarms to the management station.

Typical software components at the management station are the map, the database, third-party management applications, a generic SNMP management application and an autodiscovery utility. Some management platforms, such as IBM's *AIX SystemView Net-View/6000* and the *HP OpenView Distributed Management Platform*, also include generic management for devices supporting the Open System Interconnection (OSI) management protocols defined in the Common Management Information Protocol (CMIP) specification. OSI is a wide-ranging suite of standards developed by the International Standards Organization (ISO).

Hierarchical Network Map

All the platforms discussed in this chapter offer hierarchical maps. A hierarchical map allows the network manager to view the network at different levels of abstraction. For instance, the highest level of the map might show the world, with lines connecting different countries that contain network locations. The next level down might show the United States, with lines connecting cities. The next level might depict a single city, with network locations in the city. The next level might show a single location within the city, and so on, down to the level of a network segment, where the map would show the network devices attached to that segment.

At each level, the manager can click on a particular location or link to get a more detailed view of that location or link. Within that more detailed view, the manager can click on another location, link or piece of equipment, thus "drilling down" to a still more detailed view. The manager can usually get a view down to the port level of a particular hub or concentrator.

It is also usually possible to enter and retrieve textual information associated with the equipment, location or link, including technical, warranty and contact name information. Both the textual information and the information used to build the map are stored in a database. With an editable map, changing the map updates the database.

Device status is often indicated by colors, such as red for a serious problem, yellow for a minor problem and green for normal status.

Problem devices may also flash, and the console may beep to attract the network manager's attention.

In contrast, a nonhierarchical map shows the network in a single "flat" picture, usually at the lowest level of detail—that is, individual network devices and segments. Such a map is suitable only for managing relatively simple networks or portions of networks. Some network management utilities offer nonhierarchical maps.

Network Information Database

All platforms require some kind of database to store information about networks and network devices. For instance, the *NetWare Management System* (*NMS*) uses the NetWare standard Btrieve record handler, so any Btrieve application can access the management database. On the other hand, Hewlett-Packard does not include a user-accessible database in its *OpenView for Windows* product, although companies that create management platforms based on *OpenView* can add one if they wish.

Management Applications

Management applications are the heart of the management platform. Without applications, the platform is useless. The greater the breadth and depth of the management applications, the more valuable the platform. To support developers creating management applications, platform vendors offer application program interfaces (APIs) and developer's kits that simplify application.

The facilities available through the APIs largely determine the power of the management applications. For instance, Cabletron's *SPECTRUM*, a powerful, Unix-based platform, offers an "object modeling" feature that allows vendors to model the functioning of their devices in C++ code. With this feature, management applications no longer have to see devices as unstructured collections of parameters. They can see them as interrelated groups of parameters that form interrelated C++ objects and as C++ functions that reflect device functions. A "living model" of the managed device facilitates more powerful and sophisticated management.

Generic SNMP Management

A generic SNMP management application allows the management platform to manage any device that has an SNMP agent, without requiring a device-specific application. Generic SNMP management, in its most basic form, displays large numbers of (usually cryptic) variable names, accompanied by (usually difficult to interpret) values for those variables. Making sense of such a display requires study on the manager's part. Vendors may try to make this easier by allowing the manager to eliminate some variables from the display and to arrange the remaining variables into meaningful groups on the screen. (Some vendors call this screen-customizing feature "object modeling." However, it is entirely different from the type of object modeling discussed above.)

Almost every important network device now on the market can have an SNMP agent. Furthermore, SNMP is evolving to report on more features of more devices and to offer better supporting services, such as security. With study, work and screen customizing, generic SNMP can form the basis of a complete and highly sophisticated management system. However, something is almost always sacrificed by forgoing the vendor's device-specific management application. This is inevitable, because SNMP cannot define variables and appropriate values for every feature of every device on the market.

Vendors attempt to combine standardization and comprehensive support for device features by supporting the available SNMP variables and values appropriate to their device, and then "extending" SNMP with new variables and values that reflect unique product features. Variables are grouped into Management Information Bases (MIBs), and nonstandard variables and values make up "enterprise-specific" or proprietary MIBs. In order to access the information in MIBs, including proprietary MIBs, platforms may offer "MIB compilers" that examine MIBs and display variables and values.

Limitations of Generic SNMP

Generic SNMP allows the manager to do the following:

- Find devices communicating on the network

- Get baseline levels per device for various management parameters (e.g., traffic, errors); future levels can be compared to these baselines

- View the (usually arcane) names of MIB variables and the values those variables can take

All this is often of limited utility. Typically, there are hundreds of variables in any given MIB. The manager must know what type of device the MIB represents, what the values of the variables mean, which variables are most important and what to do in case of error conditions.

Autodiscovery

Autodiscovery is the process of automatically finding network devices, placing symbols on the network map, and inserting information in the database. This is a particularly important feature in large and dynamic networks, where otherwise it is impossible to determine what's on the network at any given moment.

Equally important in large and dynamic networks is the ability to limit autodiscovery. This is especially true for companies with TCP/IP connections to large public networks like the Internet, because without limits, the discovery process could take in hundreds of networks around the world. All the management platforms discussed in this chapter can limit discovery to a particular IP network number and its subnets, for instance. (For the *NetWare Management System*, this capability will be available starting with version 2.0.)

Agents

An agent is firmware or hardware that monitors a device or system and, when asked to or in case of emergency, forwards raw data, statistics or alarms to the management application. The agent usually resides in the managed device.

Alarms and Events

Alarms are triggered by user-defined thresholds. For instance, if a network adapter drops more than a certain number of packets per hour, the adapter agent might send an alarm to the console. Alarms may also be triggered by multiple thresholds in combination. Often, conditions that trigger alarms may be combined using Boolean logic—for instance, "If A is true, and B is true, but C is not true, then trigger an alarm." An expert system function working with the alarm system may analyze alarms, report possible causes of problems and suggest solutions.

An event is a message from the agent to the management station that reflects a normal condition rather than a fault condition.

Other Management Architectures

There are many network management products on the market today. Only a few of them are management platforms. Most are utilities, while a few are "managers of managers." The role of the management platform may be more clearly understood in relation to these other products.

Utilities

Most management products can be classified as utilities. Management utilities are much simpler and less expensive than platforms. They provide useful information—sometimes exactly the same information provided by management applications running on platforms. However, utilities don't usually offer detailed, integrated management of multivendor environments. Each utility typically focuses on just one vendor's products.

Managers of Managers

Another type of management product is the "manager of managers." There are very few of these. IBM's *NetView* is by far the most widely supported. DEC's *Polycenter Framework* (formerly *DECmcc*) and AT&T's *AccuMaster Integrator* are two other well-known managers of managers. Only *NetView* will be discussed here.

NetView, which runs on a mainframe, should not be confused with *NetView/6000*, which runs on IBM's RISC System 6000 (RS/6000). *NetView/6000* is a management platform for distributed, multiprotocol networks. Mainframe-based *NetView*, in contrast, offers a more centralized management approach and tends to be limited to managing Systems Network Architecture (SNA) networks. For instance, *NetView* offers no direct support for SNMP, the most important multivendor management protocol.

The basic function of *NetView* is to receive management information from a wide variety of devices and display it on a single screen. *NetView* provides highly sophisticated capabilities, such as expert system functionality. It's also complex and extremely expensive, in the range of $50,000 to $1 million. It provides integrated fault management for a broad range of equipment. However, it normally provides other kinds of management, such as configuration and performance management, for a limited range of equipment. In particular, *NetView* (or a similar product, *NetMaster*, from Systems Center Inc.) is nearly indispensable for day-to-day management of SNA networks. Perhaps because *NetView* evolved in a mainframe environment, it tends not to focus on PC LANs or Unix networks. (*NetView/6000*, on the other hand, does.)

In contrast to host-based management, the management platform approach is usually based on Unix, Windows or OS/2. (Since the platform has to run multiple programs simultaneously, it is most naturally based on a multitasking operating system and not on a single-tasking operating system like DOS.) Not surprisingly, the management platform, based in the PC and Unix environment and often created by a Unix or PC LAN vendor, tends to be more oriented toward providing detailed network management for PC and Unix LANs.

Management platforms can communicate with managers of managers, to provide them with summary or emergency information. Most platforms now include a gateway to *NetView*.

Management Platforms: Taking the Middle Ground

On the price-complexity scale, management platforms occupy a middle ground between simple, cheap utilities and complex, expensive managers of managers. The management platform also occupies a middle ground in terms of multivendor support. For instance, a single instance of *NetView* may receive information pertaining to products from virtually every network vendor across an entire enterprise. A utility usually gets information about one vendor's products only. A management platform typically gathers information about products from a limited number of vendors.

Selecting a Network Management Platform

In selecting a management platform for a particular network, major considerations usually include the platform operating system, the managed devices, the requirement for distributed management and connectivity to managers of managers.

The Platform Operating System

Most platforms run under Unix, Windows or OS/2. From the perspective of the operating systems they run under, there are two principles to consider when evaluating management platforms. First, if possible, select a management platform based on an operating system you already use and like. Second, the larger and more complex the network, the more robust and reliable the platform operating system needs to be.

"When you look at help desk and inventory management software, you find that you're looking at first-generation products. They are still far behind what we need to manage the kinds of networks that we've built."

— DIANE DANIELLE

Unfortunately, these two principles sometimes conflict. For instance, you may have a very large, complex network of Windows machines, with no Unix and no OS/2 workstations. However, both Unix and OS/2 make more reliable and robust platform operating systems than Windows 3.1 or DOS. In cases such as this, the network manager has to decide between the best management platform and the preferred operating system.

More fully featured network management platforms tend to be based on Unix, or sometimes OS/2. Less-expensive and simpler network management platforms tend to be based on Windows.

Windows itself is inexpensive and familiar to most PC users. However, historically, it has not offered the performance or stability that Unix has. Thus, for instance, HP (with *OpenView*) and Cabletron (with *SPECTRUM* and *Remote LANview*) provide both Windows and Unix-based management software—Unix for larger, more complex networks, and Windows for smaller, simpler networks. Windows NT may offer the performance and stability necessary for more powerful Windows-based network management platforms.

There are some OS/2-based management platforms, including IBM's version of the *NetWare Management System* (*NMS*) and Ungermann-Bass' *NetDirector*. OS/2 is technically comparable to Unix in providing a stable, high-power platform for network management software. However, developers of network management applications may be more inclined to develop for Unix due to the wider choice and greater maturity of development tools, the larger number of Unix-based management platforms and a larger available pool of Unix programmers.

Note that the platform operating system doesn't limit where agents can run. Agents can communicate with platforms as long as they're using the right protocol. Management applications may run under Unix or Windows, for instance, while agents run under proprietary, closed operating systems in devices, or under DOS or the Macintosh operating system.

Managed Devices

There are three approaches to matching management platforms to managed devices. First, select a management platform that has ready-made applications for the devices you need to manage. Second, if your network is very complex and the first approach is not possible, choose the platform that best matches your devices with ready-made applications and then create your own applications for other devices. These in-house applications are usually based on the platform's generic SNMP facility. Third, program all your own applications, based on the generic SNMP facility.

While the first two approaches tie you to vendors of particular devices (those for which you have ready-made applications), the third approach is more vendor-independent. For instance, you are not locked into a particular vendor's hubs because you need the vendor's hub management application. If you use only standard SNMP variables, they should apply equally to all vendor's hubs. This approach requires programming and detailed knowledge of management protocols and architectures. In addition, it provides "least common denominator" management by ignoring proprietary management features.

Distributed Management

Generally, distributed networks can benefit from distributed management. There are many kinds of distributed management. All the following activities might be referred to as distributed management:

- Multiple agents send data to a single console. Almost all management platforms are architected in this manner. Agents and console communicate using a protocol such as SNMP.

- One management platform queries another.

- A platform, agent or network processor reduces raw data to useful statistics close to the source of the data, and then passes those statistics to a management station. This reduces network traffic by transferring just statistics instead of raw data.

- One management platform passes alerts to another.

These different forms of distributed management have three basic benefits: First, they leverage processing resources by distributing processing. Second, they can economize network bandwidth. And third, they permit flexible deployment of management personnel. For instance, one person may manage the network in the New York office on a day-to-day basis, while an expert in Omaha may access the platform for specific problems or management areas.

Distributed management is supported within several high-end platforms, such as *SPECTRUM, HP OpenView Distributed Management Platform*, and Ungermann-Bass' *NetDirector*.

It is also possible to use management platforms from two or more vendors. Often, one vendor's platform is considered to be an integration platform, giving a network-wide overview as well as providing detailed management for a few types of devices, while other vendors' management platforms are considered to be element managers, restricted in scope to one or more limited classes of devices, such as NetWare devices. For example, on a LAN with NetWare, Sun SPARCstations, SynOptics hubs for local connectivity and Cisco routers for wide-area connectivity, you might use both *NMS* and *SunNet Manager*. *NMS* would manage the NetWare environment. *SunNet Manager* would manage the Sun workstations, the hubs and the routers; it would also manage *NMS* itself through SNMP. If you had Cabletron hubs and Wellfleet routers, you could employ a similar strategy with *NMS* and Cabletron's *SPECTRUM*. With Ungermann-Bass hubs and Wellfleet routers, UB's *NetDirector* and *NMS* might be a natural choice. Or, both *NetDirector* and *NMS* could report to *OpenView*.

Connectivity to Managers of Managers

For many users, connectivity to managers of managers is a checklist item that does not actually count for much in day-to-day operations. However, for users who are strategically focused on a manager of managers such as *NetView*, most management platforms provide a gateway to *NetView*.

Novell: The NetWare Management System

The *NetWare Management System* (*NMS*) is a Windows-based platform that focuses on NetWare LANs. It provides hierarchical mapping, alerts, a graphical user interface and a Btrieve database. Btrieve is the standard NetWare record handler. Btrieve databases can be accessed by higher-level Novell database products, such as NetWare SQL.

The *NMS* console software runs on a NetWare workstation. Agents run in devices. For instance, Novell provides a NetWare Management Agent as a NetWare Loadable Module (NLM) running in a NetWare (version 3.11 or higher) file server. The *NMS* also offers a generic SNMP capability.

NMS Components

The *NMS* has four major components: the NetWare Management Map (which is being renamed *NMS* Runtime), the NetWare Services Manager, the NetWare Management Agent and the SNMP Agent.

The NetWare Management Map

The NetWare Management Map is a Windows-based operating environment that provides the basic infrastructure for the *NetWare Management System*: an operating environment, centralized management functions and application program interfaces (APIs). "Snap-in" modules (management applications), from Novell or from third parties, run under the NetWare Management Map. The basic infrastructure features include autodiscovery, a centralized Btrieve database, a centralized alarm management system, and tools for displaying data.

The mapping function allows users to combine image files (such as floor plans or geographical maps) with *NMS* maps, which makes it easier to locate equipment visually. There is also a split-screen feature, allowing the manager to look at a detailed map of a network segment and a larger map showing how that segment fits into the network.

Autodiscovery is done through the NetExplorer NLMs, which run at one NetWare file server on the network, and the NetExplorer Manager, which runs under Windows at the management station. Optionally, you can install NetExplorer Plus NLMs on other servers to get more detailed information about those servers and the users that access them. NetExplorer can discover NetWare file servers and routers, OS/2 and DOS workstations running NetWare, third-party routers that have SNMP and Internet Protocol (IP) enabled, and Ethernet and token ring network segments. In addition, third-party developers can implement autodiscovery for their devices.

The discovery process starts with the server where the NetExplorer NLMs reside, proceeds to devices known to that server, then to devices known to those devices, and so on until the whole network is discovered. When discovery is complete, the NetExplorer Manager inserts new devices onto the map and into the database, and updates information about known devices. You can allow NetExplorer to run all the time, continually updating the map and database. However, on a large and volatile network, the disk activity involved in updating the database might interfere with other activities at the management station.

Currently, *NMS* offers only single-alarm thresholds. Compound IF-THEN Boolean logic for triggering alarms is not supported. There are five levels of alarms, three of which are represented on the map by green, yellow and red, and by different beeps. Other methods of delivering alarms, such as paging and e-mail, are not integrated into the system, but could be implemented through DDE or other NetWare APIs, such as the Message Handling Service (MHS).

The NetWare Services Manager

The NetWare Services Manager (NSM) is a Windows-based application for monitoring and managing NetWare file servers. NSM provides realtime data about all NetWare file servers (version 3.11 and above) that have a NetWare Management Agent. All the information that is available through standard NetWare management utilities is available through the NSM. NSM usually provides the information in a graphical form that makes it much easier to comprehend. For instance, memory allocation is displayed as a pie chart. In addition, NSM usually provides historical data, something the standard NetWare utilities don't. For instance, you can display a line chart showing bytes per second for file writes and reads, as well as outbound traffic, on a second-by-second basis. Some data is displayed via "gauges" that look like thermometers. For example, open files, logged-in users, current transactions and file locks can all be displayed in this way.

It would take pages to list all the information available through the NSM. You can monitor CPU utilization, determine what NLMs are loaded and see how much memory each NLM is using. You can determine volume size, how full the volume is and whether the volume is mirrored. Packet traffic, both received and sent, is monitored for various protocols. You can also monitor print servers; for example, you can see which file server a particular print server runs on, how many printers are attached and which printers are associated with each print queue.

The NetWare Management Agent

Novell's device-specific NLM for managing the NetWare file server is called the NetWare Management Agent (NMA). The NMA communicates with the NetWare Services Manager as well as the SNMP Agent. The NMA forwards statistics, such as memory usage and disk space, to the NetWare Services Manager for analysis and display. In addition, the NMA generates alarms based on user-defined thresholds. The NMA stores information in Btrieve format, making it potentially available to other Btrieve applications, including NetWare SQL.

The SNMP Agent

Novell's SNMP Agent runs at the server as an NLM. Its purpose is to allow devices managed under *NMS* to report to other SNMP-based platforms, such as *HP OpenView* or *SunNet Manager*. It is necessary to program another NLM to communicate with the SNMP Agent NLM. Novell provides the APIs and development tools that make it possible to write device-specific NLMs to communicate with the SNMP Agent.

Devices in the file server, such as uninterruptible power supplies or server-based hub cards, already have NLMs that can be "instrumented" to talk to the SNMP Agent. Devices outside the server may be able to communicate more efficiently through their own SNMP Agents directly to the other SNMP-based management platforms. Alternatively, devices outside the file server may benefit from communicating through the SNMP Agent, because they don't have to implement SNMP or the TCP/IP software that SNMP usually requires. For instance, Novell's *LANtern* network monitor communicates to the SNMP Agent, even though the monitor itself resides on the network, not in the file server.

The SNMP Agent used to be called the "Generic Agent" because it is not designed to manage any particular device or system. Instead, it acts as an intermediary between other platforms and the NetWare file server.

As the only management platform that focuses on NetWare, *NMS* is a natural platform choice for NetWare-centric environments. It is relatively inexpensive compared to the Unix-based network management platforms, particularly when you take operating system and hardware costs into account. Probably the main complaint about it has been that third parties have been slow to bring out *NMS* applications. However, support for *NMS* is growing, with vendors such as SynOptics, Cabletron, NetWorth and Compaq having announced applications.

Hewlett-Packard OpenView Products

Two separate and very different products are included under the name "*OpenView.*" One is Unix-based, running on either Sun or HP workstations, and very powerful. The other is Windows-based, less powerful, less expensive and much easier to use.

OpenView for Windows

HP does not sell *OpenView for Windows* as an end-user product. Instead, other vendors license the *OpenView for Windows* technology to produce their own management applications. *OpenView for Windows* has been used by companies like Cabletron and SynOptics to create relatively limited management platforms (SynOptics' *Basic Management* and *EZ-View,* and Cabletron's *Remote LANview)* that address equipment from just a few different vendors.

OpenView Distributed Management Platform

In contrast, HP sells its industrial-strength *OpenView SNMP Platform* and the *HP OpenView Distributed Management Platform* as products in their own right. Both HP and third parties create applications to run on these platforms. For instance, *Network Node Manager* is HP's application for TCP/IP management.

The *HP OpenView Distributed Management Platform* is a superset of the *OpenView SNMP Platform*. One major enhancement is an X/Open Management Protocol (XMP) application program interface (API). A relational database from Ingres, an ASK Company, which used to be available only with the *Distributed Management Platform*, is now available with both products. An advantage of the *Distributed Management Platform* is that it does not require any hardware other than the Unix workstation. In contrast, several hardware vendors offer distributed management based on their hardware. These are usually dependent on that hardware. For instance, the Cabletron Distributed Network Server requires the Cabletron hub.

The XMP Interface and Distributed Management

XMP is an element of the Open Software Foundation (OSF) Distributed Management Environment. OSF is an industry consortium for defining open multivendor standards that has been active primarily in Unix environments. Its Distributed Management Environment defines management APIs and applications for distributed networks. XMP is based on the Consolidated Management API (CM-API), developed by Groupe Bull and HP. HP's interface allows management applications written to the XMP API to use SNMP, CMOT (CMIP over TCP/IP) and CMIP over standard OSI. A major purpose of the XMP interface is to allow management applications running on different *OpenView* systems to communicate with one another. This is a basic requirement for distributed management, thus the name *Distributed Management Platform*.

IBM's AIX SystemView NetView/6000

NetView/6000 (now officially *AIX SystemView NetView/6000*) is a management platform that includes elements of HP's *OpenView Network Node Manager*, licensed from HP. To this basic core, IBM has added many features, including enhanced graphics, alarm filtering, enhanced auto-discovery and an enhanced SNMP agent.

NetView/6000 runs on IBM's RISC System/6000 (RS/6000) family, which runs AIX/6000, IBM's version of Unix for the RS/6000. *NetView/6000*'s role continues to grow. Integration with mainframe-based *NetView* is being continually enhanced, with applications such as AIX NetView Service Point, which provides a communications interface between *NetView/6000* and mainframe-based *NetView*. That interface is based on IBM's strategic peer-to-peer communications protocol, Advanced Program to Program Communications (APPC), also called Logical Unit 6.2 (LU6.2). In addition to advantages in integrating into IBM environments, *NetView/6000* is known for being easier to use and administer than many Unix-based management platforms.

In early releases, *NetView/6000* managed only TCP/IP networks and the IBM 6611 router. *AIX SystemView NetView/6000*, an enhanced version of *NetView/6000*, also manages token ring and Ethernet LANs, IBM hubs, RS/6000 systems and devices that support either SNMP or CMIP.

Early releases of *NetView/6000* did not offer APIs designed for third-party management applications. In *AIX SystemView NetView/6000*, the End User Interface API fills that role. There is also an SNMP API, which applications running in the *NetView/6000* environment can use to communicate with SNMP agents. Finally, *AIX SystemView NetView/6000* supports an XMP API.

However, *NetView/6000* has a lot of catching up to do when it comes to management applications. With third-party APIs dating only to the second half of 1992, *NetView/6000* is years behind *OpenView* and *SunNet Manager* in third-party support. However good the platform, it's the applications that really provide the value to users.

SunNet Manager

SunNet Manager, from SunConnect Inc., runs on Sun SPARCstations under SunOS, Sun's version of Unix. It is a natural platform for managing networks of Sun workstations. SunConnect is a subsidiary of Sun Microsystems Inc., the dominant Unix hardware vendor.

SunNet Manager is relatively simple and inexpensive for a high-end network management platform. For instance, both *SPECTRUM* and the Unix versions of *OpenView* have a richer graphical environment. However, *SunNet Manager* is also much less expensive than either HP's or Cabletron's offerings. Still, *SunNet Manager* offers all the basic platform capabilities: mapping, alerts, graphical tools and database.

SunConnect has a close relationship with leading router manufacturer Cisco Systems Inc., and with SynOptics Communications Inc., a leading manufacturer of intelligent LAN hubs. *CiscoWorks*, which was ported to *SunNet Manager* from Cisco's *NetCentral* management software, is a *SunNet Manager* application for managing Cisco routers. SynOptics's *Optivity* is a *SunNet Manager* application primarily focused on managing SynOptics hubs, but also extending to other vendors' bridges, routers and network adapter cards. Other vendors with *SunNet Manager* applications include 3Com and Wellfleet.

SPECTRUM

Cabletron sells two network management platforms. *SPECTRUM* is a high-end Unix-based system which Cabletron developed entirely on its own. *Remote LANView* is a simpler Windows-based product, based on *HP OpenView for Windows*. Both are oriented toward Cabletron hubs.

SPECTRUM is a very powerful, sophisticated and expensive management platform. It is particularly known for its excellent graphics, particularly when running on the Silicon Graphics line of graphics-optimized Unix workstations, which Cabletron recommends for *SPECTRUM*.

SPECTRUM should be of particular interest to managers who want to move management facilities out of SNA environments and into LAN environments, without sacrificing sophisticated management for SNA networks. Cabletron's *BlueVision* is an application designed to facilitate management of SNA networks from the *SPECTRUM* platform. This reverses the historical effort—largely unsuccessful—to bring LAN management to mainframes under products such as *NetView*. *NetView* is based largely on text messages, so a lot of user programming may be required to present and interpret *NetView* alerts. *BlueVision*, as a *SPECTRUM* application, is highly visual. (Cabletron also provides a *NetView* gateway for those who want to manage LAN-based equipment from mainframes.)

10 / The Foreseeable Future of Network Management

Operating Systems
High-Speed Desktop Links
SNMP Version 2
Continuous, Discontinuous Change
Network Management Strategies

Books about personal computer technology sometimes have short half-lives because of the rate at which the subject changes. This chapter first marks the point of development the technology had reached when it was written so that a reader can tell whether or not to expect the book to be aware of particular new developments. Next, it considers some of the predictable changes that are likely in the next few years and explores their impact on network management. Finally, it discusses strategies that organizations can use to maximize future productivity with network management tools.

This chapter was written in mid-1993. Several significant developments are on the verge of announcement or have just been introduced. These products or standards were not widely enough implemented to be discussed in the body of the book. They are mentioned here so that readers can readily find out what the book covers and not waste time looking for subjects not covered, and to indicate just how quickly the technology of PC network management is changing.

Operating Systems

The middle of 1993 marks several important changes in PC operating system technology. Version 4.0 of Novell NetWare is perhaps the most significant in the short term. Multiserver network administration is a much easier task on an operating system with centralized directory services, such as those provided by NetWare version 4.0 and Banyan VINES. (Network users, of course, also find a network with central directory services easier to navigate and understand.) Version 4.0 also includes security and auditing enhancements, new graphical administration tools, additional utilities for identifying faults and gauging performance on NetWare servers and improved backup capabilities. Most of the new capabilities cannot reach back into the installed base of NetWare 3.X and 2.X, however. Thus many organizations will need to make complicated decisions with time-consuming and expensive consequences.

On the workstation, the era of the 32-bit operating system is about to begin. Microsoft has announced Windows NT; Sun, Novell and NeXT have begun shipping new versions of Unix for Intel processors; Apple is shipping a Unix version for Macintoshes and preparing a wide array of new desktop operating systems; IBM's OS/2 is up to version 2.1 and proving to be flexible, capable and reliable. Because these new desktop operating systems were developed in an environment that included high-speed networks connected to the desktop, and because the target computers are so much more powerful than the original IBM PCs and Macintoshes that DOS and the Mac System were designed for, there is a good chance that these platforms will work seamlessly on existing networks. The support job will certainly grow anyway, as the world's network managers discover all the devices—CD-ROM readers, fax servers, scanners, backup drives and so forth—that have trouble supporting the new desktop operating systems.

Ideally, network management applications software would run on an operating system powerful enough to make the most of the machines it runs on. In practice, many network management utilities run only on MS-DOS, both because DOS makes up the largest installed base of network nodes and because it is difficult for a software developer (or anyone else) to predict which advanced 32-bit operating system will prove to be the most popular.

Two of the management platforms best supported by third parties—Hewlett-Packard's *OpenView* and Novell's *NetWare Management System*—make use of Windows, while some organizations have decided to use OS/2 for their internally developed management applications. Organizations with Unix installed may find that their best option is to take advantage of applications built around Sun's *SunNet Manager* or the Unix versions of *OpenView*.

High-Speed Desktop Links

Multiple competing standards for 100Mbits/sec Ethernet running on copper rather than optical cabling have been proposed to the appropriate standards bodies. At this writing, the standard has not been defined. It is clear, however, that high-capacity links are possible without running fiber-optic cabling to the desktop. Organizations with users who require more bandwidth than the existing technologies can provide will want to begin investing in cable-testing equipment that can cope with these upcoming standards, or at least be upgraded to support them.

SNMP Version 2

SNMP has been criticized for its security shortcomings. Security enhancements are among the principal improvements in SNMP version 2, which is nearing approval by the Internet standards committees. Applications built around the new version will be able to send requests and commands to SNMP version 1 agents, but version 1 applications will be unable to take advantage of the new capabilities in version 2. Network managers should plan ahead by using upgradable agents wherever possible.

Continuous and Discontinuous Change

One class of changes is reasonably predictable, with indicators that follow linear, exponential or some other kind of continuous curve. It will not surprise anyone if the cost of 1 MIPS, 16 megabytes of RAM or 100 megabytes of mass storage declines in accordance with historic trends. The other class of changes can be identified by indicators with discontinuities. People say that sales "fell off a cliff" or that "demand skyrocketed." Discontinuous changes are difficult to predict by their nature, but thinking about them in advance may enable managers to respond more quickly and appropriately than they might otherwise.

The following list of continuous changes to be expected over the next five to ten years should be unexceptionable to most readers:

- Organizations will be forced to cut costs wherever they can.
- PC and workstation platforms will become less costly faster than mainframe and minicomputer platforms will.
- Organizations will migrate more and more data and applications to networked PC and workstation platforms.
- Fault prevention, isolation and remedy will become ever more critical to these PC and workstation networks.

- Organizations will be compelled to control the costs of administering, managing and troubleshooting networks.
- To provide optimal returns on their network investment, organizations will tend to manage performance systematically.
- As organizations that are careless about security matters pay high penalties for their mistakes, network security will be managed more tightly and efficiently.

Discontinuous changes are by their nature difficult to anticipate. A few technologies and practices have been widely discussed and anticipated without producing huge financial results compared to the volume of the networking business or the PC business overall. These subjects include mobile computing, multimedia and high-speed wide area network technology.

Mobile Computing and Network Management

Remote connections to PC networks that use the switched public telephone network are usually nightmares for network managers. Fault identification and troubleshooting are time-consuming, difficult and not well served by good tools. Configurations are tricky, unreliable and support-intensive. Performance as LAN users know it is inevitably poor on a remote connection. Network managers usually feel that remote connections expose their networks to every fiendish system cracker in the world, and this conclusion is not unjustified.

On the other hand, the demand is growing rapidly for simple, reliable, secure links to the network from notebook computers, subnotebooks, palmtops, personal digital assistants, pen-based computers and other kinds of portable computing devices. The opportunity to cut the costs of real estate, facilities and furnishings by equipping the workforce with portable network nodes is tremendous. Whether or not the office of the future is paperless, it is very likely that many future offices will be officeless.

Asynchronous links with modems will most likely make up the lion's share of this kind of mobile digital communicating for at least a few more years. Whether or not the remote node has a cellular radio link to the phone system, the fundamentally cantankerous combination of quasi-standard serial ports, competing modem protocols and difficult-to-use communications software will have to be managed for years to come. Store-and-forward messaging technologies have many of the same problems of lack of standardization, clumsy administration tools and inadequate troubleshooting tools.

The developer who delivers a truly transparent method of connecting mobile computers to an organization's network such that the link is manageable and secure could be the next Bill Gates. The fact that neither Novell, Microsoft, IBM, Apple, AT&T, Hayes, nor anyone else has come close to this ideal indicates just how difficult the challenge is. In the absence of such a product, developers could also get rich by developing diagnostic and administration tools that, for example, indicate clearly, quickly and consistently which stage of a remote connection is the source of trouble.

Without greatly improved automated tools for remote network links, huge numbers of salespeople, writers and illustrators, editors, marketing specialists, auditors, accountants and other "knowledge workers" will have to be trained to be specialists in telephone/modem/serial, cable/communications, port/communications, software technology. Furthermore, another host of new jobs will appear to answer the support queries these people generate.

Network managers can anticipate the increased demands that mobile or pervasive computing will impose on them. They should begin to train themselves on remote network connection technology, install some pilots to get hands-on experience with the problems, test potential alternatives, search insistently for better tools, standardize on a platform configuration that can keep up with future changes and learn state-of-the-art deep breathing exercises so they can control their tempers in the face of the endless silly (and hard) support questions to come.

Multimedia and Network Management

The concept of multimedia is a knot with many strands running in and out of it. It adds the new data presentation options of digitized sound and digitized video to the traditional options of text and graphics. The associated technologies include video and audio compression, speech recognition, computer-generated voices and other sounds, video editing, computer animation and high-capacity storage media such as CD-ROM and videodisc. The applications most often associated with multimedia include videoconferencing, computerized phone answering, interactive training and public information kiosks. Document management systems intended to replace paper filing systems make use of some of the same devices and capacities as multimedia. The movement to integrate such office equipment as PBXs, copy machines and faxes with personal computer networks also overlaps with multimedia.

Multimedia applications that run over long distances are more compelling than those that stand alone. There are three potential media for interconnecting digitized images and sounds: electromagnetic broadcast, the telephone system and the cable TV system. The bandwidth required for widespread point-to-point digital video over the airwaves will probably never be available, but cable operators are jockeying to compete with the phone companies for many future digital services. As a result, there are many fabulous alliances forming among the usual partners from the network world (IBM, Microsoft, AT&T, Intel, Apple) and participants that are quite unfamiliar: Tele-Communications, the largest cable operator in the United States; Time-Warner, the second-largest cable operator and a major publisher, film and music studio owner and film and video library owner; Scientific Atlanta, a major producer of cable converter boxes. It is conceivable that the key application to drive down the cost of near-universal high-bandwidth networking is the interactive selection of home video.

It seems unlikely that the requirement for videoconferencing and animated presentations in the workplace will drive the development of high-bandwidth networking in most organizations. But once the infrastructure is in place for the home, organizations may well decide to take advantage of it, particularly if home offices play a larger and larger role in the way people work.

Multimedia, and digital video in particular, is the set of general-purpose technologies most likely to demand network capacities that exceed those in place today. That is not to say that most organizations need such capacities now, or in the foreseeable future. Network managers should pay attention to the potential for change that multimedia represents, but they will doubtless face many problems with greater immediate consequences.

High-Speed WAN Technology

Many manufacturers and wide area network service providers have announced products that provide increased speed. Some of these new services are Integrated Services Digital Network (ISDN), Frame Relay, Switched Multimegabit Data Services (SMDS) and Asynchronous Transfer Mode (ATM). While the highest-performing of these services would be necessary for carrying such bandwidth-greedy data types as online high-resolution digital video, the speed and capacity of these new services (and the hardware required to take advantage of them) would more likely be necessary to support many users with more mundane applications across a WAN.

Distributed databases, large workflow applications, still-image transfer and high-volume messaging are all application areas that are implemented now and certain to grow as rapidly as these new services can support them.

Most of the interface boards and routers for these high-speed services have been developed recently enough that their manufacturers understand the need for built-in management capabilities. Network managers should insist on soundly implemented SNMP agents and support for their chosen management platform as they plan to acquire this equipment.

Network managers will also be likely to resist installing the more esoteric of these technologies when they are not truly driven by the organization's needs. Prices can be expected to come down rapidly as production volumes grow and the technology matures. In addition, it is always easier to let others make the mistakes that allow learning to take place.

Network Management Strategies

A few basic principles can help guide organizations through the difficult decisions that must be made in a turbulent environment. Standardization, in several forms, is a crucial process for enhancing network management. Defining the right time to clear out an installed base that has become an obstacle is another important process to master. Finally, the practices of continuous improvement that can raise the performance of other parts of organizations will work for network management, too.

Standardization

One of the principal strategic commitments an organization can make is to subscribe to widely accepted standards whenever possible.

For most cabling and data link-level decisions, public standards are reasonably stable, and change is orderly. While there are no approved standards in place for managing desktop devices or network printers, consensus on these matters is close as this book is being written. SNMP will clearly be the management protocol best supported by the manufacturers of network hardware and software for the foreseeable future. In any functional area, unnecessary multiplicity of supported standards means additional complexity and incremental expense.

A second form standardization takes is in the uniformity of the various network nodes: What hardware and software is permissible for users? How do users load software? Where do users keep data? No outside authority like the accepted standards organizations can establish guidelines for this kind of uniformity, but there is no question that fault detection, spare parts handling, verifying correct configurations, inventory-related activities, performance monitoring and all kinds of administration can be achieved only as efficiently as the proliferation of product types is constrained.

A third form of standardization applies to management practices: Are administration, backup and virus protection centralized or decentralized? Is there a unified help desk system for tracking incidents and their solutions, escalating problems and dispatching troubleshooting and repair resources?

A fourth form of standardization is unifying the management console based on one of the network management software platforms. This kind of project may demand a multiyear commitment, and upfront expenses may possibly be higher than for a collection of unrelated utilities. Nevertheless, the long-term payoff in efficiency and reduced training costs is likely sufficient to produce an acceptable or better return on investment.

Turning Over the Installed Base

The unprecedented rate of change in the PC networking market-place can make decisions that appear promising at first glance turn out to be unwise and vice versa. For example, one cost-conscious organization migrated hundreds of its old 286-based CPUs into wiring closets to serve as NetWare-based store-and-forward messaging servers. In the course of a couple of months, the data flow from new applications increased the traffic over these systems by an order of magnitude that resulted in abominable performance for all messaging applications. Suddenly the messaging server needed to be a fast 486 machine instead of a slow 286, and the recycled machines were probably a false economy.

The installed base can shackle an organization's future. Sometimes planning, competitive bidding and standardization are unable to ensure that the system can remain competitive in the light of changes in the marketplace. The whole cable plant, or all the routers, or all the servers may need to be rooted out and replaced with equipment that can do the job.

Outsourcing

It is natural to be proud of our own problem-solving abilities and achievements. But in an unforgiving world economy, it is necessary to compare our efficiency with that of similar organizations and farm out any functions that cannot be justified as either less costly than anyone else can do them or of such strategic import that the organization must learn to do them cost-effectively. For example, small remote offices may not justify a full-time network trouble-shooter. The workload may not even justify a part-time administrator. An outside organization may provide superior support for a lower overall cost. Help desk and repair services may also be difficult for organizations to perform themselves at as low a cost as the market rate for outside providers.

Adding Value for Customers

Network management people will ultimately be held to the same standard as every other employee in the world: Am I engaged in activities that, day-in and day-out, a customer is willing to pay for? Network management customers are mostly internal, the organization's users and management. However, the spread of such applications as e-mail, Electronic Data Interchange and remote order processing leads to more and more circumstances where the PC network is expected to serve external customers directly. Whether the customers are internal or external, their perception of the availability and performance of their applications, and by extension the network, is the ultimate arbiter of whether or not the network is managed well.

Customer satisfaction is a concept foreign to many of those engaged in network management activities. Some of the reasons for this state of affairs are readily understandable. Many of the jobs in network management are highly stressful, with desperate customers, long hours, constant interruptions and limited resources in the way of tools and budget. Customers may not thank the network management staff for staying late to upgrade the routers or for recovering files after a disk crash. In spite of the difficulty of the task and the lack of appreciation, network managers must ensure that customers feel well taken care of. Common areas for improvement often include assured help desk access for any time people may be using the network; clear escalation procedures for unresolved problems and major breakdowns; orderly scheduling of limited resources so that the rest of the organization can plan for change; and tracking successful tricks, eliminated faults and past performance problems in order to leverage local experience for the future.

The practices of total quality control and continuous improvement can certainly be applied to network management practices. Because management software applications can readily capture many kinds of data about the network, measuring problems often is simple. Encouraging systematic, incremental improvements to the network can ultimately lead to significant competitive advantages as well as a more confident network management staff and more satisfied internal and external customers. While much of the literature on quality improvement is focused on manufacturing, articles and books that consider applying these practices to services have begun to appear. There is no fundamental difference between building products and delivering services as far as continuous improvement techniques are concerned.

The rest of the organization can make the job of the network management group easier by alerting them to significant upcoming changes that will affect network resources, by supporting user training efforts that can prevent unnecessary support calls and perhaps by decentralizing routine administration chores. Most of all, the organization's management must take network management sufficiently seriously to support it properly, with enough people, training and budgetary resources to ensure that the network, and all the functions that come to depend on it, will thrive.

PART FOUR

Appendices

Appendix A
Contributors

Ellen Becker, Senior Systems Analyst for a large multispecialty, nonprofit health care organization

In the fall of 1992, Ellen Becker was assigned to manage a new token ring network using Novell NetWare 3.11 for seven outpatient surgery rooms to be built in a new wing of one of the organization's clinics. The system is customized and used by many hospitals. In this case it is used for scheduling of the six rooms used by providers and anesthesiologists; it also tracks inventory, compiles preference cards and picks lists as well as tracking preoperative, intro-operative and postoperative data regarding each case. The surgery rooms have the capacity for 1,500 procedures, from cataract removal to tonsillectomies, tubal ligations and hernias. The network also connects to the other five metropolitan clinics and the company's administration mainframe.

James Brentano, Network Specialist at a West Coast utility company

The company's network uses 433 servers—all Banyan VINES—with more than 150 subnets to connect more than 20,000 personal computers, most of them IBM-compatible. It is one of the three largest VINES networks in the world. The environments are varied, ranging from sophisticated to primitive. In downtown San Francisco, there are 7,000 PCs networked with fiber optics to PCs at hydroelectric plants throughout the state, and with bridges to construction sites in other remote areas. The department does a lot of training and tutorials, which is one way to maintain control over such a large and diverse population of users.

Diane Danielle, networking writer and consultant, Danielle Associates
The president of Danielle Associates, a LAN consulting firm located in Berkeley, Diane Danielle has nine years of data processing experience, working with both mainframes and LANs, at a major university and with one of the country's largest financial institutions. She has also written for a variety of LAN-related publications. Formerly a LAN columnist for *PC Week*, she has been a monthly columnist and contributing editor for *Network Computing* magazine since October 1990. Her expertise covers LAN backup, SNA gateways, e-mail and network printing. She was the first president of the Northern California Focus Users Group (NCFUSE), has been on the boards of the International NetWare Users Group (now NUI) and the Affiliation of NetWare Users (ANU), is an active member of the San Francisco NetWare users group, and is on the Northern California Netucon Advisory Board.

Alex del Rio, Contract Network Manager for a home care nursing organization
This Houston-based home care nursing organization has 35 Banyan file servers and 400 PCs nationally. Originally a programmer at the company, and later an in-house network manager, Alex del Rio now provides the company with contracted network management services through a third-party organization.

Joe Estrada, Support Services Manager for an international chemical manufacturing corporation
Working out of a regional office in Houston, Joe Estrada's division is in charge of engineering major projects related to the chemical manufacturing process. This division has a 60-node Novell network, with TCP/ IP-based connection to an IBM RS/6000 Oracle server. The division is connected to a nationwide WAN primarily via Wellfleet routers.

Dave Fogle, LAN Development Group, ComputerLand Corporation
For several years, Dave Fogle provided the principal network support for ComputerLand Corporation's Marketing Department at the company's headquarters in Pleasanton, California. The network connected more than 100 users of both DOS-based and Macintosh equipment. He is currently working on a variety of projects to enhance communications across the company's nationwide network of 300-plus branches, distribution centers and service facilities.

Arthur Grant, an IS officer for a major commercial development corporation

Arthur Grant is in charge of a 2,000-user Novell network for the company's international locations. The network is router-based, using Cisco routers—there are 10 router nodes. Other nodes are attached via direct X.25 services. The company was strongly mainframe oriented through the mid-1980s, then began to downsize. In 1988 it went to client-server architectures, and as of today, 80 percent of the mainframe applications have moved to alternate platforms. The network is expected to expand fivefold, to 10,000 users, within 3 years.

Randy Howland, Network Manager for a Fortune 500 technology company

Randy Howland belongs to that part of the MIS department that develops common systems for the entire engineering division. His group evaluates workstations and network architectures for delivery of these common systems. They have installed and implemented LAN services at their own site, with the intention of propagating standards across the company.

Dennis Roberts, Team Leader of Network Services, Toledo Hospital

Currently, the Toledo Hospital maintains 17 networks, with 230 PCs on various network segments (ARCnet, Ethernet and token ring). The network grew according to the needs of individual departments, without an overall direction. Dennis Roberts is now instituting a Hospital Information Network, involving a shared backbone and a coherent upgrade/migration plan.

Lawrence Sachartoff, Sr. Technical Analyst for an international petrochemical firm

Lawrence Sachartoff has worked with computers for more than 21 years. He started in computer electronics in the Air Force, went into minicomputers, then became a tech support person for a reseller and took Novell training for the company. He is currently a LAN consultant at a refinery operated by a large petrochemical company. He is responsible for supporting a campus-wide LAN that includes 10 servers and more than 400 nodes, with TCP/IP connectivity to Sun, DEC and HP Unix systems. The system connects personnel involved in refinery production, refinery management, document handling, engineering and administration.

Jane Shea, Senior Network Analyst, AmSys Telemanagement

In her current position, Jane Shea specializes in integrating high-availability, mission-critical LAN/WAN applications. Previously she was a network specialist with Advanced Cardiovascular Systems, a medical equipment design and manufacturing firm based in Santa Clara, California. There she was responsible for the design, purchase, installation, configuration, security and maintenance of a 1,500-node network located across five sites in Northern California. This Network included 10 Novell 3.11 fileservers, several OS/2 database servers and 15 Sun nodes providing SNA and TCP/IP connectivity to LAN and standalone Mac/PC systems. Ms. Shea supervised 17 departmental LAN Administrators who coordinated systems implementation and upgrades, and managed service calls as well as MIS network projects and specialized training.

Richard Sherkin, MIS Manager, Biltrite Industries

Biltrite Industries of Toronto sells customized rubber compounds to shoe manufacturers, auto makers and other companies. The production process requires intensive statistical analysis and reporting. Richard Sherkin had originally installed two LANs and developed 30 *Clipper* applications to monitor and analyze data. Later, the company decided to move the data from *Clipper* to a SQL Base server, with *Forest and Trees* as a front-end query tool. The network is now composed of 35 nodes and uses two topologies, Ethernet and ARCnet.

John Thomas, Microcomputer Supervisor at a home improvement supply company

This West Coast-based company maintains retail outlets in seven states. The company recently redesigned its system to rely on file servers, and is currently expanding the network by connecting individual PCs to file servers in five locations throughout the corporate headquarters building. Approximately 150 end-users in the building are networked via small servers and one SQL database server.

Fred Vincent, Security Auditor for a public utility company

Jerry White, Network Manager at a major West Coast financial institution

Jerry White began managing LANs for a major West Coast financial institution for a 4megabyte token ring network using Novell 2.15. The network served 40 users and then expanded to a WAN for 300 users, using Novell routers. His current project involves a 10BASE-T network with Novell 3.11. The network currently serves 150 users and is being carefully documented before expansion by the end of 1993 to 5,000 users.

Appendix B
Commonly Encountered Protocols and the OSI Reference Model

	Open Systems Interconnect Protocols		Internet and Unix Protocols	Systems Network Architecture
Application Layer (LEVEL 7)	File Transfer, Access and Management (FTAM) Directory (CCITT X.500) Network Management Message-Handling Service (CCITT X.400) Distributed Transaction Processing	ISO 8571 ISO 9594 ISO 9595/96 ISO 10020/21 ISO 10026	Simple Network Management Protocol (SNMP) File Transfer Protocol (FTP) Telnet Simple Message Transfer Protocol (SMTP) Network File System (NFS)	Transaction Services
Presentation Layer (LEVEL 6)	Connection-Oriented Presentation Protocol Connectionless Presentation Protocol	ISO 8823 ISO 9576	External Data Representation (XDR)	Presentation Services
Session Layer (LEVEL 5)	Connection-oriented Session Protocol Connectionless Session Protocol	ISO 8237 ISO 9548	Remote Procedure Call (RPC)	Data Flow Control
Transport Layer (LEVEL 4)	Connection-oriented Transport Protocol Connectionless Transport Protocol	ISO 8073 ISO 8602	Transmission Control Protocol (TCP) User Datagram Protocol (UDP)	Transmission Control
Network Layer (LEVEL 3)	X.25 Connectionless Protocol End System to Intermediate System Exchange Protocol (ES-IS)	ISO 8208 ISO 8473 ISO 9542	Internet Protocol (IP) Address Resolution Protocol (ARP) Internet Control Message Protocol (ICMP)	Path Control

Data Link Layer (LEVEL 2)	Logical Link Control Sub-Layer
	Media Access Control Sub-Layer
	  CSMA/CD
	  Token Bus
	  Token Ring
	  FDDI
		ISO 8802.2, IEEE 802.2
		
		ISO 8802/3, IEEE 802.3
		ISO 8802/4, IEEE 802.4
		ISO 8802/5, IEEE 802.5
		ISO 9314
				Data Link Control

Physical Layer (LEVEL 1)	CSMA/CD Token Bus Token Ring FDDI Slotted Ring	ISO 8802/3, IEEE 802.3 ISO 8802/4, IEEE 802.4 ISO 8802/5, IEEE 802.5 ISO 9314 ISO 8802/7		Physical Control

Novell NetWare	AppleTalk	LAN Manager	Banyan VINES
NetWare Core Protocols (NCP) Service Advertising Protocol (SAP)	AppleTalk Filing Protocol (AFP)	Server Message Block (SMB)	Server Message Block (SMB) StreetTalk Directory Services
	AppleTalk Session Protocol (ASP) AppleTalk Data Stream Protocol (ADSP) Zone Information Protocol (ZIP) Printer Access Protocol (PAP)	Named Pipes	
Sequenced Packet Exchange (SPX) Transmission Control Protocol (TCP) User Datagram Protocol (UDP)	AppleTalk Transaction Protocol (ATP) AppleTalk Echo Protocol (AEP) Name Binding Protocol (NBP) Routing Table Maintenance Protocol (RTMP)	Network Adapter Basic Input/Output System (NetBIOS) Transmission Control Protocol (TCP) User Datagram Protocol (UDP)	Interprocess Communications Protocol (ICP) Sequenced Packet Protocol (SPP) Transmission Control Protocol (TCP) User Datagram Protocol (UDP)
Internetwork Packet Exchange (IPX) Internet Protocol (IP) Address Resolution Protocol (ARP) Internet Control Message Protocol (ICMP)	Datagram Delivery Protocol (DDP)	NetBIOS Extended User Interface (NetBEUI) Internet Protocol (IP) Address Resolution Protocol (ARP) Internet Control Message Protocol (ICMP)	Vines Internet Protocol (Vines IP) Vines Routing Update Protocol (RTP) Vines Address Resolution Protocol (Vines ARP) Vines Internet Control Protocol (ICP) Internet Protocol (IP) Address Resolution Protocol (ARP) Internet Control Message Protocol (ICMP)
	LocalTalk Link Access Protocol (LLAP) EtherTalk Link Access Protocol (ELAP) TokenTalk Link Access Protocol (TLAP)		

Appendix C
SNMP and Management Information Bases

What SNMP Attempts

The Internet was the first large-scale network linking together heterogeneous components from many competing manufacturers. As such, it became a natural proving ground for schemes to supply standardized management information from these many components. SNMP (the Simple Network Management Protocol) is the present form these attempts have taken.

SNMP is a protocol, a set of rules for requesting, packaging and transporting management information over a network. These rules are spelled out in Internet documents called RFCs (Requests for Comments). RFC 1157 from May 1990 is the definition of a Simple Network Management Protocol. Other RFCs define the structure of management information and define SNMP Management Information Bases (MIBs). This discussion concentrates on SNMP as an application-layer (level 7 of the OSI reference model) protocol, although the original SNMP specification also includes level 4 (transport layer) and level 3 (network layer) protocols.

The SNMP vision includes multiple independent components in different places, connected by a network, communicating with more-or-less centralized managing applications. The vision is sufficiently general to include not only routers, hubs, monitoring devices and gateways, but also network interface boards, servers, multiplexers, modems, software processes and practically anything else—the expressions of offbeat Internet humor include an SNMP-controlled toaster.

Compared to ordinary mainframe or LAN applications, an SNMP application is in many respects an extremely ambitious project. Hundreds, if not hundreds of thousands, of connected devices must execute their pieces of an SNMP system; in technical terms, SNMP management applications are distributed applications and SNMP commands are a restricted form of remote procedure calls. While a central managing process will maintain a database of management information, SNMP applications are not classic client-server applications. In fact, each SNMP device is both a client and a server for other devices and processes. While data may be gathered and stored in individual devices, it is available in realtime to the managing application. Thus the SNMP challenge was to provide: 1) a universal structure of management information that was as complete as possible, but also allowed for enhancements by individual manufacturers; 2) a mechanism to transport this information over the network; 3) a set of commands for programmers who develop management applications; and 4) a sufficiently compact implementation of these mechanisms that the overhead costs would not impede wide acceptance.

Much of the work in defining the structure of management information proceeded cooperatively with the OSI network management committees. The OSI standards (CMIP, CMIS, and others) have not been implemented nearly as widely as SNMP, although there are those in the industry who expect them to dominate the field someday.

At the most tangible level, SNMP is a set of rules for software developers who want to write multivendor distributed management applications. It is the only standard today that is widely implemented on the kinds of devices normally used on networks of PCs.

Terms and Concepts

The next several sections describe the logical and syntactical underpinnings of SNMP. The terminology and way of operating will be familiar to those who are acquainted with object-oriented programming. It will probably be quite foreign to those who are not. As many other computer-related topics do, the field of network management standards takes over perfectly meaningful, but very abstract, words from ordinary language, and uses them with precise technical meanings. The technical uses of these terms may be similar to the ordinary meaning, they may be unrelated to the ordinary meaning or they may even be the opposite of what you would expect based on the ordinary meaning. There is no agreed-upon way to italicize or highlight these special uses of words, though I attempt to put in reminders when it seems appropriate. The best way to get a grip on these concepts is to begin with the assumption that everything you know is wrong.

Name Registration

You may remember the old story that has inmates eating dinner in a prison, telling jokes to one another by standing up and saying a number. The jokes were so familiar that everyone laughed just as though the whole joke had been told. The Internet (in fact, the ISO and CCITT too—all the relevant standards organizations) has a system for registering names. Once names are registered, everyone can use numbers in place of names, making it possible to refer to significant things precisely and compactly.

Names are registered in a hierarchy (see Figure C-1); therefore a sequence of integers can unambiguously identify a name. The standard names are published and available for developers to use. There are branches of the name registration hierarchy reserved for proprietary use, too.

Figure C-1 ISO Naming Hierarchy

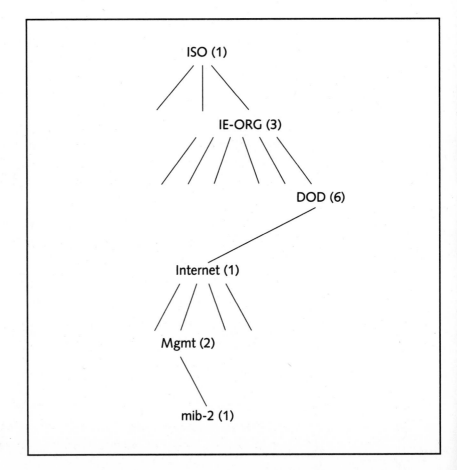

ISO	IE-ORG	DOD	Internet	Mgmt	mib-2	system	sysUpTime
1	3	6	1	2	1	1	3

Thus the sequence "1.3.6.1.2.1.1.3" is the equivalent of the name, "sysUpTime." The shorthand expression "system 3" could also be used to refer to "sysUpTime". A sequence of numbers in the format "1.3.6.1.2.1.1.3" is formally called an "object identifier."

ISO	IE-ORG	DOD	Internet	Mgmt	mib-2	interfaces	ifTable	ifType	fddi
1	3	6	1	2	1	2	1	3	15

This object identifier, "1.3.6.1.2.1.2.1.3.15", which could also be identified as "ifType 15," is the equivalent of the object "fddi."

Objects

Each registered name refers to an object. The term *object* has a technical meaning here. Each object is defined precisely by the standards documents. An object is a logical entity that may have various kinds of data associated with it and may also exhibit certain behaviors. For example, an object that is named "ipRouteAge" (also known as "1.3.6.1.2.1.4.21.1.10") has an associated text string that describes it (e.g., "The number of seconds since this route was last updated or otherwise determined to be correct..."), as well as an associated integer indicating how long the object has been active since it was last changed (e.g., "10,001" seconds), and an associated behavior that would respond to a properly formatted message by changing its value (perhaps resetting it to 0).

Managed Objects

The name "managed object" would lead an unsuspecting person to conclude that it refers to an entity that needs managing, such as a hub or server. SNMP is actually rather indifferent to these sorts of entities—ordinary devices or processes. It deals with a much higher level of abstraction, leaving concerns for devices and processes to actual implementations; i.e., specific management application software.

Managed objects are the objects in the management branch of the official SNMP naming tree. (Their full registered names all begin "1.3.6.1.2.1...") The formal definition of each managed object has five parts:

- *Object*, which is the name or descriptor of the object. (*Object* example: "ipRouteAge")

- *Syntax*, which specifies the form of the data. Possible entries can include INTEGER, OCTET STRING (octets are eight-bit characters), TimeTicks (hundredths of seconds), and lists of values from which one integer or other value may be chosen. The COUNTER data type is an integer that can only increase. The GAUGE data type is an integer that can decrease as well as increase. Other objects in the registration hierarchy can be identified as OBJECT IDEN-TIFIERs. The Syntax of a managed object is expressed in a standardized notation system known as ASN.1 (Abstract Syntax Notation 1). (*Syntax* example: "INTEGER")

- *Definition*, which provides a text description of the object. (*Definition* example: "A textual description of the entity. This value should include the full name and version identi-fication of the system's hardware type, software operating-system, and networking software. It is mandatory that this only contain printable ASCII characters.")

- *Access*, which indicates whether the managed object is read-only, write-only, read-write, or not accessible. (*Access* example: "read-only")

- *Status*, which indicates whether the object is mandatory, optional, or obsolete. (*Status* example: "mandatory")

MIBs

The Management Information Base or MIB is the template SNMP uses to describe the elements of data that will be captured and transported in a management application. Managed objects are the elemental components of a MIB. The MIB is, first of all, part of the SNMP standards definition, although the database that is inevitably *implemented* by a management application will usually be called a Management Information Base, too. RFC 1213 of March 1991 defines MIB-2, the most current version of the general SNMP MIB. RFC 1155 of May 1990 defined the first SNMP MIB.

Managed objects in MIB-2 are clustered into eleven groups. These eleven groups include:

- The system group. The objects in this group provide administrative information about an entity that is to be managed. The system group objects are mandatory for all entities, but not all system group objects must have values.

- The interfaces group. The interfaces objects are concerned with the layer below the network layer—the logical link control and media access control sublayers of the data link layer. They are also mandatory for all entities. Since an entity may have multiple interfaces, the structure of the group permits multiple rows of attributes, one row for each interface.

- The address translation group. This obsolete group was carried over to MIB-2 from MIB-1 for backward compatibility. The IP group inherited the address translation function in the more recent MIB-2.

- The IP group. IP (Internet Protocol) is the network-level (layer 3) protocol employed on the Internet and defined as part of the SNMP transport mechanism. The IP group has 19 objects with individual values about IP functions, and three additional objects that are tables of objects. One of the tables contains five attributes per row pertaining to IP addresses, one contains ten attributes for each row of the IP routing table, and the third contains five attributes per row of the address translation table.

- The ICMP group. ICMP is the Internet Control Message Protocol. It defines error and control messages for IP entities. The group consists of 26 scalar (single-item) objects.

- The TCP group. TCP (Transmission Control Protocol) is the transport-layer protocol employed on the Internet. The group consists of 15 scalar objects and one table with five attributes for each row, pertaining to the TCP connection table.

- The UDP group. UDP, the User Datagram Protocol, is another transport-layer protocol used on the Internet. Unlike TCP, which requires an established connection to transfer data, UDP is connectionless. UDP packets are broadcast to the network and confirmed receipts are the responsibility of the application, not the protocol (as would be the case with TCP). The group consists of five objects, one of which is a table with two attributes pertaining to the UDP listener.

- The EGP group. EGP, the Exterior Gateway Protocol, is a routing protocol employed on the Internet. The group consists of five objects, one of which is a table of 15 attributes for each EGP neighbor entry.

- The CMOT group. No objects are defined now for this group. It seemed like a good idea at the time.

- The Transmission group. No objects are now defined for this group either, although standards for managing the physical layer may someday be defined on this branch of the tree.

- The SNMP group. The SNMP group objects are all scalars indicating various SNMP statistics. There are 30 of these objects.

The MIB-2 Objects

The following list of the MIB-2 objects with short descriptions is provided to give the reader a little more depth of detail on the SNMP Management Information Base. The full text of RFC 1213 can provide the actual syntax, definition, access and status of these objects. This document is readily available over the Internet—I have provided availability information at the end of this Appendix.

system (mib-2 1)

sysDescr (1)	Text (octet string) to describe the entity.
sysObjectID (2)	A naming hierarchy value (object identifier) to uniquely identify the entity.
sysUpTime (3)	Time since the entity was last reinitialized in TimeTicks.
sysContact (4)	Text identifying a person or organization to contact for information about the entity.
sysName (5)	Text—a name for the entity.
sysLocation (6)	Text describing the physical location of the entity.
sysServices (7)	Integer identifying which layer the entity provides services for.

interfaces (mib-2 2)

ifNumber (1)		Integer indicating the total number of interfaces the entity has.
ifTable (2)	ifEntry (1)	The ifTable is a table of the entity's interfaces, with a row for each interface. An ifEntry is one of the rows.
	ifIndex (1)	Integer from 1 to the value of ifNumber identifying an interface specifically.
	ifDescr (2)	Text (octet string) to describe the interface.
	ifType (3)	Integer selected from list of 32 interface types. (1 = other; 6 = ethernet-csmacd; 9 = iso88025-tokenRing; 15 = fddi; etc.)
	ifMtu (4)	Integer representing maximum size datagram in octets that can pass through the interface.
	ifSpeed (5)	Integer representing the interface's bandwidth in bits per second.
	ifPhysAddress (6)	Network address of layer below the network layer, the MAC address.

interfaces (mib-2 2) (Continued)

ifAdminStatus (7)	Integer from list: 1= administratively up; 2= administratively down; 3= administratively testing.
ifOperStatus (8)	Integer from list: 1= operationally up; 2= operationally down; 3= operationally testing.
ifLastChange (9)	Counter indicating TimeTicks since the interface changed its operational state.
ifInOctets (10)	Counter indicating octets received since last reinitialization.
ifInUcastPkts (11)	Counter indicating unicast packets received since last reinitialization.
ifInNUcastPkts (12)	Counter indicating broadcast and multicast packets received since last reinitialization.
ifInDiscards (13)	Counter indicating number of inbound packets discarded at this interface for other reasons than errors.
ifInErrors (14)	Counter indicating number of inbound packets discarded at this interface because they contained errors.
ifInUnknownProtos (15)	Counter indicating number of packets discarded at this interface because they were formed according to an unknown or unsupported protocol.
ifOutOctets (16)	Counter indicating octets sent since last reinitialization.
ifOutUcastPkts (17)	Counter indicating unicast packets sent since last reinitialization.
ifOutNUcastPkts (18)	Counter indicating broadcast and multicast packets sent since last reinitialization.
ifOutDiscards (19)	Counter indicating number of outbound packets discarded at this interface for other reasons than errors.
ifOutErrors (20)	Counter indicating number of outbound packets discarded at this interface because they contained errors.
ifOutQLen (21)	Gauge indicating number of packets in the output queue.
ifSpecific (22)	May be null. Indicates media at interface.

at (mib-2 3)

atTable (2)	atEntry (1)	
	atIfIndex (1)	Integer specifying a particular interface—the same value as the object ifIndex.
	atPhyAddress (2)	MAC address or physical address of the entity.
	atNetAddress (3)	IP address of the entity.

ip (mib-2 4)

ipForwarding (1)	Integer indicating whether the entity forwards IP packets. (1 = yes, 2 = no).	
ipDefaultTTL (2)	Integer indicating default time-to-live value for packets originating at this entity.	
ipInReceives (3)	Counter indicating total packets received, errors and all.	
ipInHdrErrors (4)	Counter indicating total packets discarded because of header errors.	
ipInAddrErrors (5)	Counter indicating total packets discarded because of an invalid IP address.	
ipForwDatagrams (6)	Counter indicating total packets it attempted to route.	
ipInUnknownProtos (7)	Counter indicating total packets discarded because of an unknown or unsupported protocol.	
ipInDiscards (8)	Counter indicating packets with no problems that were discarded.	
ipInDelivers (9)	Counter indicating packets successfully delivered to IP.	
ipOutRequests (10)	Counter indicating packets supplied to IP locally.	
ipOutDiscards (11)	Counter indicating packets with no problems that were discarded.	
ipOutNoRoutes (12)	Counter indicating packets discarded because no destination could be found.	
ipReasmTimeout (13)	Integer indicating the maximum number of seconds fragments of packets are held for reassembly.	
ipReasmReqds (14)	Counter indicating the total number of fragments needing reassembly that were received.	
ipReasmOKs (15)	Counter indicating the total number of successfully reassembled packets.	
ipReasmFails (16)	Counter indicating the total number of failures detected by the IP reassembly algorithm.	
ipFragOKs (17)	Counter indicating the number of packets that have been fragmented successfully at this entity.	
ipFragFails (18)	Counter indicating the number of packets that were discarded because they needed to be fragmented but couldn't be.	
ipFragCreates (19)	Counter indicating the total number of fragments created by this entity.	
ipAddrTable (20)	ipAddrEntry (1)	The ipAddrTable has one entry, the ipAddrEntry, for each of the entity's IP addresses.
	ipAdEntAddr (1)	IP address for this entry in the table.
	ipAdEntIfIndex (2)	Integer indicating the interface to which this information applies. This index value identifies the same interface as the value of ifIndex in the interfaces group.
	ipAdEntNetMask (3)	Subnet mask associated with this IP address.
	ipAdEntBcastAddr (4)	Integer indicating the value of the least significant bit of a broadcast address.

ip (mib-2 4) (Continued)

	ipAdEntReasmMaxSize (5)	Integer indicating the size of the largest packet this entity can reassemble.
ipRoutingTable (21)	ipRouteEntry (1)	The ipRoutingTable has a row (an ipRouteEntry) for each route this entity knows about.
	ipRouteDest (1)	IP address of the destination for this route.
	ipRouteIfIndex (2)	Integer indicating which interface is to be used for this route. Indicates the same interface as ifIndex in the interfaces group.
	ipRouteMetric1 (3), ipRouteMetric2 (4), ipRouteMetric3 (5), ipRouteMetric4, (6), ipRouteMetric5, (12)	Depending on the routing protocols determined by ipRouteProto, these integer values describe the type of route metric the route uses.
	ipRouteNextHop (7)	IP address of the next hop on this route.
	ipRouteType (8)	Integer with one of four values: 1 = other; 2 = invalid; 3 = direct; 4 = indirect.
	ipRouteProto (9)	Integer with one of fourteen values indicating the routing protocol employed to find routes (e.g., rip = 8, ospf = 13...).
	ipRouteAge (10)	Integer indicating the number of seconds since the route was last updated.
	ipRouteMask (11)	Subnet mask associated with this route.
	ipRouteInfo (13)	Object identifier referring to the MIB definition for the routing protocol.
ipNetToMediaTable (22)	ipNetToMediaEntry (1)	The ipNetToMediaTable maps IP addresses to physical addresses. Each ipNetToMediaEntry is a row.
	ipNetToMediaIfIndex (1)	Integer indicating which interface this entry is for. Value refers to the same interfaces as ifIndex in the interfaces group.
	ipNetToMediaPhysAddress (2)	Physical address of this entry.
	ipNetToMediaNetAddress (3)	IP address for this entry.
	ipNetToMediaType (4)	Integer representing one of four values: 1 = other; 2 = invalid; 3 = dynamic; 4 = static.
ipRoutingDiscards (23)	Counter indicating the number of routing entries that were discarded even though they were valid.	

icmp (mib-2 6)

icmpInMsgs (1)	Counter indicating the total number of ICMP messages received by the entity.
icmpInErrors (2)	Counter indicating the number of messages received with ICMP-specific errors
icmpInDestUnreachs (3)	Counter indicating the total number of ICMP Destination Unreachable messages received.
icmpInTimeExcds (4)	Counter indicating the total number of ICMP Time Exceeded messages received.
icmpInParmProbs (5)	Counter indicating the total number of ICMP Parameter Problem messages received.
icmpInSrcQuenches (6)	Counter indicating the total number of ICMP Source Quench messages received.
icmpInRedirects (7)	Counter indicating the total number of ICMP Redirect messages received.
icmpInEchos (8)	Counter indicating the total number of ICMP Echo request messages received.
icmpInEchoReps (9)	Counter indicating the total number of ICMP Echo Reply messages received.
icmpInTimestamps (10)	Counter indicating the total number of ICMP Timestamp request messages received.
icmpInTimestampReps (11)	Counter indicating the total number of ICMP Timestamp Reply messages received.
icmpInAddrMasks (12)	Counter indicating the total number of ICMP Address Mask request messages received.
icmpInAddrMaskReps (13)	Counter indicating the total number of ICMP Address Mask Reply messages received.
icmpOutMsgs (14)	Counter indicating the total number of ICMP messages the entity attempted to send.
icmpOutErrors (15)	Counter indicating the number of messages that could not be sent because of ICMP-specific errors
icmpOutDestUnreachs (16)	Counter indicating the total number of ICMP Destination Unreachable messages sent.
icmpOutTimeExcds (17)	Counter indicating the total number of ICMP Time Exceeded messages sent.
icmpOutParmProbs (18)	Counter indicating the total number of ICMP Parameter Problem messages sent.
icmpOutSrcQuenches (19)	Counter indicating the total number of ICMP Source Quench messages sent.
icmpOutRedirects (20)	Counter indicating the total number of ICMP Redirect messages sent.
icmpOutEchos (21)	Counter indicating the total number of ICMP Echo request messages sent.
icmpOutEchoReps (22)	Counter indicating the total number of ICMP Echo Reply messages sent.
icmpOutTimestamps (23)	Counter indicating the total number of ICMP Timestamp request messages sent.
icmpOutTimestampReps (24)	Counter indicating the total number of ICMP Timestamp Reply messages sent.
icmpOutAddrMasks (25)	Counter indicating the total number of ICMP Address Mask request messages sent.
icmpOutAddrMaskReps (26)	Counter indicating the total number of ICMP Address Mask Reply messages sent.

tcp (mib-2 6)

tcpRtoAlgorithm (1)	Integer with value from 1 to 4 indicating the algorithm used to calculate the timeout value for retransmitting unacknowledged bytes.	
tcpRtoMin (2)	Integer indicating minimum value for retransmission timeout.	
tcpRtoMax (3)	Integer indicating maximum value for retransmission timeout.	
tcpMaxConn (4)	Integer indicating the maximum number of TCP connections the entity can support.	
tcpActiveOpens (5)	Counter indicating the number of active opens for this entity.	
tcpPassiveOpens (6)	Counter indicating the number of passive opens for this entity.	
tcpAttemptFails (7)	Counter indicating the number of failed connection attempts.	
tcpEstabResets (8)	Counter indicating the number of resets.	
tcpCurrEstab (9)	Gauge indicating the number of current connections with a status of either ESTABLISHED or CLOSE-WAIT.	
tcpInSegs (10)	Counter indicating the total number of segments received.	
tcpOutSegs (11)	Counter indicating the total number of segments sent.	
tcpRetransSegs (12)	Counter indicating the total number of retransmitted segments.	
tcpConnTable (13)	tcpConnEntry (1)	The tcpConnTable has one entry, the tcpConnEntry, for each current TCP connection.
	tcpConnState (1)	Integer indicating the state of a TCP connection. 1 = closed, 2 = listen, 3 = synSent, 4 = synReceived, 5 = established, 6 = finWait1, 7 = finWait2, 8 = closeWait, 9 = lastAck, 10 = closing, 11 = timeWait, 12 = deleteTCB().
	tcpConnLocalAddress (2)	The local IP address for this connection.
	tcpConnLocalPort (3)	The local port number for this connection.
	tcpConnRemAddress (4)	The remote IP address for this connection.
	tcpConnRemPort (5)	The remote port number for this connection.
tcpInErrs (14)	Counter indicating the total number of segments received in error.	
tcpOutRsts (15)	Counter indicating the total number of segments sent with the RST flag on.	

udp (mib-2 7)

udpInDatagrams (1)	Counter indicating the total number of UDP packets received.
udpInNoPorts (2)	Counter indicating the total number of received UDP packets for which there was no application at the destination port.
udpInErrors (3)	Counter indicating the total number of received UDP packets that could not be delivered for reasons other than the lack of an application at the destination port.
udpOutDatagrams (4)	Counter indicating the total number of UDP packets this entity has sent.

udp (mib-2 7) (Continued)

udpTable (5)	udpTableEntry (1)	The udpTable, informally referred to as the UDP Listener table, has one entry, a udpTableEntry, for each of the entity's UDP end-points on which a local application is currently accepting packets.
	udpLocalAddress (1)	The local IP address for this UDP listener.
	udpLocalPort (2)	Integer indicating the local port for this UDP listener.

egp (mib-2 8)

egpInMesgs (1)	Counter indicating the number of error-free EGP messages this entity received.	
egpInErrors (2)	Counter indicating the number of EGP messages received which were in error.	
egpOutMesgs (3)	Counter indicating the total number of EGP messages generated by this entity.	
egpOutErrors (4)	Counter indicating the total number of locally generated EGP messages not sent because of local problems.	
egpNeighTable (5)	egpNeighEntry (6)	The egpNeighTable has an egpNeighEntry for each of the entity's EGP neighbors. The Exterior Gateway Protocol is a routing aid often implemented on IP nodes.
	egpNeighState (1)	Integer indicating the state of the entity with respect to this neighbor: 1 = idle; 2 = acquisition; 3 = down; 4 = up; 5 = cease.
	egpNeighAddr (2)	The IP address of this neighbor.
	egpNeighAs (3)	Integer indicating the autonomous system number of this neighbor.
	egpNeighInMsgs (4)	Counter indicating the number of error-free EGP messages received from this neighbor.
	egpNeighInErrs (5)	Counter indicating the number of EGP messages received from this neighbor that were in error.
	egpNeighOutMesgs (6)	Counter indicating the total number of locally generated EGP messages sent to this neighbor.
	egpNeighOutErrs (7)	Counter indicating the total number of locally generated EGP messages not sent to this neighbor because of local problems.
	egpNeighInErrMesgs (8)	Counter indicating the number of EGP-defined error messages received from this neighbor.
	egpNeighOutErrMesgs (9)	Counter indicating the number of EGP-defined error messages sent to this neighbor.
	egpNeighStateUps (10)	Counter indicating the number of state transitions to the state "UP" with this neighbor.

egp (mib-2 8) (Continued)

	egpNeighStateDowns (11)	Counter indicating the number of state transitions from the state "UP" to any other state with this neighbor.
	egpNeighIntervalHello (12)	Integer indicating the time (in hundredths of a second) between EGP "Hello" retransmissions.
	egpNeighIntervalPoll (13)	Integer indicating the time (in hundredths of a second) between EGP poll commands.
	egpNeighMode (14)	Integer indicating the polling mode of this entity; 1 = active, 2 = passive.
	egpNeighEventTrigger (15)	Integer used to change the state of this EGP neighbor; 1 = start; 2 = stop.
egpAs (6)		Integer indicating the autonomous system number of this entity.

snmp (mib-2 11)

snmpInPkts (1)	Counter indicating the total number of messages delivered by the transport layer.
snmpOutPkts (2)	Counter indicating the total number of messages delivered to the transport layer by this SNMP entity.
snmpInBadVersions (3)	Counter indicating the total number of messages delivered that were for an unsupported version of SNMP.
snmpInBadCommunityNames (4)	Counter indicating the total number of messages delivered with unrecognized community names.
snmpInBadCommunityUses (5)	Counter indicating the number of messages delivered that represented an SNMP operation not permitted to this community.
snmpInASNParseErrs (6)	Counter indicating the number of errors encountered decoding SNMP messages.
(7)	Not used.
snmpInTooBigs (8)	Counter indicating the total number of messages delivered for which the value of the error status field is "tooBig."
snmpInNoSuchNames (9)	Counter indicating the total number of messages delivered for which the value of the error status field is "noSuchName."
snmpInBadValues (10)	Counter indicating the total number of messages delivered for which the value of the error status field is "badValue."
snmpInReadOnlys (11)	Counter indicating the total number of messages delivered for which the value of the error status field is "readOnly."
snmpInGenErrs (12)	Counter indicating the total number of messages delivered for which the value of the error status field is "genErr."

snmp (mib-2 11) (Continued)

snmpInTotalReqVars (13)	Counter indicating the total number of MIB objects that have been retrieved successfully as the result of SNMP "Get Request" and "Get Next" messages.
snmpInTotalSetVars (14)	Counter indicating the total number of MIB objects that have been altered successfully as the result of SNMP "Set Request" messages.
snmpInGetRequests (15)	Counter indicating the total number of "Get Request" messages received and processed.
snmpInGetNexts (16)	Counter indicating the total number of "Get Next" messages received and processed.
snmpInSetRequests (17)	Counter indicating the total number of "Set Request" messages received and processed.
snmpInGetResponses (18)	Counter indicating the total number of "Get Response" messages received and processed.
snmpInTraps (19)	Counter indicating the total number of "Trap" messages received and processed.
snmpOutTooBigs (20)	Counter indicating the total number of messages generated for which the value of the error status field is "tooBig."
snmpOutNoSuchNames (21)	Counter indicating the total number of messages generated for which the value of the error status field is "noSuchName."
snmpOutBadValues (22)	Counter indicating the total number of messages generated for which the value of the error status field is "badValue."
snmpOutReadOnlys (23)	Counter indicating the total number of messages generated for which the value of the error status field is "readOnly."
snmpOutGenErrs (24)	Counter indicating the total number of messages generated for which the value of the error status field is "genErr."
snmpOutGetRequests (25)	Counter indicating the total number of "Get Request" messages generated by this entity.
snmpOutGetNexts (26)	Counter indicating the total number of "Get Next" messages generated by this entity.
snmpOutSetRequests (27)	Counter indicating the total number of "Set Request" messages generated by this entity.
snmpOutGetResponses (28)	Counter indicating the total number of "Get Response" messages generated by this entity.
snmpOutTraps (29)	Counter indicating the total number of "Trap" messages generated by this entity.
snmpEnableAuthenTraps (30)	Integer indicating whether this entity's SNMP agent process is permitted to generate authentication traps. 1 = enabled; 2 = disabled.

Messages

Thus far, it is not obvious what makes SNMP a *simple* network management protocol. (Compared to the OSI MIB, the SNMP MIB is in fact quite compact and concrete.) The SNMP message set is limited and straightforward. There are five types of SNMP messages.

Get Request: This message (complete with an object identifier that indicates a specific managed object) solicits a response from the management agent that receives it.

Get Response: The management agent replies to a Get-Request by sending a Get-Response with the value of the specified managed object.

Get Next Request: This message is useful for requesting additional values from a table.

Set Request: This message can change the value of a specific managed object.

Trap: An SNMP Trap is a message initiated by the management agent without a request from the managing process. It is normally used as an alert that some important condition has changed, such as reinitialization or link failure.

An SNMP message includes one of these message types and the object identifier of the relevant object.

Figure C-2 An SNMP Dialog

Management Application	Managing Agent
Get Request 1.3.6.1.2.1.2.7 ("Tell me the value of ifAdminStatus.")	
	Get Response 2. (The administrative status of this interface is "down.")
Set Request 1.3.6.1.2.1.2.7 1 ("Set the value of ifAdminStatus to 1 [up].")	

Agents and Managers

An SNMP managed entity must have a management agent. An agent is a process that can receive and send SNMP messages and maintain the MIB objects that are implemented on the entity. Management applications, also known as managing stations or just managers, are typically the consoles that collect management data from a multitude of agents. The most common method for this is polling: the management application periodically generates request messages for every relevant agent to respond to. The advantage of polling is that the management application will find out about any bad links or devices within one polling interval—if something doesn't respond, the human network managers can get started fixing it. The disadvantage of polling is that it takes up network bandwidth. The larger the scope of the management application, the more bandwidth polling will require.

Communities

A collection of management agents and managing applications makes up an SNMP community. Authenticated community membership is required for SNMP communications to take place. An SNMP community string, the equivalent of a password, is part of any SNMP message. Access rights to particular subsets of the MIB can be controlled in a central configuration file.

Proxy Agents

Devices that do not have SNMP management agents can sometimes be managed by a proxy agent. A proxy agent is a kind of gateway, communicating with the managing application using SNMP protocols and with the managed entity using some other means of communication, perhaps a proprietary protocol. Proxy agents can play an important role in transitions from proprietary management schemes to standardized SNMP.

Access to SNMP RFCs

Internet RFCs are available from the following sources:

Internet nodes for downloading:

- NIC.DDN.MIL
- FTP.NISC.SRI.COM
- NIS.NSF.NET
- NISC.JVNC.NET
- WUARCHIVE.WUSTL.EDU
- VENERA.ISI.EDU

The filename is rfc1213.txt in a directory named pub/rfc

Source for printed copies:

Government Systems, Inc.
Attn: Network Information Center
14200 Park Meadow Drive, Suite 200
Chantilly, Virginia 22021
800 365-3642, 703 802-4535, FAX 703 802-8376
E-mail: NIC@NIC.DDN.MIL
IP Address: 192.112.36.5

Glossary

access method
The component of the data link (layer 2 of the OSI Model) functions that determines which node is next to use the LAN; a set of rules used to direct traffic on the network. The access method—how a LAN governs users' electrical access to the cable—significantly affects the LAN's features and performance. Examples of access methods are token passing, used by ARCnet and token ring, and Carrier Sense Multiple Access with Collision Detection, used by Ethernet. (See CSMA/CD.)

address
A set of numbers that uniquely identifies something: a workstation on a LAN, a location in computer memory, the next hop in a route.

Address Resolution Protocol (ARP)
Protocol used by TCP/IP to associate IP addresses with MAC-layer addresses, such as Ethernet addresses.

algorithm
A "recipe" for making a computer do something; a sequence of steps followed by a computer to accomplish a task.

ANSI

American National Standards Institute, an organization that helps set voluntary standards and also represents the United States in some international standards bodies.

AppleTalk

A software standard from Apple Computer Corporation that facilitates linking Macintosh computers and peripherals. AppleTalk may now be run over Ethernet and token ring networks—using NetWare servers and other non-Macintosh systems—at a variety of speeds. Should not be confused with LocalTalk, the 230Mbits/sec networking hardware that is built into every Macintosh computer.

AppleTalk File Protocol

The application-layer (layer 7 of the OSI Model) protocol used to provide file services to Macintosh clients.

application

A software program that carries out some useful task. Database managers, spreadsheets, communications packages, graphics programs and word processors are all applications. Application software should be distinguished from system software, the software used by the computer itself to accomplish tasks for application software. Network operating systems are also considered part of system software. DOS, OS/2, NetWare, MVS, 3+ and Unix are all examples of system software.

application layer

Layer 7 of the OSI Model. Application software, which in this context includes network and workstation operating system software, employs application-layer protocols to request and provide services over the network. Application-layer functions include file handling, message handling, directory services, network management and many others.

application program interface (API)

A set of commands and data formats, typically tied to a programming language, for programmers to use in developing applications. APIs simplify program development or furnish special functions, such as graphical user interface components. An API can make it simple for developers to implement a protocol.

architecture

The way hardware or software is structured: how the system or program is constructed, how its components fit together, and the protocols and interfaces used for communication and cooperation among modules or components of the system. Network architecture defines the functions and descriptions of data formats and procedures used for communication between nodes or workstations.

ARCnet

Attached Resource Computer Network. A 2.5Mbits/sec LAN that uses a modified token-passing protocol. The advantages of ARCnet are ease of installation and use, well-documented technology, a star-wired topology and the use of coaxial cable. Some ARCnet vendors support twisted-pair cable.

ASCII

American Standard Code for Information Interchange. A standard set of characters—alphabetical, numerical and symbolic ($, @, % and so on)—recognized by most computer systems. A presentation-layer (layer 6 of the OSI Model) protocol.

asynchronous

A type of data transmission that does not require equal time intervals between units of data. (See synchronous.)

ATM

Asynchronous Transfer Mode, a connection-oriented wide area and local area technology based on high-speed switching of 53-byte cells. Capable of transmitting high-bandwidth data, such as high-resolution video, in realtime.

audit trail

A record of events. Network operating systems can be set up to keep a record of who uses what resources at what time—an important tool for network management, especially accounting and security management.

back end

The part of a database server that performs data storage, retrieval, management and security functions. Complementary to the front end, which interfaces with the user and formats data for presentation. The back end is often called the server. The front end is often called the client. (See client-server model.)

backup

To copy in case the original is destroyed. "Backup" can be a verb, as in, "I backup the hard disk so I don't lose anything." It can be an adjective, as in, "I just bought a backup disk," or a noun, as in, "Tape backup is very important on a LAN." A backup copy of a file is a second copy, stored on tape, floppy disk or hard disk. Backup ensures that if the original copy is destroyed or damaged, the file can be restored, at least partially.

bandwidth

The capacity of a device or connection to carry information usually measured in bits per second (bps). In a network, the greater the bandwidth, the greater the information-carrying capacity of the network, and the faster the data can be transmitted from one device to another.

baseband

One of two types of LAN connections. In baseband LANs, the entire bandwidth of the cable is used to transmit a single digital signal. In the electronically more sophisticated broadband LAN, the bandwidth is divided into many channels, so it can simultaneously transmit video, voice and data. Baseband digital signals are put directly onto the cable without modulation. Multiple concurrent transmissions are achieved by time division multiplexing. (See broadband, multiplexing.)

batch processing

A type of data processing whereby related transactions are grouped, transmitted and processed together by the same computer at the same time. In batch processing, immediate responses are not needed, and no user input is required while the processing takes place. An example of batch processing is corporate payroll. All the employees' weekly times are processed at one time. The complementary class of data processing is realtime. (See realtime.) A network can handle both classes of data processing.

Bindery

The database on a Novell NetWare server that keeps track of users, groups, access privileges, passwords and other internal objects. Access to the Bindery is crucial for configuration management and administration on NetWare networks.

block
A collection of transmitted information that is seen as a discrete entity. Usually has its own address, control, routing and error checking information. (See also packet and packet switching.)

bridge
A device that can connect two or more networks, provided that they employ the same data link protocols.

broadband
One of two types of LAN connections. In broadband networks, the cable can carry video, voice and data traffic simultaneously. Signals on a cable are multiplexed by frequency division rather than by time division. Because all nodes require special modems and cable requirements are more exacting, broadband networks are more costly and complex than baseband. (See baseband.)

broadcast message
A message from one user sent to all nodes on a segment or all nodes of a certain class.

brouter
A networking device that combines some of the capabilities of a bridge with those of a router; that is, it can perform routing for some network-layer protocols but acts as a bridge when it encounters other protocols. (See bridge, router.)

buffer
Storage space in RAM (or a separate device) used to compensate for differences between the speed of data transmission and the speed with which the data can be serviced by temporarily holding the transmission.

bulletin board system (BBS)
An electronic message system with centralized mailboxes and posting areas. Users can dial in, leave messages and read messages. Sometimes confused with an electronic mail system (which has distributed mailboxes).

bus topology
A one-cable LAN, in which all workstations are connected to a single cable. On a bus network, all workstations hear all transmissions on the cable simultaneously. Each workstation then selects those transmissions addressed to it based on address information contained in the transmission. It is possible to connect bus networks together, using a bridge.

byte
A group of 8 bits, often used to represent a character. Bytes are also units of storage and transmission. The SNMP standards refer to "octets" instead of bytes, apparently because in some terminologies bytes can have more or fewer than 8 bits.

cache
An area of high-speed RAM specifically set aside to improve system performance. Blocks of data are automatically copied from a system's disk drive or main memory area into the cache, which is then used to execute instructions as quickly as possible.

CAD
Computer-Aided Design.

CCITT
Comité Consultatif Internationale Télégraphique et Téléphonique, a committee of the International Telecommunications Union, which is one of the agencies of the United Nations. The members of CCITT are the world's telephone and telegraph government agencies. CCITT standards include the V.32 modem transmission, V.42 error correction and X.25 packet switching standards.

client-server model
An architecture for applications programs under which the software is split into two parts: client and server. The server component provides services for the client part, which interacts with the user. The two parts can run on different machines. The most common client-server application is the database server. This is a database management system (DBMS) where the functions are split into a "front end" (client) that interacts with the user to enter data, issue queries and produce reports, and a "back end" (server) that stores the data, controls access, responds to queries, protects the data and makes necessary changes. The main advantages of the client-server model are reduced network traffic, much improved performance, greater flexibility in application development and improved availability of data.

CMIP (Common Management Information Protocol)
The OSI network management standard, much less commonly implemented today than SNMP.

CMOT (CMIP Over TCP/IP)
A now-defunct scheme for transporting CMIP management information over TCP/IP protocols.

coaxial cable
An electrical cable in which a solid piece of metal wire is surrounded by insulation and then surrounded by shielding whose center coincides with the center of the piece of wire—hence the term coaxial. Coaxial cables have wide bandwidth and can carry many data, voice and video conversations simultaneously. Cable TV runs on coaxial cable.

collision
The result of two nodes trying to use a shared transmission medium simultaneously. The electrical signals interfere with each other, which ruins both messages and forces the nodes to retransmit.

collision detection
The process of detecting simultaneous (and therefore mutually interfering) transmission. (See CSMA/CD.)

communications server
A type of gateway that translates the packetized information on a LAN into the formats used on telephone lines or on direct connections to minicomputers and mainframes. It allows nodes on a LAN to share modems or host connections.

concentrator
A central cabling source for physical-star wired networks. Performs the same functions as a hub, but may be larger and more modular.

configuration
The set of all variables that can be changed or adjusted for hardware devices or software routines. Configurations may be effected via switch settings, jumpers, software instructions, setup programs and the like.

configuration management
Identifying the components of the network, verifying that they have been set up correctly, tracking them as they attach and detach and changing their installation parameters as the network grows and changes or as problems are identified.

CRC

Cyclic Redundancy Check, an error detection technique that works by calculating a checksum for a piece of digital information that is appended to the information. The destination node recalculates the checksum and compares it to the appended checksum. If they don't match, it declares the existence of an error.

crosstalk

The introduction of signals from one communication channel into another.

CSMA/CD

Carrier Sense Multiple Access With Collision Detection. When access to the network is needed, this system verifies that the network is free. If it isn't, it waits a certain amount of time before checking again. If the network is free, yet two or more devices try to gain access at the very same time, it forces them to back off so that they don't collide, and then tries again.

database server

The back-end part of a client-server database. (See client-server model.) It controls the data, granting access to multiple users, updating and deleting records, performing queries and generating reports.

DBMS

Database Management System, a program or collection of programs that creates and maintains a database and allows users to retrieve information from it.

destination address

That part of a message that indicates for whom the message is intended.

diskless PC

A PC without a disk drive. Used on a LAN, a diskless PC runs by booting DOS or another operating system from the file server. It does this via a read-only memory chip on its network interface card called a remote boot ROM. When the machine is turned on, programs in this boot ROM are executed. They go out over the network to the file server and look for the operating system to be loaded into the diskless PC's memory. The file server acts as the disk for the diskless PC. Sometimes cheaper than PCs with disks, diskless PCs can also be more compact and offer better security.

distributed database

A database that has components in more than one place. Controlling access and synchronizing updates on distributed databases are very difficult problems.

distributed data processing

The processing of information in separate locations equipped with independent computers. The computers are connected by a network, even though the processing is geographically dispersed. Often a more efficient use of computer processing power because each CPU can be devoted to a certain task.

DMA

Direct Memory Access. By using a DMA channel, data can rapidly move between a computer's main memory and a peripheral, such as a LAN interface card.

DOS

Disk Operating System, a program or set of programs that instruct a disk-based computing system to schedule and supervise tasks, manage computer resources and operate and control peripheral devices, including disk drives, keyboards, screens and printers. Often used as shorthand for Microsoft's MS-DOS or IBM's PC DOS, the most commonly encountered disk operating systems on Intel chip-based computers. (See also NOS.)

downsize

To move a business application from one computing platform to a smaller, less expensive type of computer. Many applications were first downsized from mainframes to minicomputers, and are now moving from minis to microcomputer-based networks.

driver

A software program, designed as an extension to an operating system, that contains the information necessary to work with other devices or protocols.

duplex

Refers to whether a communications link can transmit and receive simultaneously or perform only one of the two functions at a time. A full-duplex link does both, while a half-duplex link can—like a two-way radio—do only one at a time.

duplexing

Providing two identical disk drives and controllers so that one of them can take over in case the other fails. Mirroring is similar but involves less hardware duplication. It uses a single disk controller to save data to two different disk drives.

EIA
Electronics Industries Association, a U.S. trade organization that issues its own standards and contributes to ANSI.

802.3
The numerical designation for the IEEE (Institute of Electrical and Electronic Engineers) standard governing the use of the CSMA/CD media-access method.

electronic mail
A messaging system operating over some sort of communications medium, often a LAN.

e-mail
Electronic mail.

Ethernet
A CSMA/CD, 10Mbits/sec network developed at Xerox's Palo Alto Research Center, one of the most popular baseband LANs in use. DEC and Intel participated with Xerox to make Ethernet a network standard that provides computers with network access on a transmit-at-will basis. If two transmissions collide, the nodes wait a random interval and try again until they get through. Ethernet runs on coaxial cable, fiber-optic cable or twisted-pair wiring.

fiber-optic cable
A data transmission medium consisting of glass fibers. Light-emitting diodes send light through the fiber to a detector, which converts the light back into electrical signals. Fiber-optic cable may be the predominant medium for LANs in the future. Fiber-optic cable offers immense bandwidth plus protection from eavesdropping, electromagnetic interference and radioactivity.

file locking
A method of ensuring data integrity. With a file-locking system, only one user can update a file at a time. Other users are locked out, unable to access the file. (See also record locking.)

file server
Any device that provides file storage and retrieval services over a LAN, typically a computer with high I/O and disk drive performance and high data storage capacity.

frame relay
A wide area technology that offers higher performance than X.25 packet switching by eliminating much of the error-checking and packet-sequencing overhead of the older technology. It allows a customer's available bandwidth to jump momentarily as much as 50 percent, which provides a good match for the "bursty" nature of network traffic.

front end
The component of a client-server system concerned with formatting and presenting data to a user. Also called the client.

gateway
A device that can connect two or more dissimilar networks, or connect a network to a mainframe or minicomputer. A gateway can convert all seven layers of the OSI Model. (See OSI Model.) In Internet terminology, a gateway is a node that can forward packets to other nodes—what would be called a router anywhere else.

groupware
Also called collaborative computing or workgroup computing. Groupware includes programs designed to handle group-related tasks such as scheduling meetings, sending messages and other information, and coauthoring documents. Other groupware includes networked bulletin board systems and group decision support systems.

handshake
A preliminary procedure, usually part of a communications protocol, to establish a connection. Sometimes, during the handshake, two computers exchange the conditions under which they will communicate. Other times, they just alert each other to the impending communication.

header
The beginning part of a message, which contains destination address, source address and other information.

host
Traditionally, a computer system, usually a mainframe or minicomputer, that provides computer service for a number of users. In Internet terminology, nodes are either hosts or gateways. Hosts are incapable of forwarding packets.

hub

The device that functions as the physical and electrical center of a star topology network or cabling system. Connections to all the nodes radiate from the hub.

interface

A demarcation between two devices, where the electrical signals, connectors, timing and handshaking meet. Often the procedures, codes and protocols that enable the two devices to interact are included or carried out by the interface. An example is an RS-232-C port. Some of its 25 pins are used to send information and make sure devices can talk to each other. The pins carry different messages, such as "request to send," "acknowledgment" and others.

interface card

A printed circuit board fitting in the expansion chassis of a computer to make the physical connection between computer and LAN cable. The interface card is responsible for getting raw bits from the computer onto the network and vice versa. This requires translation from parallel to serial form and back, buffering, packet creation, encoding/decoding, cable access, and transmission and reception.

IP

Internet Protocol. (See TCP/IP.)

ISO

The International Standards Organization (ISO) is an umbrella group of standards organizations (including the American National Standards Institute or ANSI) from some 90 countries. These nongovernmental organizations define standard industrial and commercial practices for many classes of products. The Open Standards Interconnect (OSI) committee of the ISO is responsible for electronic network standards, including the 7-layer OSI Reference Model.

K

A standard quantity measurement of computer storage. One K is loosely defined as 1,000 bytes; in fact it is 1,024 bytes, which is the equivalent of 2 to the tenth power.

LAN

Local area network.

LAN adapter

Hardware designed to permit a personal computer to attach to a LAN. Usually supplied on a removable circuit board known as a network interface card (NIC), but may also be built onto a PC's motherboard or designed as an external unit.

LAN Manager

A network operating system from Microsoft for servers running OS/2.

LAN Server

IBM's network operating system based on OS/2. It provides the traditional services of a network operating system for workstations that can run either DOS or OS/2. It runs under OS/2 on a server PC and provides file and print sharing, communications, messaging and other services.

local area network

A data communications network, also known as a LAN, spanning a limited geographical area—a few miles at most. It provides communication between computers and peripherals.

logical drive

Disk storage on a network server, represented logically by a name or letter to facilitate access from user workstations. For example, the storage available on a NetWare server might appear to users as if it were a drive E on their PCs.

log-in

The process of identifying and authenticating oneself to a computer system. Used to control access to computer systems or networks.

MAC

Medium Access Control, one of the two sublayers of the data link layer.

mainframe

A large computer usually supplied with peripherals and software by a single large vendor, often with a closed architecture. Mainframes almost always use dumb terminals, connected in star configurations.

Mbits/sec

Megabits per second, or million bits per second.

MIB

A Management Information Base (MIB) is a hierarchical structure used to define the information elements that can be employed by network management applications. The most commonly encountered MIB is called MIB-2 and is defined by the Internet Activities Board as part of the SNMP (Simple Network Management Protocol) standard. (Appendix C lists all the elements of MIB-2.)

minicomputer

A small or medium-sized computer accessed by dumb terminals. A minicomputer is bigger and may be more powerful than a PC.

mirroring

Writing identical information to two separate disk drives so that one of them can take over from the other in the event of hardware failure. Duplexing is similar, but involves more hardware duplication. (See duplexing.)

modem

A device (modulator/demodulator) that converts digital data from a transmitting device into a signal suitable for transmission over a telephone (analog) channel. At the other end, another modem reconverts the analog signal to digital data for use by the computer.

MS-DOS

Microsoft Disk Operating System, the standard operating system for computers equipped with the Intel 8086, 8088 and 80286 (and subsequent) microprocessors. PC-DOS is IBM's version of MS-DOS.

multiplexing

The transmission of multiple signals over a single communications line. Frequency domain multiplexing modulates signals onto different carrier frequencies (like the multiple signals carried over TV cables). Time domain multiplexing separates signals by sending one after the other.

multiprocessing

Running the same application on multiple processors concurrently. Symmetrical multiprocessing processors act sequentially on the next instruction when they have finished an operation. Asymmetrical multiprocessing processors have particular assigned tasks; if these tasks don't need doing, they wait idly.

multitasking

The concurrent operation of two or more programs by a single computer.

multithreading

Like multitasking, the concurrent operation of two or more tasks by a single computer. The difference here is that the tasks may be components, or "threads," of a single application rather than being separate programs.

multiuser

Having the ability to support multiple users with a single computer while providing a full range of capability to each one.

NetBIOS

Network Basic Input/Output System. Part of the original IBM PC network program. Like the BIOS of an individual computer, NetBIOS is an interface that applications use to gain access to computer resources on a network instead of in just one machine.

NetWare

The most popular network operating system, produced by Novell, and supported by almost every hardware and software manufacturer. Available in a variety of versions, including NetWare 3.11, which uses special functions of the 80386 processor for more rapid operation; NetWare 4.0, which includes enterprise-wide directory services; NetWare 2.2, which can run on computers with 80286 processors; and NetWare Lite, which offers inexpensive peer-to-peer networking services to small workgroups. NetWare for the Macintosh allows DOS PCs and Macintosh computers to be interconnected. NetWare 3.11 and above also supports OS/2 and Unix workstations.

network architecture

The structures and protocols of a computer network. (See architecture.)

network interface controller

Electronic circuitry that connects a node to a network. Usually a card that fits into one of the expansion slots inside a personal computer.

network topology

The geography of a network: whether it is a star, a bus or a ring. The physical, electrical and logical topologies of a network can be different. Token ring networks are typically physical stars but logical and electrical rings. A 10BASE-T Ethernet network is usually a physical and logical star but an electrical bus.

node

A point in a network where service is provided, service is used or communications channels are interconnected.

noise

Random electrical signals, generated by circuit components or by natural disturbances, that introduce errors into transmitted data. Noise can come from lightning, nearby cables, electrical motors, radio transmissions, sunspots and other sources.

NOS

Network Operating System, a program or set of programs that instructs a computer to provide services (especially file, print and communications services) for clients on a network. Examples of NOS software include NetWare, *LAN Manager* and the *AppleShare File Server*. NOS server software cooperates with client software components that request services. These software components, often known as redirectors or network shells, make a workstation and its disk operating system (see DOS) aware of the server and able to access it. Apple's System 7 software is a disk operating system that can also act as a NOS for small workgroups.

object

A unit of an object-oriented program, consisting of both data and rules for behavior. SNMP and CMIP define a large number of managed objects that provide developers with a framework for writing management applications software. Also, any item with an entry in the NetWare Bindery database, including users, groups, access privileges and passwords. This usage is unrelated to object-oriented programming.

online

The state of a peripheral, such as a printer, modem, terminal or LAN workstation, when it is connected and ready to operate.

Oracle

A relational database management program from Oracle Corporation. Popular as a back end for client-server databases. It supports SQL and runs on personal computers, minis and mainframes. (See client-server model.)

OSI Model

Open System Interconnection Model, a paradigm established by the International Standards Organization (ISO) for communications worldwide. It divides all networking services among seven layers: physical, data link, network, transport, session, presentation and application.

OS/2

An operating system codeveloped by Microsoft and IBM to exploit the power and speed of personal computers based on the Intel 80286, 80386 and 80486 microprocessors. Key features include support of multitasking and programs larger than 640K, sophisticated memory management capabilities, a graphical user interface and process-to-process communications facilities. OS/2's multitasking can form the basis for distributed applications on LANs.

OS/2 Extended Edition

IBM's proprietary extension to OS/2, which, among other things, allows a workstation to work in conjunction with IBM minicomputers and mainframes. Also includes a database management system.

packet

A sequence of bits, including a header, consisting of addresses, control elements and data. It constitutes a unit for the operations of a particular layer of the OSI Model. Packets are often associated with layer 3, the network layer. At the data link layer, the layer 3 packet has a header and a trailer and is often referred to as a frame.

packet buffer

Memory space set aside for storing a packet awaiting transmission or for storing a received packet. The memory may be located in the network interface controller or in the computer to which the controller is connected. (See buffer.)

packet switching

A data transmission method, using packets, whereby a channel is occupied only for the duration of transmission of the packet. The packet switch sends the different packets from different data conversations along the best route available in any order. At the other end, the packets are reassembled to form the original message, which is then sent to the receiving computer. Because packets need not be sent in a particular order, and because they can go any route as long as they reach their destination, packet-switching networks can choose the most efficient route and send the most efficient number of packets down that route before switching to another route to send more packets.

PC
Personal computer.

peer-to-peer
A description of communications between two equal devices, in contrast to terminal-host communications. Under the latter, a mainframe does all the processing, and the communicating devices, including PCs, act like terminals, just doing input and output. With peer-to-peer communications, both computers execute applications, which can request services from each other and reply to requests.

peripheral
Any hardware device connected to a computer that is not itself a computer. Examples include modems, monitors, printers, disk drives, scanners and mice.

platform
(1) A family of computers, such as the Intel platform or the Macintosh platform. (2) A software foundation for other programs, such as the Windows platform. Novell's *NetWare Management System*, Hewlett-Packard's *OpenView* and Sun's *SunNet Manager* are all software platforms for network management application software, providing basic application services for other developers. (3) A standard configuration of, for instance, a workstation, a server or a network printer. These configuration platforms provide a base system that is known to work properly; modifications to the platform can be backed out when there is any suspicion that they may be the cause of a problem.

print server
A process that runs on a file server or a workstation and provides print queues and printing services to applications on the network.

protocols
The rules that govern the format, timing, sequencing and error-control mechanisms for data moving through a network. By establishing where to look in a stream of bits to find data relevant to a particular service, protocols make network traffic intelligible. Protocols from particular vendors or other common sources often form families of protocols. These families of protocols are often referred to as suites of protocols or protocol stacks. IPX is a network-layer protocol (see OSI Model) employed by NetWare networks. EBCDIC is a presentation-layer protocol employed by IBM mainframe operating systems.

queue

A sequence or line of tasks, such as print jobs or messages, waiting for service—for processing, printing, storing, etc.

realtime

In business use, any computer system that can process multiple transactions rapidly, such as the computers for a bank's automated teller machines. More strictly, though, it refers to a computer that can respond almost instantly to signals sent to it. Examples would include an airplane autopilot or any other computer system that must monitor and control an ongoing process.

record locking

The most common and most sophisticated means for multiuser LAN applications to maintain data integrity. In a record locking system, users are prevented from working on the same data record at the same time. That way, users don't overwrite other users' changes, and data integrity is maintained. But though it doesn't allow users into the same record at the same time, record locking does allow multiple users to work on the same file simultaneously. So multiuser access is maximized. (Compare with file locking, which only allows a single user to work on a file at a time.)

repeater

A device that amplifies a signal so it can travel over a longer distance without data loss. Since it performs no other function, a repeater should not be confused with a bridge or router. (See bridge, router.)

ring

A LAN topology (organization) where each node is connected to at least two other nodes. These connections form a loop (or a ring). Data is sent from node to node around the loop in the same direction. Each node acts as a repeater by resending messages to the next node. Rings have a predictable response time, determined by the number of PCs. Network control is distributed in a ring network.

RISC

Reduced Instruction Set Computing, a microprocessor architecture designed to perform a limited number of functions, and to execute those instructions as fast as possible. Advocates of RISC processors promote their speed and low cost.

router

Routers can connect two or more networks at the network layer (layer 3 of the OSI Model) by identifying the destination network a packet is bound for and forwarding it to the next hop on the route. Because routers must unpack a packet more thoroughly than a bridge, they are often slower, more costly or both. Because they operate at the network layer, they can translate from one data link method to another (e.g., from token ring to Ethernet). Multiprotocol routers have become very desirable for the ever more common multiprotocol internetwork.

routing

The process of choosing the best path through the internetwork. Routers use various algorithms and communicate using special routing protocols to maintain routing tables. Routers look up the next hop for a packet on the table and send the packet there.

server

A computer providing a service to LAN users, such as shared access to a file system, a printer, a modem or an electronic mail system. Usually a combination of hardware and software. Servers can be PCs, minicomputers, mainframes or specialized computers designed to do nothing but dole out services to multiple users. (See file server, print server.)

shell

Novell calls its workstation client component of NetWare the shell. The shell complements DOS by redirecting service requests to the network when necessary.

SMDS

Switched Multimegabit Data Services, high-bandwidth packet switching for wide area networks, ultimately as high as 45Mbits/sec. Not currently offered by long-distance carriers, only in local telephone areas.

SNA

Systems Network Architecture (SNA) is IBM's highest-level map of the functions supplied via networking protocols. The 5 layers of SNA correspond roughly to 5 of the 7 layers of the OSI Reference Model. (Appendix B shows how the SNA layers correspond to the OSI layers.)

Sniffer
Network General Corporation's trademark for its network troubleshooting tool. A portable computer fitted with a special combination of hardware and software, the Sniffer LAN Analyzer is claimed to be the only such product that can detect problems in each of the seven layers of the OSI Model. (See OSI Model.)

SNMP
Simple Network Management Protocol, a protocol established by the Internet that allows a management station or console on a network to receive management information from and send commands to distributed management agents installed in various different entities, such as concentrators, routers or servers.

source address
The part of a message that indicates who sent the message. Often included in the header of a packet.

spooler
A program or piece of hardware that controls a buffer of data going to some output device, most commonly a printer or a tape drive. A spooler allows users to send data to a device, say a printer, even while that device is busy. The spooler controls the feeding of data to the printer by using a buffer or by creating a temporary file in which to store the data to be printed. (See buffer; compare with queue.)

SQL
Structured Query Language, a database query language invented by IBM for its mainframe databases. A version has been adopted as an ANSI standard. Most client-server database systems use SQL commands to communicate between the front end and the back end.

star topology
A topology in which each node is connected to a central hub. As an example, 10BASE-T networks use hubs or concentrators as the center of a star topology. Token ring networks that use media attachment units (MAU) consist of a physical star topology, although electrically they constitute a ring.

TCP/IP

Transmission Control Protocol/Internet Protocol, a set of communications protocols originally developed by the Department of Defense to internetwork computers. Provides file transfer and e-mail capability. Once primarily found on Unix-based and DEC VAX computers, but now supported on many other systems.

10BASE-5

The original Ethernet, a hardware implementation of the 802.3 standard (see 802.3). It is a baseband network running at 10Mbits/sec over thick coaxial cable; cable segments may be up to 500 meters in length. Also known as DIX Ethernet (for Digital, Intel and Xerox, the three vendors that worked to develop this hardware implementation). Rarely used in new network installations today because of the difficulty in handling the cable. (See 10BASE-T.)

10BASE-T

An implementation of the 802.3 standard that uses unshielded twisted-pair cabling. 10BASE-T networks run at 10Mbits/sec but cable runs are limited to 100-meter segments. Also known as twisted-pair Ethernet.

10BASE-2

Until the adoption of the 10BASE-T standard in 1990, the most common cable design for LANs. It is a baseband network running at 10Mbits/sec over thin coaxial cable; cable segments may be up to 185 meters in length. Thin coax is much cheaper and easier to handle than thick coax.

terminal emulation

The use of software on a personal computer to simulate a mainframe or mini-computer terminal. Such software is necessary because mainframes and mini-computers send terminals special characters that must be displayed as lines, boxes, alternate colors and the like. Terminals also have keys not normally found on a personal computer keyboard.

token

A unique combination of bits that circulates on a token-passing LAN. When a node receives the token, it has been given permission to transmit. (See token passing.)

token bus

A LAN with bus topology that uses token passing as its access method. ARCnet and MAP LANs are the most popular of these types of networks.

token passing

An access method. A token is passed from node to node. When a node has the token, it has permission to send a message. It then attaches the message to the token, which "carries" it around the LAN to the designated recipient. Every station in between "sees" the message, but only the receiving workstation accepts it. When the receiving station gets the message, it releases the token to be used by the next station. The entire process of generating and passing tokens around the LAN takes fractions of a second.

token ring

Type of network hardware in which individual nodes are given access to the network by a token that passes around a ring. The IEEE (Institute of Electrical and Electronic Engineers) standard for token ring (802.5) has a raw data speed of 4Mbits/sec. Versions that work at 16Mbits/sec are also available.

topology

Description of the physical connections of a network, or the description of the possible logical connections between nodes, indicating which pairs of nodes are able to communicate. A map of the "road" between all the things attached to a LAN. Examples are bus, ring, star and tree topologies.

tree

A LAN topology in which there is only one route between any two of the nodes on the network. The pattern of connections resembles a tree.

TSR

Terminate-and-stay-resident program, a program designed to load into a computer's memory and stay there while other programs are run. In this latent state, the TSR program can be executed immediately with a special keystroke combination or transparently provide services to other programs. Often required to access a LAN. (See driver.)

twisted-pair cable

Two insulated wires wrapped around (i.e., twisted around) each other.

Unix
Computer operating system originally developed by AT&T. Also works on some personal computers. Considered to be very flexible and powerful.

virtual device
A device provided to a computer—and any applications run on that computer—via a network operating system. Virtual devices mimic actual physical devices, and include disks, serial ports and printer ports. For example, a PC connected to a LAN might seem to the user as though it has a hard disk drive, when actually that drive exists only as a virtual device—an area set aside on the hard disk of the LAN's disk server. (See logical drive.) Similarly, applications may "think" they are printing to a local printer, when actually output is being sent over the LAN to a print server. Virtual devices essentially act as a "front," hiding the LAN from users and applications software that might not otherwise be able to access it easily.

wide area network
A data communications network that includes links across a public network, such as a line leased from the local telephone company or a fiber-optic link provided by one of the long distance providers. (Private networks, where an organization may own the cable and right-of-way facilities itself, would also be considered WANs.)

Windows
Software from Microsoft. It extends the DOS operating system to include a graphical user interface. Users can view side-by-side text in multiple styles and graphics, in applications written especially for Windows (such as *Word for Windows*, *Excel* and *PageMaker*). Windows applications are increasingly being written specifically for LANs. They can, for example, display a LAN's topology on screen as a graphic, thereby simplifying the chore of LAN administration. The term "windows" may also be used generically to describe any technique through which a computer's screen is split to simultaneously display output from several programs—or components of a single program.

workstation
In the most general sense, an input/output device at which an operator works. Usually restricted to devices with their own central processing units, such as personal computers. Sometimes restricted even further, to high-resolution graphics setups with CPUs capable of running a 32bit operating system, usually Unix.

X.25

The long-time international packet switching standard. Wide area networks that cross national boundaries can usually rely on the availability of these services.

Index

....